# ORMUS: M

MW00612677

## ALCHEMY

*Primer Of Ormus Collection Processes*

**Chris Emmons R.Ph.**

With Contributors

**Reference Edition**

Published by Dreamgate Press
17601 Rainier Dr
Santa Ana, CA 92705
USA
www.dreamgatepress.com
Formatting by Cordell Svengalis


Cover design by Luise Johnson
www.bluwavecreative.com
First Edition Collectors Edition
www.ormusbook.com
Web design by Jim Eleczko

ISBN: 978-0-9815840-1-0
Printed in the United States of America

+Pocketbook edition due 2010 by Chris Emmons:
*Ormus: Modern Day Alchemy*
Collection Processes for the Ormus Collector

# ❄ DISCLAIMER

The material contained in this publication was submitted as previously unpublished material, except in the instances in which credit has been given to the source from which some of the material was derived. All material in this publication is provided for information only and may not be construed as medical advice or instruction. The information in this book is presented for educational purposes only. Information in this book is not intended to be a substitute for the medical advice of your health care professional. The information contained has not been evaluated by the Food and Drug Administration. Information in this book is not intended to diagnose, treat, cure or prevent any disease. All information is for research, experimental and informational purpose only. No health claims are made. In view of ongoing and evolving Ormus experimentation, the information and opinions provided in this publication are the belief of the author at the time of this writing, except where specific cited references have been provided. The information in this book is based on personal experience and observations of the author. Because each person's training and situation is unique, the author and publisher urge the reader to know proper laboratory technique and to perform further research where there is any question as to the appropriateness of the information in the book. Readers are free to use the information contained, in their own way at their own pace, while utilizing, whenever necessary, additional research and training. While material in this manual is not intended to mitigate, diagnose or treat medical conditions, it is made in the spirit of free speech. Care has been taken in the presentation of information presented and to describe generally accepted practices and personally held beliefs. However, the authors, editors, and publisher cannot accept any responsibility for errors or omissions or for any consequences from application of the information in this manual and make no warranty, express or implied, with respect to the contents of the manual. The publisher holds no opinion regarding Ormus collection, supplementation or the contents of this book, but feels the information presented in this book should be available to the public. Ormus processes involve the use of hazardous substances. Because there is always inherent risk involved when working with caustic/hazardous substances, the author, publisher and their agents are not responsible for any adverse effects or consequences including injury to or the death of a participant resulting from the use of any of the caustic/hazardous chemicals, as well as from the use of any of the suggestions, preparations or procedures in this book. Please do not use this book if you are not willing to assume the risk. Telephone numbers, prices and web sites listed in this book are accurate at the time of publication, but they are subject to frequent change.

# *Ouroboros*

## About the front and back cover

The covers display a colorized picture from the 1621 edition of Andrea Alciato, Emblemata (Book of Emblems), Padua: Tozzi 1621 and is provided     courtesy of Dr William Barker *http://www.mun.ca/alciato*

Triton, trumpeter for Neptune, god of the sea, is the focal point and represents the lye material that is at the core of many processes. Lye is often at the center of Ormus collection chemistry and is present as a liquid solution, dry crystals or sometimes pure sodium metal.

The symbols contained in the emblem include the Ouroboros, Triton, seawater, sand, air and pyramid; and each provides insights into Ormus and its collection processes. Seawater is a widely used Ormus source material and there are Ormus collection processes utilizing sand. In addition, Ormus is also found in the air. The presence of the pyramid hints at the antiquity of this knowledge and generates a feeling of connectedness to an ancient past.

Ormus collection is part of the great work and has been defined by Paracelsus as "the ability to control, purify and transform nature by the living power of the spirit" (sic: found in all things). The symbol for the great work is a circular snake or spiraling dragon devouring its own tail and termed an "Ouroboros." This symbol presents a picture of the circle of alchemy, and the steps in Ormus collection processes follow such a circular path. Ancient alchemists have said: "What is now dry must soon become wet." This mirrors modern day Ormus collection where steps involve a "wet" followed by a "dry" followed by a "wet." Additionally, among several different Ormus collection processes, there are steps shared with those of other processes all in a circular and seamless manner.

Therefore, this Emblem symbolizes the great work performed during Ormus collection and a fitting cover for *Ormus: Modern Day Alchemy.*

## What is Ormus?

A group of essential minerals previously unknown to modern science.

## Why were they unknown?

Because they did not show up in common scientific tests.

## What kind of minerals?

Minerals like gold, silver and platinum - but they are in a different form; and in this other form, they are not toxic. We are discovering they are very common in plants, animals, air, soil and water.

## How is it beneficial?

It appears to assist communication between cells in the body and between the body and spirit.


*However, let us imagine, for a moment, that you have not heard of Ormus:*

While attending a festival you overhear conversation between four friends. Excitement is in the voices as they talk about something called Ormus. They talk about having more energy and clarity of thought. There is a silence after they have agreed about feeling peaceful and content.

You wonder, "What is this?" You have become "curious." When one asks another, "Have you begun collecting Ormus?" You listen, intent on learning more. They talk about where Ormus can be found and about a book explaining how to collect it.

The friends stop at a food court leaving you with a curiosity and the knowledge of "A Book." That book is **Ormus: Modern Day Alchemy**.

You stand at a cutting edge of the ability to glean truths regarding the nature of reality and consciousness. Those who physically do the work will gain an understanding through the work, discipline, seeing, experiencing, participating and mastership in the material outcome.

# ❀ Overview

# ✻ TABLE OF CONTENTS

## ❀ Section Eight

*Closing*

## ❀ Section Nine

*Appendices and Glossary*

Chapters with information about the Ormus material, including its history, are Italicized.

# PROLOGUE

In recent years, the search for the Philosopher's Stone of the alchemists has centered on discoveries made by an Arizona rancher named David Hudson in the late 1970s. While mining for gold on his land, he noticed some associated metallic minerals that exhibited very unusual properties. Hudson spent several million dollars over the following decade figuring out how to isolate and work with these strange materials. In 1989, he was granted several foreign patents on these materials and methods for obtaining them. During the early 1990s, He toured the United States giving lectures and workshops about what he had found.

The strange substances have been named ORMES (Orbitally Rearranged Monatomic Elements), although some researchers prefer the more general term of ORMUS. ORMES are metallic microclusters in a non-metallic state consisting of one or more atoms which Hudson felt were in a high-spin state that endows them with unusual properties such as superconductivity, superfluidity, supercurrent (or Josephson tunneling) and magnetic levitation.

ORMUS can be thought of as the natural non-metallic seed of the metals or what the alchemists called their "First Matter." Because ORMES are a new form of matter with different physical properties from normal elements, conventional chemistry equipment and lab tests have proved of little value in detecting or explaining them. Nonetheless, these special "m-state" elements are thought to be as much as 10,000 times more abundant than their corresponding metallic counterparts. So far the list of metals known to exist in this special state are cobalt, nickel, copper, ruthenium, rhodium, palladium, silver, osmium, iridium, platinum, gold and mercury.

All these ORMUS materials are abundant in volcanic soil and seawater and can also be found in biological systems. Some researchers have reported that ORMES seem to enhance energy flow in the microtubules inside living cells and even work to repair damaged DNA. ORMES have proven to be extremely beneficial to plants and animals, and people who have taken ORMES report many healing, rejuvenating and spiritually enlightening effects.

There is considerable evidence that ORMUS was known by metal craftsmen and alchemists throughout history who referred to this grouping of metals as the "noble metals." The monatomic "white powder of gold" is mentioned both in the Egyptian Book of the Dead and the Old Testament Bible. Pharaoh Akhenaten is said to have built a laboratory for the production of white powder of gold in the Sinai desert near a mountain that was a source of the ore and other raw materials.

However, according to David Hudson, the Egyptians named the monatomic material "white powder of gold" because they could not detect the other metals. Hudson suggested in his lectures that some modern methods might be similar to descriptions of the production of manna or the "food of the gods" found in Egyptian texts and the Bible.

Over the years, many newer methods of ORMES collection have been discovered that allow the general public to participate in an ancient tradition to which only high priests, pharaohs and alchemical adepts were granted access in the past. The problem has been that ORMUS collection techniques have been scattered in private researchers journals and books or shared with colleagues in private discussions. To make matters worse, the methodology varies greatly from simple to complex, from kitchen-friendly work to sophisticated lab work.

Now, for the first time, practical knowledge of how to collect and concentrate ORMUS material has been brought together in a single volume that organizes and preserves these valuable teachings of modern alchemy.

My friend and colleague Chris Emmons is the perfect person to complete this important work. Sharp-witted with a penetrating mind that stays focused on truth until she finds it, Chris is the epitome of the alchemist dedicated to exposing the hidden essences of substances.

Chris has not only organized accepted methods of ORMUS collection, but she has put them in perspective to one another, grouped them according to their methodology, and shown which methods are the most useful under differing circumstances. This work is not only a breakthrough in the sharing of ORMUS knowledge but also a powerful catalyst to new research and new horizons in understanding this mysterious and miraculous substance.

Dennis William Hauck
www.DWHauck.com

## Listed Contributors

### Barry Carter

*Organizing figure of the modern day Ormus community and Ormus speaker*
*www.subtleenergies.com*

### Chris Emmons R.Ph.

*Ormus collector, record-keeper, Pharmacist and Author*
*www.ormusbook.com*

### Don Nance

*Commercial alchemist, Ormus collector, researcher and teacher of*
*Ormus collection process*
*www.oceanalchemy.com*

## Support

### B. Joy McGinnis

*Friend of the Ormus Primer*

# Acknowledgments

Putting together a manual of this scope requires contributions by many people. I gratefully acknowledge Barry Carter and his tireless efforts that have been instrumental in creating a vibrant global Ormus community. I, as well as most, would not have had an introduction to Ormus if not for his work.

Acknowledgement is given to the work of David Hudson. Without his efforts in these modern days, the knowledge of something such as Ormus would have remained veiled.

I acknowledge the contributions made by many in the Ormus community through books, conversation, web sites, personal e-mails and information shared in forums that were joined or found while surfing. Also a big thank you to my good friend Dr. Dan, who suggested the basis for the title: "Ormus: Modern Day Alchemy."

Contributing alchemists and Ormus researchers have included Don Nance and Barry Carter. Other contributing researchers requested anonymity.

Special thanks to B. Joy McGinnis for the idea of clearly detailing Ormus processes in a published manual.

Thanks go out to the special ones whose lives have crossed the path of this manual and touched its final style and format. These include the other contributing researchers, Latitude 25 Writers Club, Dr. Dan, Rosemary Fodor, Melanie Proctor and Michael McCabe. I also imposed on knowledgeable Ormus alchemists and researchers to review sections, and they took time from their busy schedules to help.

Many thanks to Cordell Svengalis, president of DreamGate Press (www.dreamgatepress.com). When Cordell learned of Ormus he began consulting me. His input during the publishing process was a great help. Luise Johnson is a gifted artist and the covers of the book reflect this talent. I appreciate her help in formating the manuscript, and Cordell's assistance in polishing the final editing and layout. Jim Eleczko is a member of the Ormus community and a knowledgeable webmaster. Both the Ormus book and I are fortunate that Jim stepped forward to build the ormusbook.com website.

I thank my husband David for his continuous support and providing encouragement when needed.

I also acknowledge my father, who taught me to think analytically and passed from the physical world during editing.

And I cannot forget to thank you, the reader, for through your interest in Ormus lies the possibility this material may never be forgotten.

Finally, I must acknowledge and pay my respects to the Ormus itself - which is in our world and the Cosmos. Thank you.                                                    C.E.

#  SECTION ONE

INTRODUCTIONS

PREFACE

INTRODUCTION

INTRODUCING:
ORMUS: MODERN DAY ALCHEMY

# PREFACE

This work is a contribution to the world such that knowledge of the Ormus collection processes might not perish or degrade. These processes "concentrate" Ormus in the source material for collection and this book details many of them. While Ormus collectors highly value these processes, the world, at the very least, may liken them to home science projects.

After all is read and digested, indications point to a few processes considered best for most Ormus collectors. These include those that extract Ormus using "oil" or "salty solutions." The oil process is the "Live Oil Process" where Ormus collection (concentration) is based on the presence of oil. The "Wet Process" is the most useful "salty solution" type of process and uses a natural sea salt solution. In this process, the salty solution is either "reconstituted" sea or seawater that has been "drawn" from the ocean. (A reconstituted sea contains natural sea salt dissolved in distilled water.)

With this information, the average Ormus collector can place Ormus collection processes in perspective and focus first on recipes considered by many to be the most useful. (For a thumbnail overview of the Ormus collection processes see appendix VII.)

(Note: The "Wet Process" has been termed "wet" due to the Ormus source material being a wet material (seawater is wet.) Now, in the "Dry Process," the Ormus source material is always "dry" (or dried-out) and thus the process is termed dry. Section Four lists other traditional Ormus processes whose Ormus source material is always dry. In naming these processes, the word "dry" is not included. To help the reader mentally collate the processes quickly the word dry is included to reinforce that dry Ormus source material is used. Therefore, the "Lye Boil Process" is addressed as the *dry* "Lye Boil Process.")

A lot of research work has been done in the field of Ormus - but there is much still to do. My focus has been detailing the most common collection processes used by the Ormus community. However, I have detailed all traditional Ormus collection processes and made them available for information, curiosity, records, historical archives and/or the library.

For easy comparison between processes, there are seven sub-sections of information presented in each chapter:
- Definition
- Information
- Preparing the Source
- Perform the Process
- Purifying (washing)
- Storage
- Final Thought

Read each applicable appendix prior to a specific Ormus process. Therefore, each chapter first lists these appendices.

When performing a process, it is strongly advised to halt the "business of the world around" and focus on the Ormus collection process at hand becoming one with it. This is the first step in a purification process that begins with the Ormus collector. An old alchemical treatise contains this warning:

"Let none set himself up to study alchemy until, having cleared and purified his heart, he be emptied of all things impure. Let him be charitable, and let him enjoy constant tranquility, so that his mind be lifted up. For, unless it be kindled with the beam of the divine light, it will hardly be able to penetrate the mysteries of nature." - *Canons of Espagnet*

Once started, there can be no rushing through a collection process without an effect on the manna - even if subtle and "time" is spoken of in this manner: the real time is that time which it takes ... that time which IS, that time which comes around to you ... the "Patient One." In the "great work" you are utilizing the physical, psychological and spiritual levels simultaneously.

Alchemy believes "spirit" is in all things and an active part of the process. Therefore, the involvement of the spiritual level is one way to explain the difference between conventional chemistry and alchemy. Paracelsus has defined the "great work" by defining alchemy as the ability to control, purify and transform nature by the living power of the spirit (sic: found in all things).

The difference between these two sciences was explained in 1910 by the prominent English chemist of the time, *H. Stanley Redgrove*:

"If I were asked to contrast alchemy with the chemical and physical science of the nineteenth century I would say that whereas the latter abounds in a wealth of much accurate detail and much relative truth it lacks philosophical depth and insight, whilst alchemy was characterized by a greater degree of philosophical depth and insight. For the alchemist did grasp the fundamental truth of the Cosmos." - *Alchemy, Ancient and Modern*

Note: The fundamental truth is that "nature" is a living organism, every particle of which is animated by the "one life" and alchemists have declared:

"Everything is an expression of the Principle of Life in a material form. The Life is the real thing; the external form is merely the house in which it resides." - *Paracelsus: De Pestilate*

Therefore, the Ormus collector brings himself to the work as an active part of the process and if the individual is not including the spiritual level in the work, the effort is more akin to mainstream (modern) chemistry and not ancient alchemy.

Albert Einstein came to a similar conclusion and said the following regarding spirit:

"Every one who is seriously involved in the pursuit of science becomes convinced that a spirit is manifest in the laws of the Universe-a spirit vastly superior to that of man, and one in the face of which we with our modest powers must feel humble."

Chris Emmons R.Ph.

# ❀ INTRODUCTION

## Part 1

6:25 am:  In 5 minutes a small white alarm clock sitting on a white nightstand will create a volley of sound.  The clock sits within a darkened room next to a white bed where a matching white pillow rests under shaggy dark golden blonde hair framing a sleeping face.

If the small white alarm clock had feelings, it might be sorry it was soon to awaken the sleeping figure.  The clock sits quietly, among many white items in the room.  White is everywhere and this room exemplifies an artist's study in color.  White coats the furniture, phone, chair, blinds, lamps, doors, carpeting, drapes, curtain rods and a ceiling fan attached to a white ceiling.  All the white objects in the small room blend with bright white linen that dresses a king bed.  The bed is raised a full foot off the floor and lies under a white featherbed while a white feather comforter drapes it and visually meshes with layered levels of white dust ruffles.  This bundle of white is the centerpiece in the room and its oversized outline emits a brilliant white radiance.  One concession to the color white can be seen in the pale peach walls whose hue adds a restful feeling to white's feeling of stillness.

The clock knows the secret importance about this room:
that here was a bold effort in color to create a space of stillness
and rest in a life filled with the lack of them.
The little white alarm clock feels badly, knowing that in one minute
it will again send her from such a space.
Tick, tock ... Tick, tock ... Tick, tock ...

I am the sleeping figure Chris Emmons: pharmacist, friend, co-worker, wife, caretaker to a myriad of companion animals.  My dark brown eyes have opened.  With hardly a moment of transition to the world of wakefulness I swing my legs off the bed onto an unnoticed bright white rug.  Silencing the clock, I move as rapidly as a sleep-fogged mind allows, out of the room and towards it all.

Today is a repeat of yesterday.  The workday officially begins at 9 am and spans 12 hours in the busy environment of pharmacy.  However, if I can get this brain moving into higher gear, I can, for another day, also accomplish some of my work around the house.  Before leaving for work my day is tasked with finishing a load of wash, cleaning dirty dishes, feeding (and maybe loving on) the pets, making a lunch and possibly, if I am not distracted, watering those plants on the back porch.  I am very aware that I will return home when it is dark outside, just as it is now.  Therefore, these two and a half hours are important to me as I plan to balance the needs of home with those of work.

Hmmm... I have worked consistently and diligently for so many years.  I am a weathered human being.  I experienced one alcoholic parent and as a five-year-old child, the unexpected loss of my mother who left a financial legacy that flowed through me and into a dysfunctional and newly formed stepfamily created to receive it.  I survived the emotional experience, graduated from pharmacy school, ran a long-term care pharmacy, married, divorced, relocated 1,400 miles from family, married again, moved two times and rebuilt after hurricane Wilma. During the years I have lived through some events of personally epic proportion. While those have been very painful, as the decades unfold I now observe how the choices during my travails display who I am and the "who I am" directly affected directions chosen in my life's walk. The emotional fallout remained and in time drained vim and vigor and so five years earlier I thought to create a room "*devoid of color*" to help me "decompress" and *perhaps* feel "vibrant" once again.

Two hours later, the house chores almost complete, I stride towards the car and begin the drive to work. I am a conscientious methodical person who thrives on precision and accuracy and I approach the pharmacy department with the mental alertness of a general analyzing an upcoming battle and the tenacity of a foot soldier determined to make it through with my way of being intact. There is keen awareness of the many missteps that can occur during the day, causing it to turn painfully frustrating. The possibility always exists that the day can become "ruined" for me, as well as for my co-workers.

I have been in the health profession for 32 years. Currently, I am part of a 1-pharmacist/ shift pharmacy. The work days are 12 hours and contain an array of constant, rapid action and never ending challenges as the needs of everyone press into me concurrently and come with concrete time frames and deadlines that mark the day and that I truly desire to meet. The list of the everyones is very long: *doctor calls, patient counseling, creating prescriptions, many phone calls, billing* insurance claims, managing inventory, the cash register and drive-thru lane, *working with store management, corporate management* and *managing two employees*. I have learned through decades of experience the importance of sidestepping "fallouts" that may occur throughout the day. These happen when any of the everyones is not satisfied. My response to this fear of fallout is a basic "self defense" type survival technique and my mental state is on consistent high alert as it monitors for potential problems while I am also aware how fallout's may blindside me with no warning.

For example: I work with inputting insurance claims confirming the doctor, the drug and the patient are "covered." This work includes delivering "bad" news to patients when their insurance will *not* pay. A jovial friendly customer, being very happy with the birth of a long awaited firstborn son, approaches the counter carrying three prescriptions. He stopped being happy when he saw his bill, refusing to believe his insurance had been terminated. I was definitely "wrong" in his eyes and these prescription charges came between him and his antibiotic treatment. He angrily left. Now, while he did return the next day, stunned to learn how his check had not made it to the insurance company, the customers who had been present yesterday and experienced his initial response were no longer there. You see, things that upset the customers worry me, because a verbally unhappy customer causes those around to be "on edge." The others are secretly hoping they won't also have a "problem." One of them did. She was picking up a sleeping pill prescription on her way out of town. The insurance's computerized response rejected the claim, listing it is as an item they don't pay for. She was already edgy and now snappishly told me they paid for it two months ago. I had obviously done something wrong in her eyes too, and at her insistence, called the insurance company. It turns out they stopped paying for that drug one month ago and now she was bristling and venting about the $1,100/month paid for insurance that doesn't cover what she wants. I felt exasperated as I still had an unhappy customer, lost 15

minutes of time desperately needed and the customers around remained on edge, secretly hoping they wouldn't also have a "problem.
" Whew...

I have experienced enough of these occurrences to fear it happening, and it happens often enough that I have come to anticipate it. It is one big circle feeding upon itself causing me to be "unsettled" and "edgy" while at work. I may begin to dread future moments, anticipating that feelings of being overwhelmed will occur, and they do happen when too many emotional upsets happen in a row. If I mentally cross over the edge, the feeling becomes frustration as I can feel neither a way that makes this day work nor the way to make it "work for me" by leaving the job site and going home. This absolutely ruins the day while I also endure despair and feelings of how "I" as well as my team are getting further behind. As a group, we can become emotionally overwhelmed, and I can't halt the feeling of "giving up" and being convinced, at that moment, how all the needs will never get met in time. Subconsciously I begin to hold my breath or raggedly drag in air. There is no soft demeanor when I talk to the staff and soon our interactions become formal and less fluid. I feel myself being rigid and stern - a *real* battle is going on as I attempt to get the workday back in "control" and the casualty always involves the relationship I have with my staff, myself and sometimes a customer or two. Peace eludes me and I do want to feel peace while at work.

When it is 9 pm, I may return home drained, spent, and unhappy, entering the bedroom with not enough energy to even recall what this room "devoid of color" is meant to do for me. Tomorrow will be a repeat of today.

*This pretty much describes how the busy workdays were before I heard of Ormus.*

It wasn't too long after beginning to take Ormus that I remember thinking how I felt "content" all the time. I never analyzed the change or mulled it over; I was just being comfortable with every moment. The result of how I was feeling did change my life though in unexpected ways. You see, pretty much nothing fazed me as I worked to meet everyone's needs and this included an active effort to mentor the department staff towards having "a great day" together. An unexpected event occurred as district management took notice and nominated me for a company award.

What I notice is how I am able to stay in the "*present* moment" even if a past customer, phone call or event has been irritating. With the focus on the present moment, I don't have any dread. I am just doing what I am doing *without any anticipation* and this has somehow caused dread to *just not be present.* My day really "opened up." All of my moments work out fine and everything I do is just plain enjoyable: I enjoy going to work, where I used to fear fallouts, and I enjoy going home, too. I may be tired physically, but mentally I am fine.

The *main feeling* I experience now is how "*all is OK.*" Because of this, my *reaction* to just about anything that happens in the day is different: and it's better. I feel insights in my brain that open up new ways of looking at what is happening and I find that I am not being judgmental with myself, the Pharmacy workload, customers or staff. I cannot be rigid with judgmental thinking because the "right/wrong" analysis is such a small part of my focus as I realize how "all is OK." I am thinking how *being* "in the present moment" may be causing this to occur because the size of my fear and the armoring against it may be diminishing. Feeling "all is truly OK" permeates my *entire* way of being and consequently my general state is a continual feeling of contentment.

(There is even an undertone of a sort of mild happiness - because my personal experiences seem to consistently end with my being at *peace*.) Therefore, I feel a certain type of calmness and I *think* this may explain what it means to be "grounded" or "centered." I feel *comfortable* and those I interact with tell me that I am a good "life coach" because I am "balanced" and have "wisdom."

I also observe how feeling "*upset*" is not sustainable for a long period. Recently my father died without wishing to re-establish a relationship. I was stunned because my *belief* had been that he would change his mind - and that wasn't going to happen now. I attended a mental health session to address this feeling of shock. (It wasn't too very long before I carried *no* remorse over the occurrence as I couldn't maintain an upset while *knowing*, in a deep, permeating way, that "**all is OK**." This "knowing" is *not* ignorable and I feel it is an effect of Ormus because I have never in my life experienced feeling how "*all is OK*"- no matter what situation has cropped up.)

When an occurrence of this magnitude happens, another one of those insights "*lights*" my consciousness and seems to tutor me. I then really "*get*" the notion that "*it is what it is.*" By embracing this tutoring, I easily walk away from occurrences *or* make a conscious decision to stand my ground and work towards changing or altering what has happened. The difference is that I "pick my fights" with an emotional softness I have never experienced before. No matter if I walk away *or* work towards changing the occurrence, I do *not* carry "emotional baggage." I believe these responses result from my ability to realize how "*all is OK*" and "*it is what it is.*" These realizations became a part of my "way of being" after I had been taking Ormus for a while. Since they came along during times of personal upheaval and resulted in profound changes within my life, I am comfortable pointing to them as a result of the Ormus. I believe what I have experienced is an "*enlightened*" consciousness that allowed me to see things with clarity and I feel that I formed my *own* perceptions of "eternal" ideas, and brought them into *my* earthly conception with the feeling of "owning" the knowledge. To me, "enlightenment" is, at its very core, a 'consciousness' that intuits or feels insights or wisdoms that causes life to be more "workable" and Ormus, either as a form of nutritional or other supplement, appears to help this process.

Using language to attempt to describe these personal, unique moment-to-moment experiences is inadequate. I am doing my best to convey this so you may understand the underpinnings of my Ormus experience that ultimately led to writing a manual.

I first heard of Ormus on a radio program during February 2004. Barry Carter was explaining the function of the Ormus material in the body and theories about its properties. These included a mechanism of action thought to be tied to a "*field of universal energy*" that relates *directly* back to our physical form (our body.) What he said caught my attention and made me wonder if here may be answers to longstanding questions I carried in my head.

As a pharmacy student, I remember feeling that there must be an outside energy source for the body. Even while in the classroom, I doubted the nerve conduction theory presented, as I could not reason how nerve impulses throughout the body could travel fast enough for either coordination of physical movement or creation of thought. Later in life, I began to doubt the human body could power each of its one hundred thousand million cells (an approximation) or its organs (groups of cells) via calories consumed from food.

Barry explained how both the *Ormus* materials and "*biological systems*" (living things) exhibited properties of superconductivity. It was felt that this co-occurrence may actually be due to the presence of Ormus materials *in* biological systems. (The Ormus materials are generally attributed to the presence of gold, silver, copper and the platinum metal group elements in an altered state. These elements include ruthenium, rhodium, palladium, osmium, iridium and platinum.) The belief is that the action of *superconductivity* found in Ormus may enhance the "flow of energy" (as a vibrational frequency seen as light) within microtubules found inside every cell. Another theory suggests that superconductivity may cause greater "*quantum coherence*" (connectivity) between the "field of universal energy" and our physical form (the body.) Ormus may thus be acting as an "antenna," providing greater connectivity (communicating information) between our physical form (cells in the body) and the field of universal energy (called the implicate order).

(Superconductivity creates a balanced standing wave in *two* dimensions. Electrons flowing through a superconductor pair off and convert to a *light* frequency in the process. One theory is that this same superconductive process may be occurring in human cells displaying its presence by the "*light*" aura seen around the human body in Kirlian photography. This is addressed later in the book.)

Well, during my life, both before and after pharmacy schooling, I had never heard of such a "field of universal energy" and this explanation was intriguing. Consequently, I joyfully anticipated a search for more information.

I first joined an online Ormus forum that Barry moderated. Within five months, knowledgeable Ormus researchers taught me the Ormus extraction process on "Celtic" sea salt. I enjoyed learning and sharing on the Ormus forum and met a local Ormus collector who provided further information on the subject. The information I was gaining excited me a bit like Indiana Jones getting closer to the "grail."

I learned that the Ormus material is another *form* of matter, a newly discovered or *re-discovered* one that *is* present and yet spectroscopically invisible in common analytical procedures. (To be analyzed by emission spectroscopy, a less common procedure called "fractional vaporization" is performed.) The Ormus material is a *natural* substance found on the earth and in the foods we eat, water we drink and air we breathe.

Currently, Barry Carter has written what is probably the most appropriate definition when describing Ormus: "Ormus, (Orme and M-state) all are generic terms which apply to any normally metallic elements when they are in a spectroscopically 'invisible' non-metallic form. These terms apply regardless of which method was used to obtain them or the relative effectiveness of the element." (The most prominent of these elements are gold, silver, copper and the platinum group.)

The effects of Ormus revolve around the idea that, through the property of *superconductivity*, it may be interacting with a particular and unique energy field that surrounds "all."

# Part 2

This energy field surrounding "all" may have something to do with the effects of Ormus. Specifically, the effects of Ormus may have something to do with its property of "superconductivity" that allows it to *interact* with this unique field of energy. The postulation is that there exists one big ocean of "*one thing*" that is one big "*field of energy*." This field of energy, in the most direct terms, refers to the notion of a vast, unseen background of "boundless energy" and relates to the concept of a "**quantum field**," "**scalar field**," or "**scalar electromagnetics**." This boundless energy is believed to "know" all *and it is* a source of information that can be accessed. This field of energy is thought to be without time (having always existed), a *natural* occurrence that exists in an ever-present, ever-changing, always in motion "stable" state and is a part of all things - including us. Some have called it the "God Force," a part of the "Zero Point," "Super light," "Ether," "Tachyons" or simply "It." (Author's note: Ormus is thought to exhibit communication, called *quantum coherence*, with this field in such a way that both physical and mental life are benefited.) - *Resonance in Residence by Harezi*

The effects of Ormus might revolve around another postulation that it assists life by being a type of nutritional supplement. While we receive Ormus in food, water and air, a belief is that, in modern industrial days, these sources may not be as plentiful and we may benefit by Ormus supplementation. Collected Ormus is either ingested or applied topically. As a type of supplement, it is thought that Ormus may cause vibrancy in the physical body manifested as having increased stamina or achieving good health *and that the* presence of Ormus may strengthen (advance) the mind. I have seen pictures of larger sized Ormus-fed oranges, walnuts, radishes and trees as well as experienced unexpected budding in four days with my own orchid plant and changes to dark green color within four hours on my patio plant. I feel that Ormus is feeding an area of life that creates vibrancy and in this manner the Ormus material may be considered a type of "universal medicine" and thus have a similar property as the "Philosopher's Stone" that was spoken of regularly by ancient alchemists. This property of being a type of universal medicine may assist in providing better health and perhaps longer life.

Now, while the presence of Ormus can strengthen the vibrancy of the physical "*body*" resulting in better health, its presence may also strengthen the physical "*mind*" and allow it to expand towards its full potential. In this way, the mind can "grow" and become what it is meant to become. I believe this proposition has far-reaching ramifications, for when a mind is *well fed* it *grows* and thoughts created may not be the same. The strength of a well-fed mind may allow for new and different thoughts including a new way of looking at events occurring in ones life.

In addition, Ormus materials used as supplements have also been attributed to increased intuitions, possibly from having a "well-fed" mind or from greater communication with the "quantum field." Feeling *contentment* has been attributed to Ormus and explained as possibly arising from a *realization* that *each* individual moment being experienced is a pure and non-duplicateable one. Each moment requires energy to create and Ormus may facilitate the energy requirements by its action as a "*nutritional supplement*" and/or its interaction with the "*quantum field.*"

Ormus supplementation has also resulted in occurrences that relate to changes in *perception of time,* where less of a division occurs between feelings that relate to "Past-Present-Future" and in its place, the focus becomes more directed on "Here-Now-Present." *The focus on Here-Now-Present may stem from the experience of feeling content.* The concept is a circular one and awesome in its simplicity. (Note: this Here-Now-Present description matches what I feel and explains the profound positive changes that occurred in my days and life.)

Some have referred to Ormus as the "*matrix of consciousness*" since it appears it may raise our "*level of awareness*" also called our "*level of consciousness*" (LOC). Having a raised awareness causes the mind's focus to be less on "body senses" with its corresponding thoughts relating to the individuals past present and future. Actually, a body sense level of consciousness is an "ego" producing one that responds to the "*I principle*" (ego based) where "I" am defined by the following: "I" am this body, "I" am this mind, "I" am this intellect. In its place becomes a state of awareness *less* ruled by the *separating* influences that "*ego*" causes and instead a greater communication occurs between the physical "*mind*" and the ever-present, all knowing "*quantum field of energy*." The result of this communication diminishes the focus on the "I principle" as the individual experiences an underlying feeling of connectedness to a field of boundless energy (this "Zero-Point," "God Force," ever-present, ever-changing, always in motion "all"). *The sensation of connectedness often results in a deep peace and feelings of contentment* causing a decreased need to display ego-based actions or to protect ego based positions (status) in the physical world.

The effect of greater communication between the physical "*mind*" and the "*quantum field of energy*" may be the feeling of having a greater "wisdom" or manifesting "intuitive" wisdom or experiencing "insights." It may be possible that I had experienced this myself when the phrases "*all is OK*" and "*it is what it is*" "*lit*" up in my conscious mind and became part of "*who I am*."

One thing seems clear: Ormus are "transformational" elements that seem to cause deep and lasting change in an individual.

"*Ormus*" is the name most often referred to when describing materials collected from Ormus collection processes that cause a precipitate to form. However, there are other terms such as "*manna*," "*doves*" or "*the drop*" and all these terms are interchangeable. In the spring of 2004, I placed an order for an Ormus product that contained collected Ormus from dissolved sea salt. *This* Ormus product is in the form of a liquid suspension. A liquid suspension is a mixture consisting of small particles or *liquid droplets* dispersed in a liquid and the particles separate out with time. Note: an alchemist may term Ormus (manna) a "wet in liquid" because the manna contains "wet" liquid droplets in the liquid (versus solid particles such as earth particles held in a suspension of muddy water). Ormus (manna) separates out of suspension if allowed to stand and gently shaking it re-suspends the wet in liquid prior to using. A liquid suspension is the *most* common form of Ormus collected by an Ormus collector and the "*Wet Process*" *is the most common method of Ormus collection used to obtain the liquid suspension.* This process is addressed later in the book.

While Ormus collectors debate *how* the Ormus material "works," many believe that its *presence* facilitates positive effects and enables *life* to reach a fuller measure of its biological potential.

Well, I hope you can feel how I liked this "new" way of experiencing life - because I did. When I heard how Ormus is an easily collected substance, I reasoned that attaining the knowledge of the ways of collection was my ultimate "*assurance of availability*." Therefore, I turned my thoughts towards learning these processes and soon found that there was no book of present day Ormus collection methods or courses taught on the subject. Hmmm ... I strove to know specific information that wasn't readily accessible. This did not deter me though as I earnestly followed every lead towards introductions to those knowledgeable in the field.

Now, it is possible that during this personal search, my knowledge as a pharmacist and my traits of meticulousness to detail helped the progress. Perhaps it affected my "way of being" as I sought and met those who could teach or maybe during instruction it was easier to extrapolate, question, collate or absorb the knowledge. Maybe being driven facilitated my progress. I can't say. What I can say, is that I felt life "quickly and easily" directing my path to the "doorsteps" of those I needed to meet. And so, after three years of effort, the treatises (processes) of Ormus extraction and collection were gathered, collated, recorded and filed in my mind.

**My work was done!**

I felt gloriously content and I happily anticipated spending time with my Appaloosa trail horse, reading metaphysical literature and Dean Koontz books. I especially looked forward to interacting on the Ormus forums and having recreation in the company of friends!

And so it was that B. Joy, a friend, having heard about the culmination of my efforts, began a conversation. Now, some think that a conversation is the starting point of every possibility. In this conversation she verbalized how the Ormus community -both current and future- could benefit by having a manual of Ormus collection processes and that I embodied professional training and personal traits to complete such a work.

I mulled over her words and the truth in them. I remembered how I felt back then, as a seeker myself: anticipating, wanting and *hoping* the way to "*workable*" knowledge would appear. I remembered the feelings of "*boundless*" gratitude for those Ormus researchers, teachers and instructors who showed me how to collect Ormus and answered myriad questions. This feeling of gratitude has been so large I *had* to give back and in thankful appreciation I began teaching "Ormus Lab Days" in my home. Because I remember the magnitude of my feelings of gratitude, I can never forget how it feels to yearn for the knowledge of Ormus collection processes.

Therefore, I put aside for a time my horse, books and forum participation, fired up the word processor and began a manual that now lies completed in your hands. Working with Ormus has truly been a *great* adventure and I consider it the "great work" that has been described by past masters as the ability to control, purify and transform nature by the living power of the spirit (*sic:* found in all things). - Paracelsus

If you contemplate a similar path of self-discovery and empowerment, I hope the information contained within serves you well.                                   C.E.

# INTRODUCING ORMUS: MODERN DAY ALCHEMY

The *Primer of Ormus Collection Processes* endeavors to instruct interested Ormus seekers in the collection processes.

The manual provides *"practical"* information on Ormus collection with functional descriptions of the processes laid out in an organized format. The reader has an opportunity to become empowered, learning the processes and collecting Ormus themselves. These Ormus collection processes, ancient alchemists would use the term treatises, are "time-honored" and include those most commonly accepted by knowledgeable alchemists and Ormus researchers. At the very least, the processes in this manual are home science projects as they are not difficult and require few specialized utensils. An additional advantage to members of the Ormus community is that the reader becomes a more informed purchaser of Ormus products from alchemists.

Let us dispel any concerns. In a way, these recipes are "similar" to doing the work of cooking in a kitchen. In both instances, the "cook" uses fire to transform matter. The cook uses procedures and cuts, blends, measures, chops and dilutes source materials. The cook focuses the mind while forming the finished meal and takes the appropriate amount of time for each step. The cook determines the tools and supplies required by reading the recipe. The cook exercises care so no physical harm ensues during all this work. A "loving" cook also adds a part of his/her "spirit" to the finished dish. Who has not felt that distinguishable quality in a prepared meal? Therefore, just like a recipe for use in the kitchen, read and re-read an Ormus collection process until the process feels familiar. Then follow the directions with measured effort and focus on one-step at a time.

A Sufi alchemist put it this way: "All the qualities of a good spiritual alchemist can be found in the person who can cook an egg perfectly." - *Sorcerer's Stone by Hauck*

The Ormus collection processes have been based on alchemical treatises recorded from the past and some of these recipes are available in printed books such as *Collectanea Chemica* where the "thing" sought was described as the "... spirit on the salt ... ." This is the same thing we collect and call Ormus in present times. - *Collectanea Chemica by Eirenaeus Philalethes and Others 1893*

(Note: *The primary source material for this manual originates from Ormus researchers and alchemists who have been studying the subject since before there was an organized Ormus community. This serves as a footnote for the vast majority of information contained in the manual.*)

Each knew "Essene" when he was developing current Ormus collection processes and before him David Hudson. I feel (very) privileged to have attended their workshops, presentations and even scheduled personal appointments. Each has been available for many questions that have occurred. Two of these researchers are Don Nance, a commercial alchemist and Barry Carter, the organizing figure of the modern day Ormus community. Other contributing Ormus researchers requested anonymity and their contributions and efforts are greatly appreciated.

Some feel that the ancients were acquainted with the Ormus material and it may be that a *select* group knew of its ability to facilitate a growth of the "spirit." This knowledge may have become *lost* when new rulers (the Amalekites) who slaughtered the people overtook the country (Egypt). A lesson to learn is that *knowledge "owned" by a select few is always in jeopardy of being lost.*

Thanks to "Essene" and other modern alchemists, collection processes have been re-discovered and with our combined efforts, the knowledge of Ormus collection processes might not become "lost" again. However, knowledge is consistently being lost and the possibility always exists that this knowledge of Ormus collection processes could also become lost again.

Don Nance is a practicing commercial alchemist and addressed the subject of lost knowledge during a workshop on August 26 and 27, 2006.

"You must know that knowledge is being lost all the time. Thanks to "Essene" and us, it (*sic: the knowledge of Ormus*) may not get lost again. However, there is always the possibility that it could get lost again. The awareness of this possibility has come to me and I feel compelled to do what I can to ensure this does not happen. Therefore, I am having this workshop and another next month and maybe a third and I am going to teach you what I know. I am going to teach you my secrets and nothing will be held back. All alchemists have these and I am going to teach you mine (trade secrets) because it is *very* important that this knowledge is not lost again." - Don Nance

I resonate, with a sense of purposefulness, the ramifications of this loss. Don has his own poignant Ormus story (revolving around a health challenge), I have mine and we both appreciate the Ormus materials ability to benefit life. This book details Ormus collection processes to increase the possibility that the knowledge does not become lost again.

Awareness of Ormus is a starting point. After this, collection processes are learned and the growth of the global Ormus community follows. There are *many* who have and do share Ormus knowledge and I am thankful for *each* one. I hope this manual assists the efforts they have made.

An added feature is the inclusion of a section titled: "Other Substances that Attract Life Force." There is a speculation that the effect from these other substances may add to those from Ormus. If this is so, they deserve inclusion.

Know that once Ormus collection processes are learned, others will ask for assistance with their own study. It is my hope that when this occurs, the "mentor" is available in *his/her own unique way*. Unique strengths are part of a "Divine Design" and the "Mayan Galactic Signature" (similar to our horoscope) decodes them. Through understanding the "signature," sharing knowledge of Ormus collection processes is *simple* and even joyful at a "soul" level. To learn your Mayan Galactic Signature, visit *www.13moon.com*.


## Final Thought

*There is much yet to learn about Ormus and we are learning as we go.* I applaud Ormus researchers and alchemists who reach out and share their knowledge. Included in this group is Barry Carter who continues to encourage local groups to share knowledge and develop local sources.

It is important that you are comfortable extracting Ormus yourself and *self-reliance* in this matter is of chief importance. "Knowledge that is *known* is *owned*" and therefore do not rely *solely* on a supply chain from alchemists. In addition, it has been said by some the "the best Ormus is the Ormus you collect yourself."

#  SECTION TWO

TIME TO LEARN

❋ Getting Started

# GETTING STARTED

## Definition

"Collecting Ormus begins with understanding where to look."
                                                        **C. Emmons**

Ormus materials have been found everywhere: They have been collected from rock, metal, seawater, fresh water, air, organic material and some believe there is a concentration of Ormus where the first water meets with land (the sand).

Alchemists have called this material the "oil which does not burn."

Other terms describing this material include "heavenly water, not wetting the hands: not vulgar, but almost like rain water" and "a bird without wings." (Collectanea Chemica by Eirenaeus Philalethes et al., 1893.)

Indeed, the extracted Ormus from good drinking water has a soft,creamy texture and some say the 100% pure form of Ormus is oil. Our goal in collecting is to extract (concentrate) and purify Ormus from its many hiding places in nature. The uses of collected Ormus are varied and it is given internally and used topically in animals and humans as well as being applied to plants. To the ancient alchemists, collecting the life force (the spirit) in the source material was the "great work."

The Ormus collection processes are fairly easy and straightforward. This message has been conveyed from long-past alchemists: "Let it be observed, then, that all who have written on the art, from undoubted principles, assert that the genuine process is not expensive; time and fuel, with manual labour, being all allowed for." (Collectanea Chemica by Eirenaeus Philalethes et al.1893.) Once you also understand the processes, I believe you will concur how all we are doing is adding technology to something that is more of a natural element.

*Some of the collection processes form a precipitate. The precipitate that has formed and then settled out of solution during a collection process contains the Ormus. In a way we are "concentrating" the Ormus that is present in the source material and therefore the work can also be considered a concentration process.* Some call the precipitate "Ormus" or "manna" or "doves" (referring to the fluffy precipitate as it is forming in the solution) or "the drop."

Note: Most casually observe and handle the precipitate that has dropped out of the solution and say this is "Ormus." When the Ormus source material is a pure metal element it is a "single source" precipitate and contains the Ormus form of only that element. However, the vast majority of Ormus collectors do not use pure metals as the Ormus source material and consequently there are other constituents in the precipitate. These might include magnesium, calcium and other mineral elements. Therefore, realize that there is more in the precipitate than the Ormus material. It is postulated that Ormus is within the precipitate and within the liquid that hangs in the spaces around and between the precipitate. Some tests have shown that between 20 and 40 percent of the Pacific Ocean precipitate is spectroscopically invisible. (Barry Carter)

You may see or hear of additional Ormus collection recipes or variations of recipes in this manual. This book contains core Ormus collection processes and methods of knowledgeable Ormus researchers and alchemists. There are some "absolute" rights and wrongs to be aware of while performing Ormus collection methods. Beyond these rights and wrongs, the rest of the steps in the process can be modified to what draws you. However, I encourage you to follow the steps as outlined. Later, once you have gained an understanding of the Ormus collection processes you may make measured amendments.

Now, why are there different Ormus collection processes and various Ormus source materials? Because there are differences in the very nature of Ormus source materials and therefore the Ormus collector may collect Ormus from source materials better with one process versus another. In addition, the nature of people varies (because of genetic and physical differences) and some may respond better to Ormus from one Ormus source material versus another. For these reasons, there are a variety of Ormus collection processes and Ormus source materials.

To ensure that directions on performing the processes remain as uncluttered as possible, there is ancillary information in appendices near the back of the book. This information enhances understanding of the Ormus collection process at hand and the reader is to peruse these first (or read for content). Therefore, at the beginning of each chapter is a list of suggested appendices and others are also noted within the chapter. Appendices include the following:

General Ormus Information (*Appendix VI*)
Basic Explanations of Each Process (*Appendix VII*)
Source Material for the Processes (*Appendix VIII*)
Chemicals Used in the Processes (*Appendix XIII*)
Ormus Collection Labware Choices (*Appendix XIV*)

*Because learning Ormus collection processes is the focus, description of collection methods begins promptly and reading the remainder of this section is not a necessity.*

C.E.

## Information
*The history of Ormus collected during Ormus collection methods may have*
*both a recent and ancient origin.*

### What is the Recent Origin?
The history of our present day Ormus (manna) began when an Arizona agriculturist modifying his severely unproductive dirt with strong chemicals observed a "unique" compound form on top of the soil. Fortunately, the lineage of this "farmer" was a prosperous multi-generational agricultural family. Prosperity would be required because investigating the "*what then is it*" of this material was challenging and ended up costing over eight million dollars!

The farmer's name is David Hudson and because of his efforts at analyzing the compound during the 1970s and 1980s, a "new" class of materials has been discovered (or re-discovered). Re-discovered *may* be a better term, as there is compelling evidence that knowledge of these materials date back as far as ancient Egypt (perhaps further). The content of many of David Hudson's lectures, where he outlines his findings, can be found on the Internet. (One site is *www.subtleenergies.com*.)

David Hudson's research into the material that formed on his land led him to discover that his materials contained high levels of precious metal elements in an "*altered*" state. He assayed the presence of palladium, osmium, ruthenium, iridium and rhodium. The research demonstrated that "*precious metal elements*" (many are part of the "*platinum group elements*") can *naturally* form a "*different*" atomic state. Because of their "middling" location on the periodic table (being neither "metals" located on the far left nor "non-metals" located on the far right), these precious metal elements are termed "transitional" elements or "transition metals" and this may in some way explain how it is that they can show anomalous behavior such as entering into a different atomic state. The elements (thus far) known to create an altered state are: cobalt, nickel, copper, ruthenium, rhodium, palladium, silver, osmium, iridium, platinum, gold and mercury. David Hudson has said that these elements in their different state may be 10,000 times more abundant than their metallic counterparts! (*David Hudson transcripts.*)

David Hudson coined this different atomic state a "high spin" state and demonstrated these strange atomic forms as being *naturally* forming. These elements display unexpected and anomalous characteristics related to the altered state of the molecule. These materials are monoatomic (one atom per molecule) and some say they may be diatomic (two atoms per molecule) and they are capable of forming "microclusters" of up to 200 or more atoms. The unexpected characteristics observed include "superconductivity", "superfluidity," "Josephson tunneling" and "magnetic levitation." (*David Hudson transcripts.*)

It appears that David Hudson found an entirely new class of materials!

"*Superfluidity*" is a characteristic of the *David Hudson* materials. Superfluidity is defined as a liquid that flows without viscosity or inner friction. In order for this to occur, it is theorized that the *atoms or molecules* must all pair up into groups called bosons or "cooper pair" bosons and thus occupy the same "*resonance state*" ("*quantum state*"). (Elements with an even number of electrons consolidate into bosons while those with an odd number of electrons pair up into "cooper pair" bosons.)

"*Magnetic levitation*" is another characteristic of the materials that David Hudson researched. They levitate when in the presence of "*magnetic fields.*" The earth has a magnetic field (witness the mechanism of action of a compass). (Note: in Ormus collection processes, a postulation is that the Ormus (manna) is enticed to "stay put" by utilizing *sodium* which forms a "shielding" crystalline structure around the Ormus and protects it from the magnetic field of the earth. It is noted that recipes of ancient alchemists show they also used the *sodium* molecule in a substance they called the "*secret fire*" - this is addressed later in the book.)

"*Josephson tunneling*" is characteristic of the *David Hudson* materials and allows them the ability to "tunnel" across impenetrable barriers. (Note: in Ormus collection processes, these include the containers that store the collected Ormus. Creating a crystalline structure with *sodium* during an Ormus collection process is thought to also nullify this effect and cause Ormus to "stay put."

One theory regarding how these materials form is that when the elements have entered into this "*different*" state, they cease being able to form bonds that create "metal" and instead become the altered state. These materials are capable of forming *natural* micro-clusters with a characteristic of being able to disappear and avoid chemical detection by conventional means (the less conventional "fractional evaporation" test does show them). (*David Hudson transcripts.*)

David Hudson applied for patents of these materials and in his patent application, he named them "ORME:" "orbitally rearranged monatomic element." Over the decades, other names for these materials have evolved. This is due in part to cause no infringement on the David Hudson patent applications. Therefore you may hear them referred to as: "*Ormus*,"" *M-state*,"" *manna*" and even "*doves*" or the "*the drop*" (the later two indicating the visual precipitate as it forms and drops out of solution during processes that form a precipitate).

Of the three anomalous characteristics displayed by the ORME material, "*superconductivity*" is perhaps the one that holds the most interest to humans. It has been found that superconductivity occurs in our body as well as in Ormus preparations, and when Ormus enters plants, animals and humans it seems to *cause a benefit to life*. The realization of the co-occurrence of *superconductivity* in the body and Ormus materials begs the question: what may result from this seemingly natural link between the ORME material and us? (Note: Until fairly recently, *superconductivity* occurred only after a sample material was brought to a very cold "absolute zero." The absolute zero temperature requirement made every day use of *superconductors* impractical.)

Superconductivity of these materials occurring at *normal body temperatures, much higher than absolute zero*, conflicts with physics principles taught for decades. Consequently, the new knowledge caused a stir in the scientific community, although the general population largely was not aware of these findings. Since the time of David Hudson's work, new "quantum" physics theories have evolved and they encompass a paradigm that includes "*superconductivity*" and its effects in what has been termed the "*Quantum State*."

(Note: Scientific and detailed technical information on "orbitally rearranged monatomic elements," containing properties of "superconductivity," "superfluidity," "Josephson tunneling" and "magnetic levitation" are found in books and on the web for those interested and willing to do the necessary work. Appendix IX lists some of these resources. David Hudson gave lectures that explained these concepts and the content of many of the lectures can be found on the Internet. One such site is www.subtleenergies.com.)

During the state of superconductivity, *sub-particles* in the atom or molecule pair up and "groups of atoms" (called bosons or "cooper pair" bosons) "condense" into a single unified state (called a "Bose-Einstein Condensate"). These behave as a "*single*" atom, by "*resonance-coupling oscillation*" (resonating with others of its kind). *During the state of superconductivity, relaying of "information" is "instantaneous." What is especially important in the explanation of superconductivity is that when the pairing of the molecules occurs (into bosons or "cooper pair" bosons), they cease behaving as "particles" and begin to behave more like "light!"* (Note: Ormus (manna) has demonstrated the presence of superconductive properties. Since *superconductivity occurs in the body*, it is felt that the "*energy flow*" (a form of information) within every living cell is *enhanced*.

Therefore, the presence of superconductivity seems to cause a benefit to life. The greater "energy flow" within every living cell allows for increased vigor in building, repairing and maintaining the body, the plant or the animal.

It is important in the discussion that the study of Ormus is at a scientific level first. The philosophy regarding Ormus is addressed later in the chapter.

## Can there be an ancient origin?

David Hudson's research into the material that formed on his land also led him to another unique phenomenon. David Hudson studied the gold element in the laboratory and with manipulations turned it into a "white powder." The gold became a white powder and stopped looking like a metal. It was also difficult to weigh because it could not reach a constant weight as the weight continued to change over a period of time. It was determined that the white powder was responding to the smallest of "*magnetic fields*" and thus by definition the white powder was exhibiting traits of a "superconductor." (A superconductor is incredibly sensitive to even the smallest "*magnetic field*" and can levitate or sink via this effect.)

David Hudson's passionate interest in his quest led him to discover that in ancient history a *white powde*r has been spoken of. Here begins a story of the ancient origins involving material theorized to be "Ormus". What David Hudson found was that "*white powder of gold*" stories went back to ancient civilizations in the Tigris-Euphrates Valley where the knowledge of the material was attributed to have been given by the Gods. (*David Hudson transcripts.*)

Fifth Dynasty Egyptian writings on a pyramid tomb speak of the "Field of Mfkzt" as an otherworldly dimension. The walls in the Serabit temple contain the written word "mfkzt" which addresses a "mysterious" substance. The Rosetta stone speaks of mfkzt as a very valuable but unstable form of "stone." In many ways, these descriptions match David Hudson's findings for his material.

The "Egyptian Book of the Dead (The Papyrus of Ani)" by E. A. Wallis Budge, page 35, speaks of tchefa food of the gods. (Spelled literally t'efaui.) This is the "bread of the presence of God." In old kingdom Egypt it is called "the golden tear from the eye of Horus," "that which issues from the mouth of the Creator" (that being spittle *not* the *word* of God) and "the semen of the Father in Heaven." This material was fed to the pharaoh seeking terminal enlightenment of the afterlife. At every stage of an ancient Egyptian ritual (hundreds of times), a repetitive question of "*what then is it*" is asked following a declarative statement. Such declarative statements include: "I am purified of all imperfections," "What then is it." "I ascend like the golden hawk of Horus;" "What then is it." "I come by the immortals without dying;" "What then is it." "I come before my father's throne," "What then is it." (*Lost Secrets of the Sacred Ark by Laurence Gardner.*)

(The majority of our Ormus collection processes form an Ormus (manna) precipitate that is a white precipitate in liquid resembling the appearance of "spittle" or "semen.")

An analogy with semen also occurs in religious history. Religions inevitably remind a believer to cleanse, purify and prepare like a "bride in the bridal chamber." All directives are preparations geared more towards the *coming* of God and less on what "happens" when God arrives. The Egyptian rite of passage (in old kingdom Egypt) included taking the "semen of the Father in Heaven" for 30 days. (*David Hudson transcripts*)

So then, what may occur when God arrives after the cleansing, purifying and preparing? It is thought that when God arrives there is an "insemination" that causes *new life and growth*, which is experienced as a purification with the occurrence of regeneration. If so, this is an interesting and exciting prospect! (*David Hudson transcripts.*)

Because Moses and the Israelites lived and worked in Egypt for *centuries*, it is logical that they both knew of and called this material: "*what then is it?*" David Hudson has translated the word "Ma-na" as "What then is it" and it is an interesting correlation that the Israelites who were in the desert with Moses were fed "manna" that they also called "what then is it?")

The knowledge of the "what then is it" was pretty much destroyed in old kingdom Egypt when the Amalekites, known for great ferocity, entered the country and decimated it. The Israelites, however, who had recently left Egypt, may have carried the knowledge of the "what then is it" out of the country and that knowledge was safe until the destruction of the first temple. The Bible records Moses performing a gold process in Exodus 32:20. This verse describes burning the golden calf and preparing edible gold placed on water, which Moses caused the Israelites to drink. The high priests who fled the destruction of the "first temple" (Temple of Solomon) by the Babylonians (587 BC) formed a desert community that much later went by the name of the "Essene." (*David Hudson transcripts and Lost Secrets of the Sacred Ark by L.Gardner.*)

The "Essene" (circa 130BC-70 AD), the "Pharisees" and "Sadducees" were the three leading philosophical Jewish sects. The Essene was a philosophical healing community where mystics with knowledge of medicinal stones lived incredibly long lives, had a great understanding of astrology and possessed the ability of dream interpretation and divine revelation. They practiced the art of healing using knowledge from the ancients and made a mysterious white powder from gold or seawater or earth. They called *any* white precipitate that came from their processes involving the "*secret fire*" and/or salt: "*Manna*" (these two substances are discussed later in the book.) The Essene culture placed a high value on these materials and Essene workshops have been discovered which show troughs that brought Dead Sea seawater into and out of the work area. (David Hudson has shown that Dead Sea seawater contains a high quantity of Ormus gold.) The Essene called their white precipitate "manna" and later alchemists called any of these white precipitates "doves." After the publication of a book titled *the Book of the Art of Distillation* (originally published 1500), the word "dove" became synonymous with something that had been "distilled" and thus had "flown." (Note: A modern day alchemist chosing to be called "Essene" has termed all these materials "M-state," thus designating them as the "*meta-physical form*" or "*manna-form*" of the element.)

Alchemists, who lived after the publishing of *the Book of the Art of Distillation*, worked to produce a substance called the "Philosopher's Stone" or the "Elixir of Life." It is believed that our Ormus (manna) is related to the "manna" and "Philosophers Stone" of the past and indeed several of the Ormus collection processes include procedures that have been adapted from ancient alchemical texts. (Recommended texts relating to the Philosopher's stone include *The Secret Book* by Artephius; *Sacred Science* by R.A. Schwaller De Lubicz and *Le Mystere des Cathedrales* by Fulcanelli.)

## Is this the Science behind a Mind/Body/Spirit Connection?

Superconductors always display a "*Meissner effect*" (or field). The existence of a "*light field*" surrounding the human body is captured in Kirlian photography and postulated to be that field (called a "*light field*" or "*aura*") surrounding the human form. In the mind/body spirit community the "aura" is thought to demonstrate that we are composed of both a "*light*" body (called "subtle body," "spiritual body," "radiant body," "astral body" or "KA") and a "*physical*" body. When the *light body is well fed, it is said to grow into what it is meant to be*. Beliefs regarding the ingestion of either the "*white powder*" spoken of in antiquity, the superconducting "ORME" material David Hudson discovered or the "*Ormus*" *manna* collected during an Ormus collection process can be understood by phrases that have been used to describe the occurrence. Descriptive phrases are used such as: we "Swallow the Teacher of Righteousness:" "this is the light:" or "the light of the God force" and thus ingesting the material brings "the light of the God force within us." There is a nourishing of the "*light* body" and the belief is that this causes it to flourish to a point of *exceeding far out from the physical body.*

The Greeks and Egyptians believed that feeding the "Ka" (or light body) generated "enlightenment" (an enlightened consciousness that intuits or feels insights or wisdoms that cause life to be more workable) In addition, you may have also experienced a person whom upon walking into a room *lit* it up with their *natural* presence. That person may have a strong "*animating* sprit" (the KA).

Other observations seen or felt when a strong "*light* body" is in place may be greater "intuition" and a *knowing* of the presence of good or evil in people or rooms. In addition, there may be an openness of thinking receptive to higher "*innate*" wisdoms (after which wisdoms *are* received). A "willingness to be guided" can occur and if so then a greater *acceptance* of life as it presents itself is felt. Telepathy, healing by the "laying on of hands" or the projection of thoughts are also considered possibilities. *The core action responsible for this phenomenon is surmised to be interactions between this material in us (both naturally and in supplemented form) and the material in the "Quantum Field."* These two areas are thought to be communicating via "resonance-coupling oscillation" (resonating with others of its kind) that results in greater "flow of information" between the "*Quantum Field*" and our "*light body.*"

## Final Thought

Now, the reader may subscribe to the possibility that Ormus collected from Ormus collection processes is of a "*benefit to life*" from a *scientific* standpoint, a *mind/body/spirit* standpoint or a *combination* of both. What is clearly observable is that pictures of plants before and after Ormus supplementation display increased growth and larger fruit and I have experienced this in plants on my own patio. This is compelling *visual* evidence suggestive that, at the very least, Ormus is in some manner enhancing *vitality* in biological systems.

#  SECTION THREE

Best Processes for the Ormus Collector

Live Oil Process

Lye (NaOH) Solution Preparation

Wet Process

Hydrochloric Acid (HCl) Preparation

Dry Process (Cold Fire Process)

# LIVE OIL PROCESS

Note: There are appendices that may have cross-referencing information to that in the "Live Oil Process" chapter.

These appendices include:

"List of Ormus Resources and Supplies,"

"Common Measurement Conversions,"

"Best Practices Labware Choices"

## Labware and Supplies to perform a "Live Oil Process"

"Grape seed" oil, sea salt *or* Ormus (manna) *or* "drawn" seawater (from the ocean), glass container (with non-metallic top), aluminum foil, paper towels, flat strainer or funnel, filters (*unbleached coffee filters*).

If using Ormus (manna) precipitate or seawater as the Ormus source material a barrel syringe or turkey baster (the type with the bulb at the end not the brush) is helpful.

To best ensure electromagnetic waves cause no interference on the stability of Ormus in source material or finished Ormus product, it is prudent to keep the work and storage area six feet or more away from them. For more information, see "Labware Choices - Aluminum Foil." (Appendix XIV.)

## Definition

This process infuses Ormus from sea salt or Ormus precipitate (manna) or "drawn" seawater (from the ocean) *into* oil. The infused oil is termed "Live Oil." Depending on the oil chosen, the "Live Oil" may be *ingested*, applied *topically* or *both*. (This process is performed *most often* on *sea salt and oil*.)

## Information

Appearance: The Ormus in "Live Oil" cannot be seen. The Ormus product looks and feels like oil.

Because the "Live Oil Process" is quick, easy and provides a good Ormus product, the average Ormus collector often performs it. For these reasons, this method of collection is the first one described.

"Live Oil" can be made at *any time or on any day of the year*. To alchemists, there *is* an ideal time for an Ormus collection process and this is three days before a full moon or an equinox as these are energetically active times. Some say that the Ormus product produced during these time frames is exceptional. For detailed information, see "Moon Chart." (Appendix X.)

**Ormus is thought to have an affinity for oil and this is the basis of the "Live Oil Process."**

"Grape seed" oil may be the *best* oil to choose since both the *grape* and the *grape's seed* are said to be good Ormus sources. (Note: it may be beneficial to chew the grape's seeds when eating grapes.) Because grape seeds are considered a good source of Ormus, *Grape seed oil* can be considered a form of "live" oil by itself. *Grape seed oil can be either ingested or used topically.* If

"Kosher" grape seed oil can be located, that brand should be exceptional since the amount of processing done to foods in kosher products is minimal.

Examples of other oils include flax seed, olive, coconut and hemp.

(I have given a massage therapist two "Live Oil" products for evaluation. One made with Sesame Seed oil and sea salt, and the other made with Grape Seed oil and sea salt. She especially enjoyed the "Live Oil" made with Grape Seed oil explaining how she could feel energy going through her hands with the Grape Seed oil and that her hands generated a lot of heat.)

The following information about "Olive" oil can make you a well-informed oil purchaser of oil from any source: "First Cold Pressed" olive oil contains mashed olives (including the seed) that have undergone a "first press." (The material is not heated.) The "California Olive Oil Council" is in the process of developing industry standards. Under current manufacturing processes the olives called "First Cold Press" may contain older olives that have started to oxidize (over ripen) with a resultant decrease in shelf life. The shelf life of properly prepared "Olive" oil is two years from the date of processing and better brands list the date of processing on the label. A "Seal of Approval" by the "California Olive Oil Council" is due on approved bottles of olive oil sometime in the future. For an approved list of oil suppliers visit their website at *www.cooc.com*.

(*Olive oil is used as "finishing oil" in food and for topical use.* Olive oil is not used for cooking purposes as heat causes a breakdown of the oil's profile [perhaps peanut oil may be best suited for cooking]. Finishing oil is added to pasta or cooked hamburgers, in salad, on bread, etc. Olive oil can also be applied topically.)

## Perform the Process
## "Live Oil Process from Sea Salt"

The "Live Oil Process" can be performed using oil plus dry sea salt as the Ormus source material. Be sure the dry sea salt is *known* to contain Ormus. To confirm this, perform an Ormus collection method called the "Wet Process" on sea salt. If Ormus is present, a precipitate forms (the precipitate contains the Ormus). Dead Sea salt is often used as the sea salt source in the "Live Oil Process." Celtic sea salt is also used and any natural sea salt can be chosen as well. For more information, see "Sources for the Ormus Processes." (Appendix VIII.)

**Place 1/2 sea salt and 1/2 Grape Seed oil to the top of a glass jar with a non-metallic lid.** (The dry natural sea salt is to have no anti-caking agent or coloring added.) *Leave no room for air.* If the lid is metal, first place a layer of plastic wrap over the top of the glass container. This acts as a barrier between the metal lid and the "Live Oil." (Metal is not to come in contact with the "Live Oil" product.)

**Shake the jar vigorously 21 times and then let the sea salt settle for a few minutes.**

**Repeat this nine times.** The reason the jar is shaken 21 times is because 21 is a "Fibonacci" series number and the number nine, representing three sets of three, is also a Fibonacci series number.

(Fibonacci Series: This series of numbers appears in every corner of the natural world. These numbers are found, among other areas, as defining how a nautilus shell grows, how sunflower seeds are distributed in the flower cone and in the number of petals on flowers from such families as the daisy, the rose and all the flowers of the edible fruit bearing plants. The Fibonacci series is a measurable link between art, science and spirituality; and it has been suggested to include them in the "Live Oil Process.")

**After the final shake and settling, the "Live Oil Process" is considered complete.** The "Live Oil" product can be filtered or used immediately and some have said to allow the oil and sea salt to settle as long as 24 hours for fullest infusion.

**Separate the Grape Seed oil from the sea salt using a single (oil) wetted coffee filter or two of them stacked together. Wet with oil first and change to a new filter when the pores clog.** The sea salt filtered from the "Live Oil" can be used as a "skin scrub" or a "bath salt." Some suggest leaving the salt in the oil as it does not dissolve and once the oil is used, oily salt remains on the bottom. This oily salt finds use as a body scrub, facial scrub or bath salt. (Caution: If placed in a tub of water, the bottom of the tub will be slippery.)

### "Live Oil Process from Ormus (manna)"

The "Live Oil Process" can also be performed using oil and Ormus (manna) collected when performing an Ormus collection process. The Ormus is often the Ormus (manna) collected during a "Wet Process." Ormus collected from other Ormus collection processes is *not* used because less volume of Ormus is collected from other Ormus collection processes *and* those processes cost more (in terms of time, effort and price of materials).

**Perform a "Wet Process" on Dead Sea salt.** (Other natural sea salts can be chosen in place of Dead Sea salt.)

**Draw the Ormus (manna) up from the bottom of the container.** Wash the Ormus (manna) *one* time only (not the three times as is usually done.)

**Place 1/2 Ormus (manna) and 1/2 Grape Seed oil to the top of a glass jar with a non-metallic lid.** *Leave no room for air.* If the lid is metal, first place a layer of plastic wrap over the top of the glass container. This acts as a barrier between the metal lid and the "Live Oil." (Metal is not to come in contact with the "Live Oil" product.) Because effort was expended to collect Ormus from a "Wet Process," it makes sense to choose *Grape Seed oil when making "Live Oil" from Ormus* (manna).

**Shake the jar vigorously 21 times and then let the Ormus (manna) settle for a few minutes.**

**Repeat this nine times.** The reason for these specific numbers has been explained above.

**After the final shake and settling, the "Live Oil Process" is considered** *complete.* The "Live Oil" product can be filtered immediately and some have said to allow the oil and Ormus to settle as long as 24 hours for fullest infusion.

**Separate the Grape Seed oil from the Ormus (manna) using a single (oil) wetted coffee filter or two of them stacked together. Wet with oil first and change to a new filter when the pores clog.** (Note: The Ormus (manna) filtered from the "Live Oil" can be used as a *poultice* on pest bites, psoriasis and bruises. The poultice is made by mixing the filtered Ormus (manna) with dry oatmeal, applying it to the skin area, covering and then allowing it to set.)

**Allow the "Live Oil" time to fully** *settle away* **from any water that came from the Ormus (manna.)** The Ormus (manna) contains a small portion of water and some of this water is now in the "Live Oil." The "Live Oil" and this little bit of water completely separate from each other and display a clear line of demarcation between them. *It is important that the finished "Live Oil" product contains no water* as water is a *nurturing* medium and when stored with oil becomes a breeding ground for microbes. Microbe cultures can grow in this medium and would make the "Live Oil" undesirable for ingestion or topical application. In addition, the presence of water makes oil less stable and causes it to become rancid more quickly.

**Draw off the "Live Oil" floating over the water** with an oral baby syringe, turkey baster or marinating syringe (without the needle).

**Stop as the "Live Oil" line gets close to the water line** even if this means that some of the "Live Oil" is discarded. (Now, this last bit of "Live Oil" containing that small bit of water can be used right now - perhaps topically.)


## "Live Oil Process from Seawater"

The "Live Oil Process" can be performed using oil plus "drawn" seawater (from the ocean) as the Ormus source material. (for more information see Appendix XX)

**Filter the seawater and then boil gently for 10-15 minutes.** (It is important to boil the seawater because seawater contains living (organic) microorganisms that will putrefy in the finished "Live Oil" product.)

**Place 1/2 boiled seawater (while it is still warm) and 1/2 Grape Seed oil to the top of a glass jar with a non-metallic lid.** *Leave no room for air.* If the lid is metal, first place a layer of plastic wrap over the top of the glass container. This acts as a barrier between the metal lid and the "Live Oil." (Metal is not to come in contact with the "Live Oil" product.)

**Shake the jar vigorously 21 times and then let the seawater settle for a few minutes.**

**Repeat this shake and settle nine times.** The reason for these specific numbers has been explained above.

**After the final shake and settling, the "Live Oil Process" is considered** *complete.* The "Live Oil" product can be separated from the seawater immediately. Some allow the oil and seawater to settle as long as 24 hours for fullest infusion.

Separating the Ormus source material from the "Live Oil" when made with seawater is performed differently. The task is *to separate the "Live Oil" from seawater, leaving no water in the "Live Oil" product.* There is no need to filter for particulate matter as seawater has been filtered prior to beginning the "Live Oil Process" and "Grape Seed" oil is particulate-free at time of purchase.

**Allow the "Live Oil" and seawater to fully settle away from each other.** The oil and water completely separate from each other and display a clear line of demarcation between them. It is important that no water remain in the finished "Live Oil" product to provide a breeding ground for microbes. (This has been explained previously.) In addition, the presence of water makes the oil less stabile and causes it to become rancid more quickly.

**Draw off the Ormus infused Grape Seed oil floating over the seawater** with an oral baby syringe, turkey baster or marinating syringe (without the needle).

**Stop as the oil line gets close to the water line** even if this means that some of the "Live Oil" is discarded. (Now, this last bit of "Live Oil" containing that small bit of water can be used right now - perhaps topically.)

### Storage

A theory holds that "Live Oil" contains Ormus in its "free" state. Ormus has moved to the oil from the Ormus source material because Ormus is thought to have an affinity for oil. (Some feel that Ormus in its pure state is an oil.) Other Ormus collection processes thought to contain Ormus in the "free" state are the "Magnet Vortex Water Trap" and "Vortex Water Trap," "Concord Grape Process" and "Dew Collection Process."

Because the Ormus in "Live Oil" is in a "free" state, some have said that the Ormus can "wander off" more easily and therefore a suggestion is to store "Live Oil" away from sunlight and electromagnetic waves such as those associated with refrigerators or TVs. Because the Ormus is in a "free to roam" state, the length of storage time is lessened (in comparison to Ormus collection processes that make a precipitate), and it has been suggested to use the "Live Oil" within 30 days.

**Store the "Live Oil" in a glass container with a tight fitting *non-metallic* lid.** If the lid *is* metal, first place a layer of plastic wrap over the top of the glass container. This acts as a barrier between the metal lid and the "Live Oil." Plastic containers are *not* suggested for storage because the pores of plastic are larger - possibly making it easier for the Ormus to tunnel out.

"Live Oil" is a *nutritive* product and can support the growth of bacteria and fungi (mold is a fungi.) Keep the "Live Oil" storage container free of these contaminants by drawing out what is to be used into a separate container first to ensure that the stock container remains uncontaminated.

**Wrap the "Live Oil" container in aluminum foil.** Keep the container away from sunlight. For more information, see "Labware Choices-Aluminum." (Appendix XIV.)

Containers of "Live Oil" are *always* wrapped in aluminum foil, stored out of sunlight and at least six feet from EMF wave producing appliances. Store the containers away from all forms of light, the most offending of which is UV rays (sunlight). The aluminum foil wrap seems to help retard scalar (spin) fields and provide some shielding from radio frequency waves. For more information, see "Labware Choices-Aluminum Foil." (Appendix XIV.)

**Use the "Live Oil" within 30 days.**


## Final Thought

The uses for "Live Oil" are many and varied. Use it on food (when edible oil, such as "Grape Seed" and "Olive" oil, has been used.) For example, add it as "finishing" oil to salads and cooked vegetables. Use "Live Oil" topically for skin care such as softening the skin and during massages. (If used for the latter application, both the client and the massage therapist benefit.) When used on the soles of the feet, it penetrates through the skin quickly because of the large pores in that location. Some feel that "Live Oil" is helpful for painful conditions such as arthritis, neuropathy and sunburn.

"Live Oil" can be enhanced with the addition of a good quality "essential oil," either alone or in combination. If the "Live Oil" is for food preparation, essential oils such as thyme, sage, rosemary, lemon, garlic, pepper, oregano, black cumin, carrot seed and marjoram are recommendations. If the "Live Oil" is for topical use essential oils such as lavender, frankincense or myrrh, grapefruit, helichrysum rose, cedar, geranium, hyssop and ylang ylang are popular. When choosing an essential oil, select a fragrance that is pleasing to you. This is as important as the essential oils listed beneficial qualities or its popularity. For essential oil sources see "Resources and Supplies." (Appendix I.)

The most potent "Live Oil" produced is when Ormus (manna) has been used as the Ormus source material. The next potent is that made with sea salt and the least potent is that made with seawater. The potency of the "Live Oil" product directly correlates to the Ormus content in the source material. Since Ormus in manna is concentrated, the "Live Oil" made with it is thought the most potent. Sea salt is less concentrated and seawater even less.

NOTES:

> *"When the student is ready,*
> *a master will come"*
> old saying from India

## LYE (Sodium Hydroxide, NaOH) SOLUTION PREPARATION

Note: There are appendices that have cross-referencing information to that in this chapter. These include: "List of Ormus Resources and Supplies," "Common Measurement Conversions," "Best Practices Labware Choices"

### Labware and Supplies to make lye solution

(Food grade) sodium hydroxide (granules, crystals or pellets preferred over powder), distilled water, glass container (borosilicate glass preferred), measuring cup, measuring spoon, plastic stirrer (or borosilicate glass), catch basin, safety clothing/equipment and HDPE storage bottle. For more information, see "Labware Choices." (Appendix XIV.)

As a safety measure, always place containers used in the process into a larger non-metallic catch basin (*in case of leakage or breakage*). For example: A (new) cat litter box or the bottom of an under-the-bed storage container.

---

**CAUTION!!**

Note: Cautions are a form of education so that you may work with lye in awareness and respect not fear.

Lye (sodium hydroxide, NaOH) is a "caustic." It is also a caustic agent and if it is in contact with eyes, it can damage them by rendering the cornea opaque, a form of eye damage that is irreparable. If lye gets into eyes, flush the eyeball with water immediately and seek medical attention if the burning persists.

If lye contacts skin it hurts and damages it. If lye contacts clothes, it damages them. If lye gets onto your clothes or body, immediately flush the area with lots of water and seek medical attention if necessary.

It is very helpful to work near a sink, faucet or other source of wash water.

The area must be well-ventilated as breathing fumes from lye is harmful and can damage air passages and the lungs. Lye solution creates caustic fumes. Do not breathe in these fumes. Handle lye with adequate ventilation such as a laboratory range hood vented outside or conduct the work outside. It is advisable to keep a spray bottle of distilled white vinegar handy to use against spills.

For more information and cautions when using lye, see "The Chemicals of the Processes." (Appendix XIII.)

When working with lye, or any chemical, avoid touching your face or rubbing your eyes. Do not handle around food. Do not dump wastewater on the ground. Lye is generally safe to put down the drain, but first run water in the sink while slowly pouring the lye directly into the drain and don't mix it with any acid that may be in the drain as it can react explosively.

When working with lye, please wear goggles or a full-face visor (an industrial face protector), neoprene gloves and a PVC lab apron as well as protective clothing such as long sleeves and long pants.

Keep children and pets away from the work area and do not leave it unattended. Even if no one is around, an unsuspecting person could venture by and be at risk.

Glass can shatter with hot liquids. Allow lye solution that has been prepared time to cool prior to pouring it into another glass container.

## Definition

Oxidized metals make a "pH basic" material. For example, lye (sodium hydroxide) is an oxidized metal. (Sodium [Na+] is the metal). The chemical formula of sodium hydroxide is NaOH and it is a caustic (an alkaline substance). **An alkaline substance has a pH of greater than pH 7 and an acidic substance has a pH of less than pH 7.** A pH of pH 7 is termed neutral.

## Information

Appearance: Lye solution looks like clear liquid.

Because lye is a caustic it can hurt us if handled improperly (see above). Some express concern about using a chemical that they consider toxic in a process whose product may be ingested. Following is an answer to this concern:

In the "Wet Process" lye is added to arrive at a "target" pH point (that point is pH 10.78) during which the Ormus (manna) precipitate can form and fall out of solution (lye does not act as a reagent in the "Wet process.") (A reagent is a substance used in a "chemical reaction" for the purpose of producing other substances that exhibit distinctly different characteristics.) *In the "Wet Process" any un-reacted lye solution that was added during the work is rinsed out during purifying (washing). Therefore its presence is "gone."*

In a *dry* Ormus collection process, lye acts as a reagent in the process. (A reagent produces other substances during a "chemical reaction.") *It is understood that in all the dry Ormus collection processes lye solution used in the process "changes" by means of a" chemical reaction" from lye (NaOH) to harmless salty (NaCl) water that is rinsed out and its presence gone during the rinsing step.*

Lye is central to the Ormus collection processes because it reacts with *all* the kingdoms of the earth: the animal, the vegetable and the mineral. This makes lye extremely useful as it can be used in all of its *pure* forms to interact with every Ormus source material. The *pure* forms of lye include *granular, pellet* and *flake* (flake form not preferred). **Do not use lye mixtures as might be found in toilet bowl cleaners and etc.**

For the Ormus collection processes, a 12.5% lye *solution* made from *solid* pure lye (crystals, pellets, granular or powder form) is used. This is the same strength of lye solution used in all the Ormus collection processes that form a precipitate.

Potassium Hydroxide (KOH, potash lye) can be chosen in place of Sodium Hydroxide (NaOH) however sodium hydroxide is favored. We prefer sodium hydroxide because it is both less costly and stronger than potassium hydroxide. (Therefore less sodium hydroxide is used in an Ormus collection process because 56 parts of potassium hydroxide are required to perform what 40 parts of sodium hydroxide performs.)

Make sure you understand the procedure and are prepared with your equipment and supplies before you start.

Do not work with lye in fear. *Work with lye in" respect" not "fear."* The emotions surrounding fear also cause a mind to "close off;" this results in making the steps of a procedure very difficult to absorb.

### Perform the Process

**Choose an appropriately sized glass container (borosilicate glass suggested and preferred).** This work generates heat and borosilicate glass withstands heat changes (without cracking) better than regular glass. *Place a catch basin under the glass container.* For more information, see Appendix XIV and Appendix I.

**Select a working area that is well ventilated preferably outside in the open air.** Do not breathe in the lye fumes.

**The solid pure lye (crystals, pellets, granular or powder) is carefully added to distilled water and** *never the other way around.* Adding water to lye causes sputtering, splashing and boiling. (Use *only* distilled water.)

**Stir to mix the lye with the distilled water.** Use only a plastic utensil or glass stirring rod. These are the amounts of lye and distilled water needed.

## Add:

1 level tablespoon food grade lye to 1/2 cup distilled water
Or
2 level tablespoons food grade lye to 1cup distilled water
1/2 cup food grade lye to 1quart distilled water
Or
2 cups (1 pound) food grade lye to 1gallon distilled water

The above measurements reflect the standard ratio of lye to distilled water and this is a 1/8 dilution ratio. *This is the dilution rate used in all Ormus collection processes.* This dilution ratio is especially good when using a large quantity of seawater in the "Wet Process" (one gallon or more) because these are *strong* concentrations of lye solution.

When performing a "Wet Process" on **small quantities (less than one gallon) of seawater it may be advantageous to use a more dilute solution by mixing 1/2 tablespoon of lye to one cup of distilled water.** This gives a person more control of the resultant pH rise with each addition of lye solution.

Standardize the concentration of lye solution made so there can be a feel for how reactive the lye solution is when used in the "Wet Process." Standardized concentrations also make it easier to analyze results from multiple ongoing experiment documentation reports. For more information, see Appendix XI.

(Note: lye flakes have less volume than granules, pellets or crystals because they are a fluffy and less dense form of lye. If lye *flakes* are used, measure *125gm of lye flakes per quart of distilled water.* Weigh the lye flakes on a weight scale because the "Measurement Conversions" listed in Appendix XII are not accurate for fluffy less dense flakes. For this reason, it is preferred that lye crystals, granules or pellets be purchased. However if you have lye flakes, the Ormus collection process is not going to be hampered: it is only that the 125gm of the lye *flakes* need to be weighed on a scale.)

After adding the lye to distilled water, **the liquid becomes warm then hot.  This has been known to break the glass container.**  Always use a catch basin.

You may assume the heat generated when lye is added to distilled water is a *chemical* reaction, but it is not.  Sodium hydroxide is *dissolving* into water.  *Dissolving substances into liquid, results in a solution while a "chemical reaction" results in new compounds.*  Lye *dissolves* in the water and separates into Na+ and OH- that move around the water freely as a *solution.*  A *chemical* reaction occurs when a new third substance forms out of the initial two and the *new* third substance exhibits distinctly different characteristics.

We experience a *chemical* reaction during all the Ormus *dry* collection processes.  This is explained so you may appreciate the reaction occurring in the Ormus processes on a different level.

A chemical reaction results in new compounds.  In the *dry* Ormus processes, *hydrochloric acid* is added to *lye* solution and this is discussed later.  Two *new* compounds form: *salt and water.*  This is why the solution at the end of any of the *dry* processes is *salty!*

Here is the chemical equation for those who are interested:
$$HCl + NaOH = NaCl + H_2O$$

## Storage

**Store in an HDPE plastic bottle once the lye solution has cooled,** The HDPE bottle that has a plastic triangle on the bottom and the number 2 inside the triangle is the type to use.  Do not store in glass because lye eats away at it and, with time, weakens the glass.  (Note that while performing an Ormus process, the lye solution can be placed in glass containers.)

**Label the bottle of lye solution "Lye (NaOH) - Poison"** so the bottle is not confused with something else.

*Store the bottle in a plastic catch basin.*  This is a safety measure against possible leaks.

## Final Thought

The ancients called lye solution the "Secret Fire" because of the chemical burning that lye produces.  You feel the heat when the lye is first added to the water however, this heat continues at a *chemical* level.  This secret fire is useful in the *dry* Ormus collection processes as the chemical burning of the Ormus source material releases the Ormus attached to it.  (The same chemical *principle* finds use when lye dissolves clogged hair in the drain of a tub.  The lye solution is chemically "burning" the hair and thereby disaggregating it.)  As mentioned earlier, potassium hydroxide solution may be chosen in place of a sodium hydroxide solution and ancient alchemists depicted the potassium hydroxide solution as a "lion."  Ancient alchemists knew both sodium hydroxide and potassium hydroxide as the secret fire and when the two were used together, they were referred to as the "double" secret fire.

In fact, ancient alchemists have described the secret fire in this manner: "...a Fiery Water, an uncompounded and immortal *ens*, which is penetrative, resolving all things into their first Liquid Matter, nor can anything resist its power, for it acteth without any reaction from the patient, nor doth it suffer from anything but its equal, by which it is brought into subjectaion: but after it hath dissolved all other things, it remaineth entire in its former nature, and is of the same virtue after a thousand operations as at the first." (*Collectanea Chemica by Eirenaeus Philalethes et al.* 1893.)

There are tools that can add controlled amounts of lye solution to the seawater in a "Wet Process." These include *glass eyedropper bottles, oral baby syringes and (HDPE) plastic bottles with an elongated spout cap.* A measuring cup can also be used to add lye solution when working with a large volume of seawater in the "Wet Process" (five or more gallons of seawater).

(As a point of interest: Both sodium hydroxide and potassium hydroxide can be made from wood ash and water. The process involves leaching metallic oxides from the burned ash of hardwood trees into the water.)

(In the past, Red Devil® Lye was a popular brand within the Ormus community. Consequently, there is a possibility that the name may be mentioned by any who are not aware that the company re-formulated the product and it now contains a *mixture* of ingredients and not just pure lye (sodium hydroxide). Therefore, *Red Devil® Lye is not to be used* in Ormus collection processes.)

Government, through its bureaus, departments and agencies, controls many areas of life. They have determined to make it difficult (not impossible) to procure lye. Therefore, you may have to work to procure a lye source. For more information, see Appendix I.

**NOTES:**

"Alchemy is one part art, one part science."

## WET PROCESS

Note: There are appendices that have cross-referencing information to that in this chapter. These include:
"List of Ormus Resources and Supplies," "Common Measurement Conversions,"
"Best Practices Labware Choices," "pH Meter" and
"Seawater Collection with Pump and Filter,"
For "Lye Solution Preparation" see previous chapter.

Manna from a "Wet Process" settling to the bottom of a beaker filled to the 500ml. mark. (Note: The Ormus precipitate doesn't always have to be white. The color can vary with different Ormus source materials used.)

**Labware and supplies to perform a "Wet Process".**
Sea salt or "drawn" seawater, lye solution, distilled water, pH meter, aluminum foil, barrel syringe or baster, flat strainer or funnel, filters (*unbleached* coffee filters), enamel pan or stainless steel pan, focus beam flashlight, heat source, measuring cup, plastic catch basin, stirrer of plastic or borosilicate glass (stainless steel *not* preferred), safety clothing/equipment and container made of HDPE plastic or borosilicate glass (regular glass may also be used). Do *not* use leaded glass (lead may contaminate the product). Therefore, if you have a leaded crystal punch bowl that seems to be a good size for the process, don't use it because lead or iron contamination is not desired. Store the finished Ormus (manna) in HDPE plastic. Long-term storage of lye solution is in HDPE plastic containers however during the Ormus collection process, it can be placed in HDPE plastic or glass containers. For more information, see Appendix XIV.

As a safety measure, always place containers used in the process into a larger non-metallic catch basin (*in case of leakage or breakage*). For example: A (new) cat litter box or the bottom of an under-the-bed storage container.

To best ensure electromagnetic waves cause no interference on the stability of Ormus in source material or the manna (precipitate), it is prudent to keep the work and storage area 6 feet or more away from them. For more information, see "Labware Choices-Aluminum Foil." (Appendix XIV.)

### Definition

Because the Ormus source material is wet, this collection method is termed the "Wet Process."

The object of the "Wet Process" is to have a precipitate form and then fall out of "reconstituted" sea or "drawn" seawater (from the ocean) by adding lye solution until the pH rises to a maximum of 10.78. This is an actual target point maximum pH and should not be exceeded. The precipitate that forms contains Ormus and is termed: manna or the wet precipitate. In a way we are harvesting or concentrating the Ormus that is present in the seawater.

**CAUTION!!**

Note: Cautions are a form of education so that you may work with lye in awareness and respect not fear.

Lye (sodium hydroxide, NaOH) is a "caustic." It is also a caustic agent and if it is in contact with eyes, it can damage them by rendering the cornea opaque, a form of eye damage that is irreparable. If lye gets into eyes, flush the eyeball with water immediately and seek medical attention if the burning persists.

If lye contacts skin it hurts and damages it. If lye contacts clothes, it damages them. If lye gets onto your clothes or body, immediately flush the area with lots of water and seek medical attention if necessary.

It is very helpful to work near a sink, faucet or other source of wash water.

The area must be well-ventilated as breathing fumes from lye is harmful and can damage air passages and the lungs. Lye solution creates caustic fumes. Do not breathe in these fumes. Handle lye with adequate ventilation such as a laboratory range hood vented outside or conduct the work outside. It is advisable to keep a spray bottle of distilled white vinegar handy to use against spills.

For more information and cautions when using lye, see "The Chemicals of the Processes." (Appendix XIII.)

When working with lye, or any chemical, avoid touching your face or rubbing your eyes. Do not handle around food. Do not dump wastewater on the ground. Lye is generally safe to put down the drain, but first run water in the sink while slowly pouring the lye directly into the drain and don't mix it with any acid that may be in the drain as it can react explosively.

When working with lye, please wear goggles or a full-face visor (an industrial face protector), neoprene gloves and a PVC lab apron as well as protective clothing such as long sleeves and long pants.

Keep children and pets away from the work area and do not leave it unattended. Even if no one is around, an unsuspecting person could venture by and be at risk.

Glass can shatter with hot liquids. Allow lye solution that has been prepared time to cool prior to pouring it into another glass container.

## Information

Appearance:The collected Ormus is observed as a fluffy white precipitate in clear liquid.

After the "Live Oil Process," the "Wet Process" is the easiest method for collecting Ormus.

A pH meter is used in the process to measure "pH." Use an accurate meter and determine the accuracy with a standard pH buffer solution. These standard buffers are often included with pH meters or purchased separately.

*Ormus (manna) can be collected at any time or on any day of the year.* To alchemists, there *is* an ideal time for the collection of Ormus (manna) from Ormus source material and this is three days *before* a full moon or an equinox. These are energetically active times during the year and some have said that Ormus (manna) collected during these periods is exceptional. To facilitate performing a "Wet Process" (or any Ormus process) during an energetically active period gather the Ormus source material and supplies *three* days prior to the day of the event. The procedure during an *ideal* time frame involves *precipitating* the Ormus three days prior to the day of the event, allowing it to be *settling* the night *prior* to the event followed by purifying (rinsing) it beginning the day *after* the event. For more information, see "Moon Chart." (Appendix X.) By doing an

Ormus process during one or two of these energetically active times of the year you can with a large enough volume of seawater (Ormus source material), procure enough Ormus (manna) for use during the entire year.

When performing a "Wet Process" as much as 20% of the liquid can form a precipitate. Some evaluate the amount of precipitate after eight hours and some after 12 hours. (There is no consensus at this time.) After 24 hours, the precipitated amount may appear less as it settles with time.

The "Wet Process" can be finished in one sitting but does not need to be completed in one sitting. You can take a week to do the precipitation part of the "Wet Process" by checking the pH *daily* to see if the pH has gone down from the target pH of 10.78. If it has, you know more Ormus (manna) has been collected. (Add more lye solution to arrive at the target pH, and additional Ormus precipitate may form.) Continued daily checking of the pH is not a necessity and when the pH target is met during the first sitting, the process may be considered finished. I can suggest you check the pH the next day to ensure it did not rise instead! This has happened to me. The pH rose to well above pH 10.78. I cannot explain how this occurred. While it may be the garage was hot from the summer heat, it is also known that Ormus collection processes are based on chemistry and "energetic phenomena" sometimes not explainable. Therefore, check the pH each day the precipitate is allowed to stand overnight. If the pH exceeds pH 10.78, undesirable material *may* be in the precipitate (if they were present in the source material).

Now if while making (or washing) the precipitate, it is forgotten and weeks later has mold in it -give it to the plants - do not "eat" it. For information, see "Manna Use in Agriculture." (Appendix XXI.)

Dr. Massaru Emoto has shown that sound, words and thought influence water. (Therefore, it is important to be aware of your way of being and verbalizing when preparing the source material, making the manna or purifying it.) (*Messages from Water* by Emoto.)

Distilled water is the standard water used in the process. The distilled water may be placed in sunlight to "charge" it (some have said for an hour and a half). Once the distilled water has been in the sun, it can be expected to hold its vibrational resonance - sometimes called *charge* or *charge frequency* - for three days (some say seven days). For more information, see "Vedic Alchemy" (Section Eight). (It is not vital to the Ormus process that the distilled water is placed in the sun.)

**The Ormus source material in a "Wet Process" is "artificial" sea or "drawn" seawater. Artificial sea is a "reconstituted" sea made by dissolving natural sea salt with distilled water. The terminology used from here on is reconstituted sea when referring to artificial sea.**

Do not use table salt or any salt with anti-caking (anti-clumping) agents or coloring agents added. Many feel that Celtic sea salt contains a more balanced mix of the different Ormus elements and therefore this sea salt may make the overall best Ormus (manna) from a sea salt source. The Dead Sea has more of some Ormus elements such as gold, as well as a lot of magnesium. Because of its magnesium content, the Ormus (manna) yield from Dead Sea salt by volume is more than the yield of Celtic sea salt by volume. The salt from other seas can also be chosen. For more information, see "Sources for the Ormus Processes-Sea Salt." (Appendix VIII.)

### PERCENTAGE OF M-STATE ELEMENTS IN PRECIPITATE
### FROM VARIOUS SEA WATERS

| Water Source | Gold | Rhodium | Iridium | Magnesium |
|---|---|---|---|---|
| Dead Sea | 70% | - | - | 30% |
| Salt Lake | 19% | 30% | 5% | 46% |
| Pacific | 8-14% | 30% | 6-9% | ? |

*Every ocean has its own unique Ormus value. Courtesy B. Carter ( www.subtleenergies.com )*
*(Other interesting chart comparisons are at this site)*

Information on sea salt is in Appendix VIII under "Sea Salt" and information on purchasing sea salt can be located in Appendix I: "Sea Salt."

Once distilled water is added to the sea salt, it becomes *reconstituted sea* and the theory holds that Ormus binds tightly to the crystalline salt structure. If there was Ormus in the sea salt, it is now in the *reconstituted sea* and is freer to travel (leave). A suggestion has been made to use the reconstituted sea in a timely manner to perform a "Wet Process".

(An experiment using Morton® Safe-T-Salt Rock Salt as the Ormus source material was performed. Morton® Safe-T-Salt Rock Salt is sold in large bags and used to de-ice steps and walkways during the winter months. This salt originates from an ancient seabed deep under the earth. It is so old that while there is little Ormus left in it (there was very little Ormus (manna) precipitate) the fact that there is any left in the ancient salt at all is fascinating. This experiment is mentioned for a couple reasons. First, the Ormus community needs to find new Ormus source materials and a part of the search begins with mulling over potential source materials. Choosing to try Morton® Safe-T-Salt Rock Salt as an Ormus source material is an example of work done by an Ormus researcher to determine if this material may be a good source of Ormus (it wasn't). The example shows how once Ormus collection processes are learned - you are capable of investigating potential Ormus source materials. The *knowledge* of the Ormus collection processes is the beginning of a *new* relationship with the Ormus community as you have become equipped to continue the search for new Ormus source materials. In this manner, you have become a researcher! Therefore, be open to the idea of exploring potential Ormus sources. Remember: *If a source is non-toxic, the Ormus (manna) is non-toxic and if you don't know if the source is non-toxic, first have an analysis done on it and/or the Ormus that forms from it.* For information on having a source or precipitate analyzed, see Appendices I and VIII.

The pH of "drawn" seawater is fairly standard at about pH 7.8 to pH 8.4. The pH range occurs because different areas of the ocean have varying factors. Often when seawater is collected from deep or mid ocean levels, the pH is around 7.4 to pH 7.8. As one draws water closer to reefs, the calcium carbonate and calcium hydroxide in the reef acts like a base by adding OH- to the seawater and this can raise the pH of the water to as high as pH 8.4.

Now, in generalized terms, this is one theory regarding the reaction that is occurring during a "Wet Process." Both "reconstituted" sea and "drawn" seawater are in a stable equilibrium. The addition of lye does two things. First it breaks this equilibrium, and secondly it raises the pH level. The lye molecules dissolve into Na+ and OH- (observed as a rising pH level). When the lye molecules (NaOH) have dissolved into Na+ and OH-, one theory holds that the Ormus material forms a complex observed as "particles." These particles grow larger and have the appearance of a flake. The flakes coalesce together and slowly sink to the bottom of the container. This precipitate contains the Ormus. These particles (the manna) become visible at around pH8.

There is a "pH plateau" associated with a "Wet Process:" the pH stops rising even as lye solution is added. This occurs because the hydroxide ions (OH-) from the lye solution is being used to form the complexes that are observed as "particles" *instead* of raising the pH. It is during the pH plateau that the *great work* of collecting Ormus is occurring. Once you break free of the pH plateau, the pH begins rising again, and the great work performed in the "Wet Process" is done. The collection process may, in general terms, be considered finished. Some alchemists look for the pH plateau, go through it and then stop the work once they have broken free of it. Most Ormus collectors continue up to pH 10.78 or near to it. (This is explained later.) To recap: The pH plateau has been passed when a small amount of lye solution makes a larger rise in the pH reading. Watching for this pH plateau is an example when experiment documentation sheets are helpful as the quantity of lye solution added is recorded with any resultant change in pH. This is an easy way to notice a *break* from the pH plateau. For more information, see Appendix XI.

Ormus does continue to precipitate past the pH plateau. For example: Copper has been said to drop at a pH range of 9-14 (we never exceed pH 10.78). For this reason, there are strong proponents of continuing a "Wet Process" up to pH 10.78 (if this causes great fear, stop at pH 10.4). When the pH is allowed to continue to rise past the pH plateau, it is expected that the precipitate also contains more of the magnesium and calcium present in the reconstituted sea or drawn seawater. Since both of these minerals are beneficial to the body and a majority of people are said to be deficient in one or both, the average Ormus collector often chooses to continue to raise the pH and collect as much Ormus (manna) as possible as well as these beneficial minerals. Now, magnesium can cause griping in the intestinal tract (some are more sensitive to this and not everyone experiences it). This griping can give a laxative effect. A belief held by some is that: "If an individual gets a cleansing, then they needed a cleansing."

When choosing between stopping the process once the pH plateau has been passed or continuing towards pH 10.78 consider this: If I plan to ingest the Ormus (manna), what amount is to be taken? If supplementing with higher amounts of Ormus (manna), the higher amounts of magnesium in the finished Ormus (manna) may not be preferred. For more information, see "Manna Supplement Usage." (Appendix XXI.) Regardless, most Ormus collectors continue the "Wet Process" up to pH 10.78.

If the pH continues to be raised towards pH 10.78, do not raise it beyond the pH of 10.78 and if there is fear regarding the possibility of overshooting pH 10.78 a suggestion is to not go above pH 10.4. Some are comfortable choosing Ph end points in the pH 10.5 - pH 10.7 range. The major focus is to remove the feeling of fear, as we do not want "fear" to imprint onto the Ormus (manna).

*The target pH of 10.78 is an "actual" pH value.* Calibrate the pH meter, determine any variance in its readings and factor the variance into the pH readings. For more information, see "pH Meter." (Appendix XV.)

Now, magnesium in reconstituted sea or drawn seawater acts as a *protective* barrier preventing toxic metals (if they are present) from precipitating out. This protectant action - this buffering so to speak - works up to pH 10.78 and this *is why we never go beyond the pH reading of pH 10.78.* The precipitate of toxic metals is not visually distinguishable from the Ormus (manna) being precipitated. **Toxic metals are metals that accumulate in the body and cause health challenges. Therefore their ingestion should be avoided.** It is mentioned that toxic metals usually are not present because of the care taken when harvesting the sea salt or drawing the seawater from the ocean. However, unless the Ormus source material had been sent in for assay, it is not known if toxic metals are present. *When performing Ormus collection processes always proceed on the side of caution.* Therefore, never take the process beyond the pH point where magnesium's protective barrier action is occurring and that pH is 10.78. (Note: If the pH went above pH 10.78, the Ormus (manna) still finds use on plants. For more information, see "Usage and Directions-Plants/Agriculture." (Appendix XXI.)


## Preparing the Source

If "*drawn*" seawater is the Ormus source material, collect it from the sea. For more information, review Appendix XX. Even after filtering, living things are always in seawater. Plan to kill the living things by sterilizing the filtered seawater prior to performing the "Wet Process." For more information, see "Pump and Filter Seawater Collection-Information." (Appendix XX.)

If "*reconstituted*" sea is the Ormus source material, it is made by combining one-gallon distilled water with one-cup sea salt and is mixed in a *specific* order. The resultant solution is one-gallon reconstituted sea and this is explained later.

**Start an experiment sheet to document the work.** For more information, see Appendix XI.

**To make reconstituted sea place one-cup of sea salt into an enameled pan or good quality stainless steel pan.** (The dry natural sea salt is to have no anti-caking agent or coloring added.) If an enameled pan is used, make sure there are no chips or breaks in the enameling that show the metal iron underneath and if stainless steel, the pan is to have *no* rusting, *no* flaking, *no* pitting, *no* chipping, *nor* breeching of the stainless steel coating or discoloration that can't be polished away with stainless steel cleansers. See "Labware Choices-Stainless Steel." (Appendix XIV.)

(The generally accepted sea salt to water ratio is one-cup of dry sea salt per gallon distilled water. Others use two-cups sea salt or 1/2 cup sea salt per gallon distilled water. *All these quantities work.* To make a smaller quantity of reconstituted sea, 1/2 cup sea salt is added to 1/2 gallon distilled water. Note: 1/2 gallon is equal to eight cups or two quarts. For more information, see Appendix XII.)

(Adding a lot of sea salt does not make a better reconstituted sea. The reconstituted sea is not to be a concentrated or saturated solution of sea salt as the pH does not rise above pH 9 in concentrated solutions of sea salt.)

**Remove any large visual impurities, by hand, which may be seen in the one-cup of sea salt.**

**Add about four cups and no less than two cups of distilled water to the sea salt.** Add just enough water to dissolve the sea salt and make a highly salted liquid. Purists say to use distilled water - and most Ormus collectors do. However, it is acceptable to use "Magnet Vortex Water Trap" water, "Vortex Water Trap Water" or even good tap water. For more information, see "Magnet Vortex Water Trap." (Section Five.)

(If "water trap" water or (good) tap water is used, organic material has been introduced because there is organic material in these waters, which spoil with time. If the plan is to mail the manna, it is *not* suggested to use these waters and Ormus (manna) collected in the presence of these waters should be stored in the refrigerator (wrapped in aluminum). This potential spoilage is why Ormus collectors usually choose distilled water.)

**Heat the pan over** *low* **heat and a gas flame is** *generally* **preferred**. There is not a consensus on the topic of using "gas" versus "electric" heat in an Ormus process. This is discussed in "Labware Choices-Heat." (Appendix XIV.)

What is generally agreed is that external heat, *especially when heat is applied to cause a "boil,"* places a slightly higher energy state (higher spin) on the Ormus material and this is felt to cause a bit more potency. External heat also causes some of the lighter Ormus material to boil off and these are lost to the collection. Therefore, external heat is another factor said to drive Ormus "away," and in this manner, affects the Ormus (manna). Consequently, when adding external heat, an alchemist will direct you to: "Always use heat as we must - but *only* as much heat needed to do the job." In this step of the "Wet Process" use only the amount of heat necessary to dissolve the salt.

(While standing next to the stove and observing the sea salt dissolving in the pan, you may notice the steam draws towards you. (There is no need to bend over the pot to notice this.) It is possible some of the escaping Ormus will come to you as some believe that Ormus prefers human warmth. This is not readily seen but may be felt and is one reason some say: "the Ormus (product) you make yourself is better than anything you can purchase.")

**Allow the highly salted liquid to cool and then filter it through coffee filters or paper towels dampened with distilled water.** (If the liquid contains "Dead Sea" sea salt it is usually free of particulates and often does not need straining while the highly salted liquid made from "Celtic" sea salt may need multiple filtering.) One dampened filter or paper towel can be used although most stack two or three of them together. The object is to filter out large impurities, which may include sand, from the highly salted liquid. Because the pores of the filter or the paper towel do clog up, use a fresh dampened filter or paper towel as needed. Strain until the highly salted liquid runs through clear.

**Add the remainder of the one-gallon distilled water directly into the filtered and highly salted liquid.** The resulting mixture is now "reconstituted" sea and the Ormus source material in a "Wet Process."

Now, there may be seen a little scum floating on the surface of a reconstituted sea or it may be observed as a small amount of a type of particulate matter. Both are acceptable and some feel the floating material may be Ormus (M-state).

A *warmed* reconstituted sea or drawn seawater is preferred as the precipitation step then occurs as quickly as possible. The drawn seawater (taken from the ocean) can be *gently* heated OR the distilled water used to make a reconstituted sea can first be placed in the sunlight. When the liquid is warm, the precipitation step in a "Wet Process" does proceed noticeably quicker. (Note: A potential idea for another form of *gentle* heating *may* be the heat produced by a small candle as used in chafing dish. It is a thought - and if it works may be helpful.)

**(If Celtic sea salt is used as the sea salt source, the reconstituted sea is covered and boiled gently.)** Use heat as low as possible to maintain the boil for 10-15 minutes to kill any living things that may be there. The Celtic sea is known as a "living" sea while the "Dead Sea" and the "Great Salt *Lake*" in Utah (not to be confused with the "Great Salt Lake *flats*") contain *fewer living organisms* in them because of higher salt content and therefore usually do not need to be boiled. No additional filtering is required after the reconstituted Celtic sea is boiled and cooled.

**Place the reconstituted sea or drawn seawater in an HDPE plastic container.** As a safety measure, place a catch basin under the container. A 5-gallon paint bucket purchased at the hardware store is the appropriate HDPE plastic material. For more information, see "Labware Choices-HDPE." (Appendix XIV.) Borosilicate glass containers are the absolute best but HDPE plastic works fine and are a lot less expensive. You can use a regular glass container instead, but some feel that gold Ormus seems to have an affinity for regular glass and it may hang onto the sides of regular glass and be uncollectible. For this reason and because gold Ormus is prized, many choose to perform a "Wet Process" in HDPE plastic containers versus regular glass containers. This is not to mean regular glass containers cannot be used - regular glass containers can be used to drop Ormus.

**Never use leaded glass containers because the salt and the lye leach out the lead, which is a toxic metal and should not be in the manna.**

### Perform the Process

Add lye solution to reconstituted sea or drawn seawater to obtain a precipitate termed *Ormus* *(manna or Wet Precipitate)*. The longer it takes before the Ormus (manna) ceases to form means more Ormus (manna) is contained in the seawater.

Keep the container out of the sunlight while precipitation is occurring. The presence of sunlight is thought to place a stress on Ormus that causes the finer (lighter) particles of Ormus to be lost. (Iridium Ormus has been said to be the lightest Ormus and is considered one of the three most precious Ormus to the human [the other two are rhodium Ormus and gold Ormus].)

When precipitating Ormus (manna) from a reconstituted sea or drawn seawater, it is helpful to have an easy way of adding lye solution to the liquid. Using an HDPE bottle with an elongated spout cap gives control of the lye solution stream as it enters the liquid. For more information, see appendix XIV and "Resources and Supplies." (Appendix I.) Another useful tool to add controlled amounts of lye solution to the liquid is a "barrel syringe." These are commonly called "oral baby syringes" and are available in barrel sizes of 1ml, 5ml and 10ml. The barrel syringe allows great control over the amount of lye solution entering the seawater. Barrel syringes allow easy calculation of the amount of lye added to the seawater and they are especially handy when processing smaller volumes (one-gallon or less) of a reconstituted sea or drawn seawater.

Lye solution is added to the seawater while stirring constantly until reaching a maximum pH of 10.78. NEVER exceed pH 10.78. Continually stir with a plastic cooking spoon. (A stainless steel spoon is not suggested because of the precautions that revolve around the use of stainless steel.) For more information, see "Labware Choices-Stainless Steel." (Appendix XIV.) Because of the stainless steel precautions, plastic utensils are often used. Add the lye solution until the pH passes the "pH plateau" as described above or rises to a maximum of pH 10.78.

To observe the pH readings, hang the probes of the pH meter into the salty solution. The electrical energy generated from hands affects the pH meter so it is important to clip it to the container or hang it over the side. The use of magnets or electric stirrers is *generally* not preferred as the electric and especially the EMF field may affect the Ormus. There is not a consensus on the topic of using an electric stirrer versus manual stirring in an Ormus process. This is discussed in "Labware Choices-Aluminum" (Appendix XIV). Now, if you choose to use something electric, like an electric beater to help with the stirring, it is preferred that the beaters be made of plastic because if they are made of *stainless steel* there are stringent stainless steel *precautions* to follow. For more information, see "Stainless Steel *Precautions*" (Appendix XIV).

Stir *constantly*, first in a clockwise direction as lye solution is added so there are no areas where the pH may spike to higher than pH 10.78. These areas are called **hot spots** and stirring keeps the distribution of lye solution optimal. (Some have said once Ormus [manna] is seen forming, stir in a counter clockwise manner.) If the pH rises higher than pH 10.78, the Ormus (manna) is considered good only for plant use because the *possibility* of toxic metals exists (as described earlier in this section). Therefore, if this happens consider it a lesson on the Ormus collection "learning curve." It is helpful to establish that mindset now because passing pH 10.78 has happened to all and when it occurs, there is an emotional moment upon realization of "lost" time, effort and expectation. Therefore, a common desire among those new to Ormus processes is to salvage the Ormus (manna). *Don't do it:* Let this be a lesson in learning better techniques then let it go and move on to a fresh batch of reconstituted sea or drawn seawater. *This is the best approach* and alchemists and Ormus collection method presenters will direct you towards it. (The Ormus (manna) that has formed is not a loss in the fullest sense as it can be diluted and given to plants. Appendix XXI explains how this is done.)

---

Now, it is possible, with many restrictions, to lower the pH and re-do a "Wet Process" on this batch of Ormus (manna). This is addressed both for information and because I understand how those new to Ormus collection processes can be hesitant to give up on Ormus (manna) whose pH went too high.

### Here is the Method

You must lower the pH to below pH 9 while never allowing any pocket of pH in the liquid to dip below the pH of 5. (When the pH dips below the pH of 5 the Ormus is felt by some to be lost all together.) To accomplish this, a weak solution of acid is used. A one-half strength solution of the hydrochloric acid (HCl) used in the Ormus dry processes is utilized. For more information, see "Hydrochloric Acid Preparation" (Section Three). An alternative acid is white distilled vinegar as it comes from the bottle, which is 5% strength.

> The pH of the Ormus (manna) containing solution must be reduced to pH 9 while never having hot spots where the pH hits below 5 and a weak solution of acid is used to lower the pH. This is accomplished by adding acid very slowly - maybe a drop or two at a time (depending on the amount of seawater) while constantly stirring. The acid cannot be streamed in or there will surely be a pocket where a pH lower than pH 5 has occurred.
>
> Once the pH is brought to pH 9, a "Wet Process" can be re-performed with lye solution to raise the pH to no higher than pH 10.78.
>
> This is the process to bring the pH back down from precipitated Ormus (manna) and I trust you see value in choosing to use Ormus (manna) that went above pH 10.78 for plants only. There is less energy spent preparing a fresh batch of reconstituted sea or drawn seawater than going through the process of bringing the pH back down.

At pH 8 a few particles may become visible, grow larger and then fall to the bottom of the container. The more Ormus present the more particles are seen to form, and if this occurs, the process takes (a little) longer and more lye solution is used. If Ormus is present, the particles present themselves visibly. They form to the extent of appearing like snow flurries, a snowfall or blizzard. It all depends on how much Ormus is present in the reconstituted sea or drawn seawater. If a lot of particles are seen, more Ormus (manna) is collected and the pH won't substantially rise until a lot of the Ormus (manna) particles have formed (the more particles the more lye solution used). Remember that the cooler the reconstituted sea or drawn seawater, the longer (a little longer) the "drop" takes.

A postulation regarding the Ormus (manna) forming is that Ormus hides in "tight" places to get away from scalar fields and these particles that form during a "Wet Process" create tight places for the Ormus (manna) to go. In addition, the theory holds that Ormus *likes* Ormus and therefore is attracted to "its kind." A focused beam flashlight can be used to watch particles (the doves) form by shining it through the liquid.

The end result of adding lye solution and constantly stirring is the formation of many particles that slowly fall to the bottom (providing there was Ormus present in the source material). The particles seen forming and dropping to the bottom are considered to be "in the box" Ormus (manna) and it is up to the body to pull the Ormus back out of the box to use it. The particles start out as little flakes and grow bigger. When they are large, they are called "doves" because they are big, fluffy, and kind of look like they have wings. This has also been called "Philosopher's Milk." A belief held by some is that they are "superconducting" and line up, thereby becoming heavier (this is what is seen as the doves), then slowly sink to the bottom of the container.

There is the possibility no precipitate occurs ("drawn" seawater always has Ormus in it). If a "reconstituted" sea doesn't form a precipitate, it is because this batch of sea salt had no Ormus left in it. The processing method, the storage method or the shipping method caused the Ormus to leave. This salt is not useful in the body and it is suggested that you do not even bother adding it in the preparation of food. (There are certain applications for this non Ormus-containing salt. First, this sea salt can be utilized as a "nesting" material when storing the aluminum foil clad bottle of washed and diluted Ormus (manna). As a nesting material, pour this *sea salt known to contain no* Ormus all around the bottle(s) of Ormus (manna) as another way of encouraging Ormus not to "wander off." The *presence of the salt acts as some sort of shielding* for the Ormus material and causes the Ormus not to be disturbed and wander off. The Ormus in the manna is considered "locked in the box" and unless disturbed by outside influences, stays put.)

There are times when performing a "Wet Process" that having sea salt with no Ormus in it is useful. For example, I was performing a "Wet Process" on mineral water from the "Warm Mineral Springs" in Northport, Florida. The water from the "Warm Mineral Springs" is purported to be healing waters and I wanted to see if Ormus might be present. The "Warm Mineral Springs," formerly called "Salt Springs," has drinkable mineral water with a high mineral and sodium content (the suggested amount to drink for its minerals is 2oz once a day). Water analysis of the "Warm Mineral Springs" showed a lot of sodium and my line of reasoning was that Ormus might be found in association with this sodium. I observed that water from the "Warm Mineral Springs" did not have a salty taste and wondered if there was enough sodium present for a "Wet Process" to work well. There was very little precipitate while performing a "Wet Process" and I determined to add sodium to the water by adding *sea salt known to contain no Ormus*. By doing this, any precipitate that formed could only have come from the "Warm Mineral Springs" water. For more information, see "Chemistry of the Ormus Processes." (Appendix XXII.)

(Another example that utilized sea salt containing no Ormus occurred when performing a "Wet Process" on pool water from my "Laminar Crystal" swimming pool. A dozen "Laminar Crystals" of varying sizes had been added to the pool (for more information, see "Laminar Crystals" (Section Seven) and the water often changed consistency feeling "thicker" (similar to thin syrup) and routinely displayed a white material of varying thickness, shape and texture floating on the top of the pool. The pool water is clear from the top down, and viewed from under water contained small white round particles that appear suspended in the pool water. (I could not remain in place to determine if they eventually rose to the surface and I saw no evidence that there was a precipitate on the bottom.) Both the water and these particles felt greasy when squeezed in my hand. Since pure Ormus is thought by some to be oil, I wondered if the Laminar Crystal pool water contained Ormus and performed a "Wet Process" on 480ml. of pool water concurrently with 480ml. of tap water. *Sea salt known to contain no Ormus* was added to both the pool water and tap water to make a "reconstituted" sea. The pool water dropped 20ml. of precipitate during the "Wet Process" and no precipitate was observed from tap water.)

If during a "Wet Process" the precipitate doesn't drop until pH10.7 it's not very good - don't even bother eating it or the sea salt used to make it.

**Once particles are observed dropping and the target pH has been met, cover the Ormus (manna) and allow it to settle in the dark for at least 8-12 hours.** It is placed in the dark because Ormus reacts to light. If the Ormus (manna) settles slowly, let it settle 24 hours. Letting the Ormus (manna) settle 24 hours is always better because some Ormus take more time to form the dove (a flake) that drifts to the bottom. By giving the liquid 24 hours to settle, more of this slower forming Ormus (manna) has an opportunity to precipitate. If the precipitate is slow to settle to the bottom, a speculation is that it contains more iridium in it because iridium is said to be light and not settle well. *While iridium is the heaviest element on the planet, in the Ormus form it is said to be the lightest.*

The Ormus (manna) and the liquid over it may be placed in the moonlight of the full moon to charge (energize) it. Actually, leaving items (crystals for example) in the moonlight of the full moon is a way of charging them. To make energetic Ormus (manna) place the precipitate in moonlight and do not let the sunlight strike it. The vibrational resonance of the moon, which is reflected light of the sun, is different form the vibrational resonance of the sun as its rays shine directly.

To recap: Place the *Distilled* water used to reconstitute a "sea" in the sunlight to charge it and place the *precipitated Ormus (manna)* in the moonlight to charge it.

When a glass container is used instead of an HDPE plastic container, particles of Ormus (manna) may be seen clinging to the sides.   Even if they loosen, they re-cling and so it is nearly impossible to capture them with the Ormus (manna) that settles and this is one reason many use an HDPE plastic container in place of glass. (There seems to be an affinity with some Ormus to glass.)

As the precipitate settles, a clear liquid barrier forms over the Ormus (manna) fallen to the bottom of the container.  Up to three gallons of Ormus (manna) may be seen from 15 gallons of reconstituted sea or drawn seawater.

There are *secondary* processes of the "Wet Process" and they are called "Double Drop Processes."   A "Double Drop Process" is performed to coax more Ormus (manna) out of reconstituted sea or drawn seawater.  The volume of Ormus (manna) that forms during a "Double Drop Process" is less than the amount formed during the initial "Wet Process."  There are three different "Double Drop Processes" and the idea behind all of them is the liquid over the settled Ormus (manna) is reused as new Ormus source material.  There are two reasons that a "Double Drop Process" is surmised to work.  The first is that Ormus is still in the clear liquid because it is taking time to make a "dove" (a flake) and therefore didn't fall out when the first "Wet Process" was performed.  For example, rhodium has been said to need two weeks to one month for it to *fully* drop out.  The second reason is that while Ormus is still in the liquid the elements are in a "different state," and with time become a state of Ormus that does precipitate out.

### "Double Drop Process #1"
After the process of precipitating Ormus (manna) in a "Wet Process" is completed, remove the precipitate from *under* the lye liquid.  A turkey baster is a useful tool for this process. If available, a separatory funnel is preferred.  For more information, see "Labware Choices." (Appendix XIV.) Now put a lid or a covering on the container of lye liquid and set it aside in the dark, where it is room temperature, for 24 hours to a week.

When this time has elapsed, test the pH of the lye liquid.  If the pH has gone down, try another "Wet Process" on it by adding lye solution to the target pH of 10.78.  A little bit more Ormus (manna) has been observed to drop.

### "Double Drop Process #2"
After the process of precipitating Ormus (manna) in a "Wet Process" is completed, remove the lye liquid *over* the precipitate (pour the liquid off or remove the precipitate from under the lye liquid). If you remove the Ormus (manna) from below, turkey basters and separatory funnels are useful tools.  Cover the lye liquid with a lid and save.

The *next* time a "Wet Process" is completed, keep the lye liquid resulting from that and combine with the first. Continue combining the lye liquids from completed "Wet Processes" and when enough has been collected, perform "Double Drop Process #2."

This is done by using one gallon of the lye liquid and one-cup of sea salt to make a "reconstituted" sea pretty much as described in "Preparation of the Source Material." (Note: dissolve the sea salt in a little distilled water and then add to the one gallon lye liquid.) Perform a "Wet Process" on the "reconstituted" sea by adding lye solution to the target pH of 10.78. Note: performing the "Double Drop Process #2" also saves on lye solution.

## "Double Drop Process #3"

This may be best called "coaxing a little more out of the lye water." After the process of precipitating Ormus (manna) in the "Wet Process," remove the lye liquid over the Ormus (manna) (pour the liquid off or remove the Ormus (manna) from under the clear liquid). If removing the Ormus (manna) from below, a turkey baster is a useful tool or a separatory funnel. Now *dissolve* one teaspoon or one tablespoon of sea salt (or use one cup of filtered and sterilized "drawn" seawater). *Dissolve* the sea salt by placing one teaspoon (or one tablespoon) of sea salt in one cup of heated distilled water. Add the dissolved sea salt (filter if necessary) or "drawn" seawater to the lye liquid. See if this coaxes more Ormus (manna) from the lye liquid. One teaspoon to 1/2 cup more Ormus (manna) has been observed.

## Purifying (washing)

**Begin purifying the Ormus (manna) by washing it.** Washing is a form of purifying. The Ormus (manna) is washed three times (some do rinse a fourth time). If the Ormus (manna) was made based on any of the moon phases, follow the time frame outlined in "Moon Chart." (Appendix XX.)

Once the Ormus (manna) has settled, covered and in the dark, it is ready to be washed with water (distilled water preferred). Washing removes lye solution and reduces pH. Washing is a form of purifying.

**For the first rinse, the liquid can be drawn from the top of the Ormus (manna) or the Ormus (manna) can be removed from the bottom of the liquid.** This "first" rinse lye solution is a high pH, caustic liquid and *will* burn skin, clothes and eyes if it gets onto them. Follow the cautions for lye at the front of the chapter.

If removing the Ormus (manna) from the bottom of the liquid, turkey basters or separatory funnels are good tools to use. A useful suggestion when drawing out the Ormus (manna) is to put it in a pilsner style beer glass (or any other container narrower on the bottom than at the top). When the container is this shape, rinsing the Ormus (manna) is more efficient because as the rinse water is poured off there is more control of the Ormus (manna) on the bottom and therefore little of it is lost. This shaped glassware works well for smaller batches (under two gallons) of "reconstituted" sea or "drawn" seawater. When processing higher volumes of reconstituted sea or drawn seawater a larger container than pilsner glassware is needed to collect the Ormus (manna) for rinsing.

The other method of washing involves decanting the liquid by slowly tipping the container and pouring out the top liquid. Be careful not to pour out the precipitate! If the precipitate drifts up, stop pouring and let it settle again before continuing to pour. Decant as much liquid as possible. If the precipitate drifts up, let it settle. Then a turkey baster (or barrel syringe) can be used to draw off additional liquid. Next, pour the Ormus (manna) into a pilsner style beer glass - or any approved container. Note: *Any container shape can be chosen and the container can also be HDPE plastic.*

**Add an equal amount of distilled water to the Ormus (manna) filled container as you see Ormus (manna) precipitate plus any remaining liquid over it.** Purists say to use distilled water - and most Ormus collectors do. However, it is acceptable to use "Magnet Vortex Water Trap" water, "Vortex Water Trap" water or even good tap water. (For more information, see "Magnet Vortex Water Trap" in Section Five). If "Magnet Vortex Water Trap" water or (good) tap water is used, organic material has been introduced because there is organic material in these waters, which spoil with time. If the plan is to mail the Ormus (manna), it is not suggested to use these waters and Ormus (manna) collected in the presence of these waters should be stored in the refrigerator (wrapped in aluminum). This potential spoilage is why Ormus collectors usually choose distilled water.

*It does make a difference how much rinse water is added* to the Ormus (manna). With every batch of rinse water, some of the manna is thought to dissolve and once dissolved it doesn't re-precipitate back to Ormus (manna). Additionally, with every batch of rinse water, the Ormus said to be in the liquid is lost. Therefore, using more water than is necessary per wash, or washing the Ormus (manna) too often, causes it to become less potent. Consequently, this washing step is performed *three times* (*some* do wash the precipitate four times).

(Note: The original liquid from the first wash can be diluted in bathwater or *much* diluted as a foot soak because Ormus is contained in that water. *Dilute this first wash water very well* to a pH of 7. Normal *skin tolerates acids* (pH less than 7) *more than bases* (pH greater than 7) because skin is naturally mildly acidic having a general pH range of pH 4.0 to pH 5.5. Normal skin can generally tolerate pH ranges of pH 4.5 to pH 7. However, the pH of liquid from this first wash is a *strongly* "alkaline" solution of pH 10.78 - or very close to it. Therefore, this solution is *corrosive* and will burn and scar the skin. Lye solution also has a degreasing action that removes the skins protective barrier. *Even* **well** *diluted, the lye solution may act as an irritant to the skin therefore dilute the lye solution with a great deal of fresh water).* If rinse water is used for plants, it is said to use the rinse water from the third (or fourth) wash. Don't use the first or second rinse water for plants because of the corrosiveness and salt content of the liquid. For information on Ormus (manna) use in plants, see "Usage in Plants/Agriculture." (Appendix XXI.)

**Stir the Ormus (manna) OR stir and bubble air downward from a turkey baster into it.** If stirring, use a plastic or glass stirrer. If bubbling, use a turkey baster by squeezing the bulb so air injects into the precipitate on the bottom of the container. By bubbling air through the precipitate in this manner the Ormus (manna) is fluffed and washed by both the moving air and water. By adding bubbling air the Ormus (manna) may be more thoroughly rinsed.

**When finished stirring or stirring and bubbling, cover the Ormus (manna) and let it settle again before removing the liquid from the top of the precipitate.**

**Remove the liquid from the top of the Ormus (manna).** If the Ormus (manna) had been drawn *up* from the bottom during the first wash, it is only drawn up from the bottom for the *first* wash. After the first wash, decant the liquid from the top in subsequent rinses. Once a lot of the liquid is removed off the top, a turkey baster (or barrel syringe) can be used to draw off even more water from the top leaving the Ormus (manna) on the bottom of the container.

**For the second time, add an equal amount of distilled water plus any remaining liquid over the Ormus (manna).** Distilled water is preferred as explained above.

**Rinse the Ormus (manna) by stirring or stirring and bubbling (as explained above).**

**Cover the Ormus (manna) and let it settle again before removing the liquid from the top of the precipitate.**

**For the third time add an equal amount of distilled water as there is Ormus (manna) plus any remaining liquid over it.**

**Rinse again using the same guidelines.**
It has been said that there are no concerns about overwashing the Ormus (manna) when these guidelines (three rinses) are followed, (some do a fourth rinse). After the third wash, dilute the Ormus (manna) as described below and store it.

**To dilute the Ormus (manna) add distilled water.** The most common ratio is 1:1. Add an equal amount of distilled water *plus* any remaining liquid over the Ormus (manna). Twice-as-much or half-as-much distilled water may be used. It depends on how thick an Ormus product is desired. (Too little water may cause the texture of the Ormus (manna) to be less palatable). Note: when adding the water, this is a good time to imprint/charge the Ormus (manna). For more information, see "Imprinting/Charging." (Appendix XVIII.)
(Aloe juice, "Magnet Vortex Water Trap" water, "Vortex Water Trap" water or tap water may be used *in place of distilled water to dilute the Ormus (manna).* If they are used, the Ormus (manna) must be stored under refrigeration as these materials are organic and will spoil. Aloe is said to enhance absorption and is a source of rhodium and iridium. Therefore, it can make sense to use aloe juice to dilute the Ormus (manna) *currently* used.)

**If, after adding the distilled water the Ormus (manna) doesn't taste a little salty, add sea salt crystals (to taste).** This may take one or two or a number of the individual sea salt crystals - it depends on how much Ormus (manna) there is. I use Celtic sea salt. It is generally felt that the Ormus (manna) needs to be a *little* salty. Salt protects it and gives it a "happy" home and therefore it stays put, allowing for prolonged storage time. (**Do not use Dead Sea salt** for this application because Dead Sea salt is not "salty" tasting. Dead Sea Salt contains a lot of magnesium and it tastes like concentrated milk of magnesia. Adding it to Ormus (manna) causes the manna to be unpalatable.)

**Storage**

**Store the Ormus (manna) in HDPE containers in a cool, dry dark place.** HDPE is chosen over glass because Ormus has been observed to tunnel into glass in order to get away from cold and spin-disturbing waves. It is thought that over time, this may cause the glass to break. For more information, see Appendix XIV. It is noted that Ormus (manna) collected from a "Wet Process" is considered "locked in the box" of the particles of the Ormus (manna) so it is considered relatively stable and generally doesn't travel off.

**Individual bottles of washed and diluted Ormus (manna) are always wrapped in aluminum foil and stored out of the sunlight and at least six feet from EMF wave producing appliances.** The presence of light is thought by many to (slowly) degrade the Ormus (manna) - even bringing a portion back to the metal element. Although this conversion to metal is a slow process, store the bottles away from all forms of light, the most offending of which is UV rays (sunlight). The aluminum foil wrap seems to help retard scalar (spin) fields and provide some shielding from radio frequency waves. For more information, see "Labware Choices-Aluminum Foil." (Appendix XIV.)

**Label the containers of Ormus (manna) using mailing labels covered with clear shipping tape.** It is helpful to record the date the Ormus (manna) was collected and the Ormus source material used. Place another label on the outside of the aluminum foil over wrap so information about the manna is easily seen.

It has been suggested by some that Ormus (manna) is used within one year. To be on the safe side while storing Ormus (manna) *long term*, keep it away from electromagnetic fields (EMF) of electrical appliances like stoves and refrigerators. For more information, see Appendix XIV. For storage of the bottle of Ormus (manna) currently being used, refrigeration may be ok. There is no clear consensus regarding this. Some say to refrigerate the container because the Ormus supplement gravitates to body heat - others say not to refrigerate because the Ormus (manna) is near the electromagnetic field of the refrigerator motor.

(Adding aloe, "Magnet Vortex Water Trap" water, "Vortex Water Trap" water or tap water is *not* advised for long-term storage or if mailing and if mailing Ormus (manna) it is suggested to follow guidelines outlined in "General Ormus Information.") (Appendix VI.)

*A suggestion is to store the Ormus (manna) in metal cans (the type that draws a magnet) with or without sea salt placed between the can and the Ormus (manna) container.* The salt used for this application can be sea salt that demonstrated it had no Ormus in it (not forming a precipitate during a "Wet Process.") This is a way to find use for sea salt that otherwise would have no use. The salt chosen can also be the inexpensive Morton® Safe-T-Salt Rock Salt and another salt source for this application is the salt used in making ice cream. Sources for metal cans include paint cans, holiday popcorn cans, cans that held potato chips and those that contained candy or bottles of liquor. I have seen garden seeds packed in metal cans.

For additional protection from electromagnetic fields, the metal canister may be stored inside a *metal* (the type that a magnet is drawn to) file cabinet. Metal (made of steel) is thought to be the best storage material because it *shunts* electromagnetic fields around it and somehow shields the state of the Ormus material.

### Final Thought

*It is noteworthy that a precipitate does not drop from every batch of sea salt (a precipitate always forms in "drawn" seawater). This causes pause and a realization of how there must be "a" something in sea salt that can either be present or not be present: A something that can be there or can be driven away. If each batch of sea salt were to make a precipitate and make it to the same degree, it would be easy to categorize this work as "conventional" chemistry.*

In addition, varying amounts of Ormus (manna) have dropped from the same batch of *sea salt on different days of the year.* Much experimental work can be done to "quantify" this statement. For example: In this observation, questions may be asked and refined tests performed such that more definitive statements are made. These questions include: Are the varying amounts of precipitate the *same* amounts when collected on the *same* day of *different* years? It may be possible that when different years are factored in a variation does not occur. What is the accuracy of the weight of sea salt? Is a cup dipped into the bulk supply or is the sea salt weighed on a scale? What storage provisions are made to ensure that the Ormus in the sea salt does not leave? Who is performing the "Wet Process?" Is it the same individual or different individuals? Are their techniques becoming more refined with time? How quickly is the lye solution added? What is the rate of stirring and the temperature? All these variables are known to affect the appearance of a precipitate. (This train of thought has been included to reinforce by examples how the study of Ormus is in its infancy.)

Do not work with lye in "fear" as it is thought that feeling fear at the time of the work causes an "imprint" of fear onto the Ormus (manna). *Work with lye in "respect" rather than "fear."* The emotions surrounding fear also cause a mind to "close off;" this results in making the steps of an Ormus collection process very difficult to absorb.

The use of pH test papers (litmus tests) in place of a pH meter is not addressed. These papers are not as accurate and in this day of fairly inexpensive pH meters, there is little point in using pH test papers and risking the possibility of overshooting the pH 10.78 endpoint. If test papers are used, a suggestion is to bring the pH only up to pH 9.5. This ensures the liquid is less than pH 10.78. (Some of the Ormus from the seawater is not collected because Ormus (manna) drops out of solution up to (and even through) pH 10.78.)

Those who wish to ingest Ormus (manna) must find their own dosage from an Ormus product because some individuals may be more sensitive than others. In one cup of Ormus (manna) there is often enough for a month of supplementation. Ormus (manna) has also been given to plants and animals and used in agriculture. For more information, see "Usage and Directions." (Appendix XXI.)

When washing containers and other equipment used during a "Wet Process", there may be observed a dried white ring in the container and dried white spots on it. These are easily removed with a solution of 3/4 part white vinegar and 1/4 part water.

As a point of interest, *well* water can drop an Ormus precipitate and it can also taste salty and fishy, however, unless performing an experiment, the amount of Ormus precipitate is not worth the time. It is interesting that Ormus (manna) can have a "fishy" taste about it no matter if sea salt or well water was used as the Ormus source material. (It may be interesting to see if "fish" have a high Ormus content.)

After a "Wet Process" is completed and the Ormus (manna) has settled, there may be a small amount of particulate matter floating on the surface. Some feel that the floating material may be

Ormus (M-state). It is not possible to collect this material although it has been said that ancient alchemists may have lifted it from the top of the liquid with a feather. (Note: A potential idea to collect this floating particulate material *may* be to lift it up with a piece of filter paper. It is a thought - and may be worth experimentation.)

Performing a "Wet Process" on city water, unless performing an experiment is not recommended if fluoride has been added. If you choose to experiment with city water, draw water the night before and let it sit out overnight - or at least a day or so to dissipate the chlorine which is often present. Be aware that any fluoride will still be present.

*Once you understand Ormus processes, it may be seen how all we are doing is adding technology to something that is more of a natural element.*

How is it known that Ormus is in the Ormus (manna)? When the wet precipitate is assayed, the metal form of the element does not show as present. After the precipitate is dried and fired (burned) with sulfur (the sulfur drops it to a metal form) metal shows up as present in an assay. *Consequently, it may be argued that the metal element was in the precipitate in a different state and was not detected in that state.*

Superconductivity in Ormus (manna) may be demonstrated. For more information, see "Basic Explanation-Final Thought." (Appendix VII.)

The following note regards bottles that have color. While this information does not directly relate to a "Wet Process", you may find it interesting or useful. It is written that water placed in a blue bottle and set in the sun for about an hour and a half creates highly charged water beneficial to the body. You may wish to experiment with blue glass containers if "charging" (as described in "Information") the distilled water used to make "reconstituted" sea. (*http://www.PsiTek.net*) (Web search: *Blue Solar Water*)

## Detailed Composition of Seawater
### at 3.5% salinity

| Element | Atweight | ppm | Element | Atweight | ppm |
|---|---|---|---|---|---|
| Hydrogen H2O | 1.00797 | 110,000 | Molybdenum Mo | 0.09594 | 0.01 |
| Oxygen H2O | 15.9994 | 883,000 | Ruthenium Ru | 101.07 | 0.0000007 |
| Sodium NaCl | 22.9898 | 10,800 | Rhodium Rh | 102.905 | . |
| Chlorine NaCl | 35.453 | 19,400 | Palladium Pd | 106.4 | . |
| Magnesium Mg | 24.312 | 1,290 | Argentum (silver) Ag | 107.870 | 0.00028 |
| Sulfur S | 32.064 | 904 | Cadmium Cd | 112.4 | 0.00011 |
| Potassium K | 39.102 | 392 | Indium In | 114.82 | . |
| Calcium Ca | 10.08 | 411 | Stannum (tin) Sn | 118.69 | 0.00081 |
| Bromine Br | 79.909 | 67.3 | Antimony Sb | 121.75 | 0.00033 |
| | | | Tellurium Te | 127.6 | . |
| Helium He | 4.0026 | 0.0000072 | Iodine I | 166.904 | 0.064 |
| Lithium Li | 6.939 | 0.170 | Xenon Xe | 131.30 | 0.000047 |
| Beryllium Be | 9.0133 | 0.0000006 | Cesium Cs | 132.905 | 0.0003 |
| Boron B | 10.811 | 4.450 | Barium Ba | 137.34 | 0.021 |
| Carbon C | 12.011 | 28.0 | Lanthanum La | 138.91 | 0.0000029 |
| Nitrogen ion | 14.007 | 15.5 | Cerium Ce | 140.12 | 0.0000012 |
| Fluorine F | 18.998 | 13 | Praesodymium Pr | 140.907 | 0.00000064 |
| Neon Ne | 20.183 | 0.00012 | Neodymium Nd | 144.24 | 0.0000028 |
| Aluminium Al | 26.982 | 0.001 | Samarium Sm | 150.35 | 0.00000045 |
| Silicon Si | 28.086 | 2.9 | Europium Eu | 151.96 | 0.0000013 |
| Phosphorus P | 30.974 | 0.088 | Gadolinium Gd | 157.25 | 0.0000007 |
| Argon Ar | 39.948 | 0.450 | Terbium Tb | 158.924 | 0.00000014 |
| Scandium Sc | 44.956 | <0.000004 | Dysprosium Dy | 162.50 | 0.00000091 |
| Titanium Ti | 47.90 | 0.001 | Holmium Ho | 164.930 | 0.00000022 |
| Vanadium V | 50.942 | 0.0019 | Erbium Er | 167.26 | 0.00000087 |
| Chromium Cr | 51.996 | 0.0002 | Thulium Tm | 168.934 | 0.00000017 |
| Manganese Mn | 54.938 | 0.0004 | Ytterbium Yb | 173.04 | 0.00000082 |
| Ferrum (Iron) Fe | 55.847 | 0.0034 | Lutetium Lu | 174.97 | 0.00000015 |
| Cobalt Co | 58.933 | 0.00039 | Hafnium Hf | 178.49 | <0.000008 |
| Nickel Ni | 58.71 | 0.0066 | | | |
| | | | Tantalum Ta | 180.948 | <0.0000025 |
| Copper Cu | 63.54 | 0.0009 | Tungsten W | 183.85 | <0.000001 |
| Zinc Zn | 65.37 | 0.005 | Rhenium Re | 186.2 | 0.0000084 |
| Gallium Ga | 69.72 | 0.00003 | Osmium Os | 190.2 | . |
| Germanium Ge | 72.59 | 0.00006 | Iridium Ir | 192.2 | . |
| Arsenic As | 74.922 | 0.0026 | Platinum Pt | 195.09 | . |
| Selenium Se | 78.96 | 0.0009 | Aurum (gold) Au | 196.967 | 0.000011 |
| Krypton Kr | 83.80 | 0.00021 | Mercury Hg | 200.59 | 0.00015 |
| Rubidium Rb | 85.47 | 0.120 | Thallium Tl | 204.37 | . |
| Strontium Sr | 87.62 | 8.1 | Lead Pb | 207.19 | 0.00003 |
| Yttrium Y | 88.905 | 0.000013 | Bismuth Bi | 208.980 | 0.00002 |
| Zirconium Zr | 91.22 | 0.000026 | Thorium Th | 232.04 | 0.0000004 |
| Niobium Nb | 92.906 | 0.000015 | Uranium U | 238.03 | 0.0033 |
| | | | Plutonimu Pu | (244) | . |

ppm= parts per million = mg/liter = 0.001g/kg
Source: Karl K Turekian: Oceans, 1968, Prentice-Hall
Reprinted by SeaAgri Inc., P.O. Box 88237
Dunwoody, GA 30356  (770) 361-7003

NOTES:

> *"To him who concerns himself with Alchemy, may Nature, Reason, Experience, and Reading be guide, staff, spectacles and lantern."*
>
>                                    Atalanta Fgiens, by Michael Maier

# HYDROCHLORIC ACID (HCl) PREPARATION

Note:  There are appendices that have cross-referencing information to that in this chapter. These include: "List of Resources and Supplies,"
"Common Measurement Conversions"
"Best Practices Labware Choices"

---

**CAUTION!!**
Note:  Cautions are a form of education so that you may work with hydrochloric acid in awareness and respect not fear.

Hydrochloric acid is an acidic reagent and if it is in contact with eyes, it can damage them by rendering the cornea opaque, a form of irreparable eye damage. If hydrochloric acid gets into eyes, **flush the eyeball with water immediately** and seek medical attention if the burning persists.  If hydrochloric acid contacts the skin, it hurts and damages it.  Hydrochloric acid reacts with skin tissue and can cause permanent damage and scarring if severe.  Even minor reactions can be very painful.  If hydrochloric acid contacts clothes, it damages them.  If hydrochloric acid gets onto your clothes or body, immediately **flush the area with lots of water** and seek medical attention if necessary.

It is very helpful to work near a sink, faucet or other source of wash water.

The area must be well ventilated as breathing fumes from hydrochloric acid can damage air passages and lungs.  Handle hydrochloric acid with adequate ventilation such as a laboratory range hood vented outside or conduct the work outside.  An open stock bottle of hydrochloric acid creates corrosive fumes and when added to water a pungent corrosive "fog" forms.  Do not breathe fumes or fog.  It is advisable to keep a bottle of baking soda solution handy to use against spills and baking soda powder can be sprinkled on if the spill is large.

For more information and cautions when using hydrochloric acid, see "The Chemicals of the Processes." (Appendix XIII.)

When working with hydrochloric acid, or any chemical, avoid touching your face or rubbing your eyes.  Do not handle around food.  Do not dump wastewater on the ground.  Hydrochloric acid is generally safe to put down the drain, but first run water in the sink while slowly pouring the hydrochloric acid directly into the drain and don't mix it with any "pH alkaline" material that may be in the drain as it can react explosively.

When working with hydrochloric acid, please wear goggles or a full-face visor (an industrial face protector), neoprene gloves and a PVC lab apron as well as protective clothing such as long sleeves and long pants.

Keep children and pets away from the work area and do not leave it unattended. Even if no one is around, an unsuspecting person could venture by and be at risk.

---

## Labware and Supplies to make hydrochloric acid

Food grade hydrochloric acid, distilled water, stirrer of plastic or borosilicate glass, glass container (borosilicate glass preferred), glass container for storage, safety clothing and equipment.

For more information, see "Best Practices Labware Choices" (Appendix XIV).

As a safety measure, always place containers used in the process into a larger non-metallic catch basin (*in case of leakage or breakage*).  For example: A (new) cat litter box or the bottom of an under-the-bed storage container.

## Definition

Oxidized non-metals make a "pH acidic" material. For example, hydrochloric acid is an oxidized non-metal. Hydrogen (H+) is the non-metal. The chemical formula of hydrochloric acid is HCl and it is an acid-an "acidic" substance. **An "acidic" substance has a pH of less than pH 7 (a "basic" substance, termed alkaline, has a pH of greater than 7)**. A pH of pH 7 is "neutral."

## Information

Appearance: Hydrochloric acid is a clear liquid. Hydrochloric acid is an acid and can hurt us if handled improperly (see above).

Hydrochloric acid has many uses including that of a strong cleaning agent for tile, grout and concrete. Therefore, it is seen in cleaning mixtures. **Do not use hydrochloric acid mixtures** as might be found as a common ingredient mixed into grout cleaners, tile cleaners, some lime away products, some toilet cleaners, humidifier cleaners, some spa cleansers, etc. (We use hydrochloric acid in its *pure* form in the Ormus collection processes. The pure form comes as a clear liquid.)

The pure form of hydrochloric acid (HCl) is used to make the diluted hydrochloric acid used in the *dry* Ormus collection processes. The pure form of hydrochloric acid also goes by the name "Muriatic acid."

Hydrochloric acid is a chemical that maintains proper pH in swimming pool water. Therefore, a common source for pure hydrochloric acid is pool supply stores. Either pure hydrochloric acid or sulfuric acid maintains proper pH in swimming pool water and therefore pool supply stores stock them both. Therefore, *visually confirm that the container is hydrochloric acid and not sulfuric acid*

Hydrochloric acid has been seen sporadically at *Lowe's* or *Home Depot*.

Hydrochloric acid (Muratic acid) is sold in 31% and 35% concentration. *All of the dry* Ormus collection processes use 20% strength hydrochloric acid. Therefore, the stock bottle of hydrochloric acid is diluted with distilled water to achieve 20% strength.

Make sure you understand the procedure and have the proper equipment and supplies before starting.

Do not work with hydrochloric acid in fear. *Work with hydrochloric acid in "respect" not "fear."* The emotions surrounding fear" also cause a mind to "close off;" this results in making the steps of a procedure very difficult to absorb.

## Perform the Process

**These are the mathematical figures in diluting hydrochloric acid:**

- If hydrochloric acid is 31% strength, add 65ml. into 35ml. distilled water to make 100ml.
- If hydrochloric acid is 35% strength, add 57ml. into 43ml. distilled water to make 100ml.

These mathematical figures *do not* have to be met *exactly*; it is adequate to use roughly half-and-half the ratio or a little more acid than water. (The *useful* hydrochloric acid concentration in the Ormus processes is a range of strengths from 18-20 %.) The reason that the 18-20% range is chosen is that the "target pH" point in *dry* Ormus collection processes is pH 8.5 (this is discussed later) and the hydrochloric acid concentration is not to be so weak that an unwieldy amount of acid must be added to attain this pH or so strong that the target pH is easily overshot.

**Measure the hydrochloric acid and distilled water in separate (glass) measuring containers.** These materials should be handled outside.

**Slowly add hydrochloric acid to distilled water (in a glass container).** The liquid can splash out of the container if the hydrochloric acid is dumped into the water rather than being added slowly. When diluting hydrochloric always add the acid into distilled water and always use a catch basin. (If water is added to hydrochloric acid it may sputter and could splatter on you.)

**Stir to mix the hydrochloric acid and the distilled water.** Use a plastic utensil or glass-stirring rod.

## Storage

**Store the diluted hydrochloric acid in glass.** Borosilicate glass is the best type to use although regular glass also works. For more information, see "Labware Choices-Borosilicate Glass." (Appendix XIV.) For safety, store the glass bottle containing diluted hydrochloric acid in a catch basin (in the event the bottle breaks).

(Note: A household type item that can be useful for storage is the glass container of a 40oz beer bottle covered with a plastic lid. A metal lid is not used because fumes from hydrochloric acid corrode metal. Saran Wrap® cannot be placed as a dividing material between metal and glass because it corrodes.)

**Label the bottle of hydrochloric acid "Hydrochloric Acid (HCl)-Poison"** so the bottle is not to be confused with something else.

**While performing an Ormus Collection Process, the diluted hydrochloric acid may be placed in HDPE bottles.**

You may remember the white precipitate from the "Wet Process" and expect that all Ormus precipitates are white. All Ormus precipitates are not pure white.

## DRY PROCESS
## (Cold Fire Process)

Note: There are appendices that have cross-referencing information to that in this chapter. These include: "List of Ormus Resources and Supplies," "Common Measurement Conversions," "Best Practices Labware Choices," "pH Meter" and "Sources for the Ormus Processes." For "Lye Solution Preparation" and "Hydrochloric Acid Preparation" see previous chapters in this section.

### Labware and Supplies to perform a "Dry Process" (Cold Fire Process)

Ormus source material, lye solution, hydrochloric acid, distilled water, pH meter, container made of HDPE plastic (to house the lye solution as it disaggregates the Ormus source material), borosilicate glass container (to perform the process in), measuring cup, aluminum foil, barrel syringe or baster, funnel or flat strainer, filters (*unbleached* coffee filters), focus beam flashlight, catch basin, plastic stirrer (or borosilicate glass), safety clothing/equipment and HDPE container (to store finished manna). The hydrochloric acid used as "reagent" in the process can be placed in an HDPE plastic bottle. For more information, see "Best Practices Labware Choices." (Appendix XIV.)

As a safety measure, always place containers used in the process into a larger non-metallic catch basin (*in case of leakage or breakage*). For example: A (new) cat litter box or the bottom of an under-the-bed storage container. (Note: When adding the hydrochloric acid, a lot of heat is generated that could break the glass.)

To best ensure electromagnetic waves cause no interference on the stability of Ormus in source material or the manna (precipitate), it is prudent to keep the work and storage area six feet or more away from them. For more information, see "Labware Choices-Aluminum Foil." (Appendix XIV.)

---

**CAUTION!!**

Note:  Cautions are a form of education so that you may work with lye and hydrochloric acid in awareness and respect not fear.

Lye is a "caustic." Hydrochloric acid is an acid.  Both lye and hydrochloric acid are strong chemicals and can damage eyes by rendering the cornea opaque, a form of irreparable eye damage.  If lye or hydrochloric acid gets into eyes flush the eyeball with water immediately and seek medical attention if the burning persists.

If lye or hydrochloric acid contacts the skin it hurts and damages it.  Lye or hydrochloric acid reacts with skin tissue and can cause permanent damage and scarring if severe.  Even minor reactions can be painful.  If lye or hydrochloric acid contacts clothes it damages them.  If lye or hydrochloric acid gets onto your clothes or body, immediately flush the area with lots of water and seek medical attention if necessary.

It is very helpful to work near a sink, faucet or other source of wash water.

The area must be well ventilated as breathing fumes from lye or hydrochloric acid can damage air passages and lungs.  Lye solution creates caustic fumes.  Do not breathe in these fumes.  Hydrochloric acid creates a pungent, corrosive "fog" when added to water.  Do not breathe in this fog.  Handle lye or hydrochloric acid with adequate ventilation such as a laboratory range hood vented outside or conduct the work outside.  It is advisable to keep a bottle of baking soda solution handy to use against hydrochloric acid spills (baking soda powder can be sprinkled on if the spill is large) and a spray bottle of distilled white vinegar handy to use against lye spills.

For more information, see "The Chemicals of the Processes." (Appendix XIII.)

When working with lye or hydrochloric acid, (or any chemical) avoid touching your face or rubbing your eyes.  Do not handle around food.  Do not dump wastewater on the ground.  Lye is generally safe to put down the drain, but first run water in the sink while slowly pouring the lye directly into the drain and don't mix it with any acid that may be in the drain as it can react explosively.  Hydrochloric acid is generally safe to put down the drain, but first run water in the sink while slowly pouring the hydrochloric acid directly into the drain and don't mix it with any "pH alkaline" material that may be in the drain as it can react explosively.

When working with lye or hydrochloric acid, please wear goggles or a full-face visor (an industrial face protector), neoprene gloves and a PVC lab apron as well as protective clothing such as long sleeves and long pants.

Keep children and pets away from the work area and do not leave it unattended.  Even if no one is around, an unsuspecting person could venture by and be at risk.

---

## Definition

Because the Ormus source material is dry (or dried-out), this collection method is termed the "Dry Process."

The "Dry Process (Cold Fire Process)" as well as any of the other *dry* processes allows Ormus to be extracted from *dry* or dried-out material.

The heat for this process comes from the lye solution (the "secret fire").  The secret fire is explained in "Lye Solution Preparation-Final Thought."

Source material for this process includes organic (biological) material such as carrot pulp, material from the mineral kingdom (such as ancient seabeds or dry land minerals like black sand) and other non-*metallic* material.

**Information**

Appearance: The collected Ormus is observed as a fluffy precipitate (not always a brilliant white color) in liquid.

Since the "Dry Process (Cold Fire Process)" does not add heat from an external source (external heat), this process is considered both a valuable Ormus collection process and a process that the average Ormus collector is able to perform. Any Ormus process which uses external heat *especially when heat is applied to cause a "boil,"* is generally thought to place a slightly higher energy state (higher spin) on the Ormus material and this is felt to cause a bit more potency. It is also felt that more precipitate forms during a process that does not cause a boil. When boiling, some of the lighter Ormus boils off and therefore lost to the collection. For more information, see "Labware Choices-Heat." (Appendix XIV.)

The *chemical* burning created by the lye solution (not external heat) is utilized in this Ormus collection process to physically *disaggregate* (disintegrate) the Ormus source material and release the Ormus within. Ancient alchemists referred to lye solution as the "secret fire" therefore the "Dry Process" is also referred to as the "Cold Fire Process." The secret fire has been explained in "Lye Solution Preparation-Final Thought."

All Ormus collection processes use the *same* lye solution concentration. For more information, see "Lye Solution Preparation." (Section Three.) The pH of the lye solution is a little higher than pH 12.

The *"Living Menstruum"*: By soaking the *dry* Ormus source in lye solution (the "secret fire"), an "Ormus-containing lye medium" forms. This is termed "living menstruum" because Ormus is now *in* the lye liquid. This soaking step is theorized to allow Ormus to break free from the dry Ormus source material and "tie" to the lye solution. The Ormus is "tied" to the lye solution in one of two ways. First, the source material can be soaked in lye solution and the mixture *stirred* twice a day for several weeks *or* the source material can be added to the lye liquid and the mixture *boiled* as done in the *dry* "Lye Boil Process" explained in the next chapter. During a later step of the process, the "collection" step, hydrochloric acid is added to the living menstruum. A precipitate forms and falls to the bottom of the container where it is collected.

*Any* process where the Ormus source material is a *dry* (or dried-out) source falls under a general heading of a *dry* process and Section Four lists *several specific dry processes*. Even if the Ormus source material starts out a wet source - such as an organic item like carrot - it is reduced to a *dry* state before the process begins. *All* source materials used in *dry* processes must be clean (rinsed or washed), in small particle size and drained of all water (being completely dry is even better). If performing a process that includes a *burn*, such as the *dry* "Lye Burn Process, the *dry* "Lye Burn and Boil Process or the *dry* "Sodium Burn Process, the source material must be *completely dry* and this is explained in a later chapter. For information on Ormus source materials see "Sources for the Ormus Processes." (Appendix VIII.)

Dried carrot pulp is used as the Ormus source material while explaining the "Dry Process." Carrots are a good source material for the "Dry Process (Cold Fire Process)" because they are rich in iridium and rhodium and these elements are valued in the Ormus processes. (Iridium, rhodium and gold are the three elements most valued in the Ormus collection processes). For more information, see "Ormus Information." (Appendix VI.)

Carrots are a physically aggregated cellular material. To prepare any source material for an Ormus process it must first be physically disaggregated (disintegrated). Using common vernacular it may be said that we "tear it apart." Ancient alchemists would use terms such as: *disassociate, decompound* and cause *decomposition*. (From *Collectanea Chemica* by *Eirenaeus Philalethes et al, 1893*.)

The tighter the physical aggregation of molecules in an Ormus source, the more energetically active (dangerous) processes are required to unlock the Ormus from the source material. (These more energetically active processes add varying degrees of *heat*.) We use the term "unlock" and ancient alchemists would have termed it "opening" the source as the now opened molecules of source material allow Ormus to leach out and thereby becomes available for collection. The molecules of some Ormus source materials are *not highly physically aggregated*, (such as carrots), and therefore require *less* energetically active (dangerous) Ormus collection processes. (It does become more difficult when physically disaggregating the aggregation of molecules in tightly bound materials such as the metallic bonds in gold or copper. The "Dry Process" is not useful for this purpose as the lye solution (the "secret fire") does not provide enough *energetics to properly* disaggregate (disintegrate) metal bonds.)

Other sources for the "Dry Process" may include minerals like magnetite, pureganic minerals®, humic shale and volcanic ash. Platinum group Ormus or rare earths may be present in these source materials and therefore the Ormus made from them would be expected to be good. These minerals are in a *powdered or granulated* form and while the molecules in these materials are more aggregated than dried carrot, the particles are small and the materials not overly dense. Therefore, the "Dry Process (Cold Fire Process)" disaggregates the molecules and allows the formation of collectable Ormus.

(These minerals are also good Ormus source materials in the *dry* "Lye Boil Process" where *external* heat is added to produce a boiling of the lye solution. This boiling disintegrates the molecules in the powdered or granulated minerals to a greater degree than the "Dry Process." The *dry* "Lye Boil Process" is discussed in Section Four and has been mentioned now to describe how there *are* Ormus collection processes which provide greater heat than the "secret fire" of lye solution utilized in the "Dry Process.")

Any organic or mineral source known to be *edible* (non-toxic) is a candidate for the "Dry Process." If using an Ormus source material you do not know is edible and it makes a precipitate, at the very least send the *precipitate* off or an assay. For more information on laboratory assays, see "Sources for the Processes-Information" (Appendix VIII).

**Note:** There is an exception regarding silver as an Ormus source material. This is discussed in "Sources for the Processes-Metal." (Appendix VIII).

The "Dry Process" (and all of the dry processes) involves two noticeable occurrences: an *"energetic phenomenon"* and a *"pH Plateau."*

The energetic phenomenon is observed as the pH of the lye menstruum *rises* when hydrochloric acid is added. Because hydrochloric acid is *acidic*, the pH is expected to *lower*. *Observing the pH rise is not initially expected, but does happen in the Ormus processes.*

A "pH plateau" is also observed. The pH first rises and then it *levels off* as hydrochloric acid continues to be added. Once passing the pH plateau, the pH begins to lower rather quickly. When the pH of the "living menstruum" reaches pH 8.5 the process is finished.

Remember: *The process is finished when the living menstruum reaches pH 8.5.* The target pH of

8.5 is an "actual" pH. Calibrate the pH meter, determine any variance in its readings and factor that variance into pH readings. For more information, see "pH Meter." (Appendix XV.)

Some say that many of the Ormus materials precipitate at pH 6 - 8 (gold, osmium, palladium, platinum and rhodium are included in this group) and therefore, by stopping at pH 8.5, there have been localized areas of lower pH in the range of pH 6 - 8. The pH is *not allowed* to dip to pH 6 or 7 because then there have been localized areas of lower pH in the range of pH 5 or below. *When the pH dips below pH 5 the Ormus is thought by some to be lost all together.*

**Note:** If hydrochloric acid is added to the "living menstruum" and the pH initially goes *down* and not up, this is an indicator that Ormus is *not* present in that batch.

The use of a magnetic stirrer to stir the living menstruum is generally not suggested because of the electromagnetic (EMF) field generated by the motor. Some feel electromagnetic fields may disturb the state of the Ormus. There is not a consensus on this point. For more information, see "Labware Choices-Aluminum Foil." (Appendix XIV.)

## Preparing the Source Part 1
### Drying the Source/Reducing Particle Size of the Source
Dried carrot pulp is used as Ormus source material during the explanation of the "Dry Process."

**Juice the carrots to remove as much *water* and *sugar* as possible.** A theory holds that Ormus likes "tight" places and the crystalline structure of salt and sugar provide these. Since Ormus is generally thought to have an even greater affinity for sugar than for salt, the carrot is often juiced twice to maximize the sugar loss.

**Dry the moist carrot pulp on a stainless steel pan in a gas oven at 120 degrees.** This allows the carrot pulp to *slowly* dry with no charring. (If a gas oven is not available, use a gas flame. Place the carrot pulp in a stainless steel pan over very low flame.) Stir occasionally and do not leave unattended or allow charring to occur. Charring an Ormus source material introduces carbon; and this is not desired because Ormus is thought to attach to carbon. The end result of drying is the formation of *small* particles of Ormus source material in a *dry* state. (The smaller the pieces of source material the better the process works. I have ground the dried particles in a mortar and pestle to reduce their size even more.) In the case of carrots, it may be said that the carrots have been reduced to *dirt* as they are small, dark brown, crumbly particles. For more information, see "Labware Choices-Heat." (Appendix XIV.)

## Preparing the Source Part 2
### Boiling the Source
Lye embodies a "secret fire" and this step in the process utilizes that "chemical" fire in lye solution to disaggregate the molecules in the *dry* Ormus source material and unlock the Ormus within. Secret fire is explained in "Lye Solution Preparation-Final Thought."

**Prepare one gallon lye solution.** For more information, see "Lye Solution Preparation." (Section Three.)

**Place the lye solution into a clean HDPE plastic container.** The container used to house the dry Ormus source and lye solution can be HDPE plastic or stainless steel. Because external heat is not added in the "Dry Process," HDPE plastic containers are more commonly used. (Not only is it easier to find them in various sizes, but there are no precautions associated with their use as with stainless steel containers.) Glass is not recommended because lye solution is in contact with the glass for a *long* period of time and silica etches (a non-toxic contaminate) from the glass. For more information, see "Labware Choices." (Appendix XIV.)

**Add the fine *dry* particles of Ormus source material to the lye solution at a ratio of roughly one cup of *dry* Ormus source material to one gallon of lye solution.** Stir while combining. The order of combining is specific and *it is important that the Ormus source material is always added to the lye solution.* If this order is not followed, the lye solution may sputter, boil and splatter onto you. (In this example the dry Ormus source is *dry* carrot *pulp.*) To make smaller volumes, use the same proportions, such as 1/2 cup dry Ormus source material to 1/2 gallon lye solution. Note: 1/2 gallon is equal to 8 cups or 2 quarts. For more information, see "Measurement Conversions." (Appendix XII.)

**Cover the container of lye solution and Ormus source material then place it in the *dark*.** Stir with a plastic utensil or glass stirring rod at least twice a day. Stirring is important as it allows the lye solution to more fully reach all of the particles of Ormus source material. *Stir regularly for several weeks.* This allows *time* for the Ormus in the dry source material to break free and *move into* the lye solution.

(*Lye solution releases noxious fumes that are harmful if inhaled.* Therefore, it is suggested that this soaking step in the "Dry Process" is *performed in a well-ventilated space.* Placing it out of the house is strongly suggested.)

**After several weeks, pour the "living menstruum" (Ormus-containing lye solution)** *off the* **top of the Ormus source material and filter it.** The same filtering process is performed as described in the "Wet Process-Preparing the Source," (Section Three) *with one difference*: a paper towel is never used because lye solution disintegrates the paper towel. The filtering process is repeated here for your convenience.

**Filter the "living menstruum" through a wetted coffee filter.** Always use distilled water to moisten the filter. One filter can be used or two or three stacked together if necessary. Pores of the filter do clog up so use a fresh dampened filter for each pour. Repeat the straining until the menstruum runs through clear.

**Place a "candy/deep fry thermometer" on a thick cloth (to "seat" it) under a clean *borosilicate glass* container.** If the thermometer is constructed of all glass (containing no metal), it may be attached to the inside of the container. The thermometer allows us to monitor the temperature of the living menstruum as hydrochloric acid is added. The temperature during the process does rise and Ormus has been speculated to "boil off" (gassing) if it rises above 140 degrees farenheit. Consequently it is important not to exceed this temperature.

Fill the *borosilicate glass* container less than 1/2 full of "living menstruum" because the next step requires a lot of hydrochloric acid. (*High heat is generated when hydrochloric acid is added. Always* choose borosilicate glass containers and place a catch basin underneath.) When a reaction releases heat, it is called an "exothermic" reaction and this heat causes the borosilicate glass container to become very hot. For more information, see "Labware Choices-Borosilicate Glass." (Appendix XIV.)

(*What has been created is a filtered living menstruum that is central to the chemical reaction in all the dry Ormus collection processes.*)

(Point of information: In other *dry* Ormus collection processes described later in the book, the dry Ormus source material is further prepared by *boiling* the lye solution or *burning* the Ormus source material with solid lye crystals to *further* disaggregate the molecules of the material and unlock the Ormus in it.)

## Perform the Process

**This is important:** The filtered "living menstruum" (Ormus-containing lye solution) must be at a *room temperature*. *If the solution is warm the next step of the process will not work.*

### Adding the Hydrochloric Acid

The pH of the cool and filtered living menstruum (in the borosilicate container) is lowered to pH 8.5 by adding hydrochloric acid. A precipitate forms called "Ormus" (manna). The hydrochloric acid required is usually about 40- 50% of the amount of living menstruum. (The amount of hydrochloric acid needed is dependant on how much Ormus is in the living menstruum.)

(Some have said that it may be helpful to stir in a clockwise direction and once Ormus (manna) is seen forming begin stirring in a counter-clockwise direction.)

**Add hydrochloric acid in a steady stream to the "living menstruum" in the borosilicate glass container.** The hydrochloric acid is continually added in a steady *stream* because this step *must* be completed in one sitting and in a timely fashion.

To accomplish this *continuous and steady* stream, place hydrochloric acid in an HDPE plastic bottle that has a "spout" cap. Constantly stir the living menstruum with a plastic (or borosilicate) utensil so there are no "hot spots" (areas in the menstruum that the pH drops to pH 5 or below). A hot spot is very detrimental to the reaction as some feel that pH 5 is the pH where Ormus leaves all together.

**Do not dawdle. Add the hydrochloric acid in a steady continuous stream and stir without interruption.** *DO NOT STOP THE PROCESS* - it must be completed in one sitting. If the process is stopped, the liquid cools, the pH goes up and we lose control of knowing when to consider the process done. The process is completed when the pH is brought down, in one sitting, to pH 8.5.

**Initially the pH is observed to (unexpectedly) rise and then crest and hold the pH point before lowering.** This initial rise in the pH and then leveling off are the "energetic phenomenon" discussed earlier in "Information." I have experienced the pH rise, crest at pH 12.5, hold that pH and then (relatively slowly) lower to pH 12 then pH 11 on its way down. When the pH lowers below pH 11, it drops faster than you may expect.

**A fog is seen hanging onto the inside of the glass beaker.** This fog is called an "indicator point" and its presence alerts the astute Ormus collector to add hydrochloric acid more slowly as the pH is close to maximum and will begin to decrease soon. (This fog indicates that the end point of the process is close.)

**There is a point where the beaker becomes very hot to the touch and a fine vapor collects on the inside of the container.** The vapor is another "indicator point" and its presence is directing you to add the hydrochloric acid *more* slowly (stir continuously). When the fine vapor is seen, the "living menstruum" is so hot that Ormus is "boiling off" ("gassing"). Add the hydrochloric acid a *little slower* because losing Ormus to the air is not desired. Monitor the temperature reading on the candy/deep fry thermometer. *Do not let the temperature of the "living menstruum" rise above 140 degrees* Fahrenheit. (I have experienced the heat rising above 140 degrees.)

**At pH 11, fluffy precipitate may begin to be observed.** (A focused beam flashlight can be used to view the Ormus (manna) "cloud" that forms in the liquid.) The closer the pH gets to the neutral pH of pH 7, the faster the pH lowers. Therefore, once pH 11 has been attained, continue adding hydrochloric acid more slowly and in smaller amounts (even drops) until pH 8.5 is achieved. *Continually stir the living menstruum* so no "hot spots" form.

**There is a point where foam forms around the edges of the stirring utensil.** This occurs near the end point of pH 8.5 and is another "indicator point." The end of the process is very close so add hydrochloric acid in *small* amounts until the target pH of pH 8.5 is achieved. When pH 8.5 is reached, stop adding hydrochloric acid.

At pH 8.5 the drop is done. *Do not bring the pH to lower than pH 8.5.* Now, as the liquid cools, the pH meter displays a "drifting up" of the pH values as the pH does rise a little as the liquid cools - but relative to the drop - the "work" is done.

(If pH 8.5 is passed, for example the pH lowers to pH 8.3, the Ormus (manna) is still all right because the difference is so small. (Since some feel that Ormus leaves altogether at pH 5 this pH of pH 8.3 is very far from pH 5.) Because of both the wide spread between the two pH values and the constant stirring that was done, "hot spots" as have been discussed earlier are not a factor.)

**At the end of the reaction, the "living menstruum" has become a very salty tasting and safe to touch liquid.** For more information, see "Chemistry of the Processes." (Appendix XXII.)

Note: The Ormus collected from carrots in a "Dry Process" is more luminescent than the Ormus collected from sea salt or drawn seawater in a "Wet Process." The precipitate from the carrot source looks like fluffy clouds or a "cake-like" material.


## Purifying (Washing)

Purify (wash) the Ormus (manna) three times as described in the "Wet Process." *There are two differences.* First, the rinse water used is always *distilled* water. (Distilled water is used because organic material is always present in "Magnet Vortex Water Trap" water, "Vortex Water Trap" water and tap water that can result in spoilage of the Ormus (manna) over time. Because this process requires more time, energy and resources in the collection of Ormus the *longest* shelf life is desired.) The second difference in the washing technique is that salt *never* need be added to the finished Ormus (manna) since salt is produced in the reaction and the liquid over the precipitate becomes *very* "salty."

For your convenience, the "Wet Process" washing (purifying) directions are repeated, with modifications, below.

**Once the precipitate has settled, is covered and in the dark, the manna can be washed with distilled water.** Excess salt is removed during the washing. Washing is a form of purifying and the manna is washed *three times* (some rinse a fourth time). If the manna was made based on a moon phase, follow the time frame outlined in "Moon Chart." (Appendix XX.)

**For the *first* rinse, the liquid can be removed from the top of the Ormus (manna) or the Ormus (manna) can be removed from the bottom of the liquid.** Turkey basters or separatory funnels are good tools for removing the manna from the bottom of the liquid. Draw out the manna - a useful suggestion is to put it in a pilsner style beer glass (or any other container narrower on the bottom than at the top). When the container is this shape, rinsing the Ormus (manna) is more efficient because as rinse water is poured off there is more control of the manna on the bottom and therefore little of it is lost. This shaped glassware works well for smaller batches of Ormus. When processing over two gallons of "living menstruum" a larger container than pilsner glassware may be required to hold the collected manna for rinsing.

The other method of washing is to decant the liquid from the top by slowly tipping the container over and pouring out the liquid. Be careful not to pour out the precipitate! If the precipitate drifts up, stop pouring and let it settle again before continuing to pour. Decant as much liquid as possible. Then a turkey baster (or barrel syringe) can be used to draw off additional liquid. Next, pour the manna into a pilsner style beer glass or any container.

(Note: Any container shape can be chosen. HDPE plastic containers can also be used.)

**Add an equal amount of distilled water to the Ormus precipitate (manna) filled container as you see Ormus (manna) plus any remaining liquid over it.**

*It does make a difference how much rinse water is added.* With every batch of rinse water, some of the manna precipitate is thought to dissolve and once dissolved, it doesn't re-precipitate back to manna. In addition, with every batch of rinse water, the Ormus oil said to be in the liquid is lost. Therefore, using more water than is necessary per wash or washing the precipitate too often causes the manna to become less potent. Consequently, this washing step is performed *three times* (*some* do wash the precipitate four times).

(Note: Save the original liquid from the *first* wash in case the Ormus (manna) has been washed too much. This should not happen as the rinsing is performed three times, however, if this does occur, some of the liquid can be added back into the manna. The original liquid from the *first* wash can also be used in bathwater or as a foot soak because Ormus is contained in that water. If rinse water is used for plants, it is said to use the rinse water from the third or fourth wash. Don't use the first or second rinse water for plants because the *salt* contained in the initial washes of Ormus (manna) is considered to be too much. (At the end of the Ormus collection reaction in any of the *dry processes*, the living menstruum becomes a very salty non-toxic solution.) For information on Ormus use in plants, see "Usage in Plants/Agriculture." (Appendix XXI.)

**Stir the manna or stir and bubble air downward from a turkey baster into the manna precipitate.** If stirring, use a plastic or glass stirrer. If bubbling, use a turkey baster. When bubbling, the manna is fluffed and washed by the moving air and water. By bubbling air the manna may be more thoroughly rinsed.

**When finished stirring or stirring and bubbling, cover the manna and let it settle again before removing the liquid from the top of the precipitate.**

**Remove the liquid from the top of the Ormus precipitate.** If the Ormus (manna) had been drawn *up* from the bottom during the first wash, it is only drawn up from the bottom for the *first* wash.
After the first wash, the liquid is decanted from the *top* in subsequent rinses. Once a lot of the liquid is decanted, a turkey baster (or barrel syringe) can be used to draw off additional liquid.

**For the second time, add an equal amount of distilled water as there is manna (precipitate) plus any remaining liquid over it.**

- Rinse the Ormus (manna) by stirring or stirring and bubbling (as explained above).
- Cover the Ormus (manna) and let it settle and then again decant the liquid from the top of the precipitate.
- For the third time, add an equal amount of distilled water as there is manna plus any remaining liquid over it.
- Rinse again using the same guidelines.

It has been said that there are no concerns about over-washing the Ormus (manna) when these guidelines (three rinses) are followed (some do rinse a fourth time). After the third wash, dilute the Ormus (manna) as described below and store.

**Add distilled water to dilute the Ormus.** The most common ratio is 1:1. Add an equal amount of distilled water *plus* any remaining liquid over the Ormus (manna). Twice-as-much or half-as-much distilled water may be used. It depends on how concentrated an Ormus product is desired. (Too little water may cause the texture of the Ormus [manna] to be less palatable.) Note: When adding the water, this is a good time to imprint/charge the Ormus. For more information, see "Imprinting/Charging." (Appendix XVIII.)
   *Note: Salt never needs to be added to the finished Ormus (manna) because at the end of the reaction the solution has become very salty.*

## Storage
*Storage of the manna is the same as described in "Wet Process-Storage." (page 52)*

## Final Thought

*Ormus (manna) can be collected at any time or on any day of the year.* To alchemists, there *is* an ideal time for the collection of Ormus (manna) and this is three days before a full moon or an equinox. These are energetically active times during the year and some feel that Ormus (manna) collected during these periods is exceptional. For more information, see "Moon Chart." (Appendix X.) By doing an Ormus process during one or two of these energetically active times of the year, you can with a large enough volume of Ormus source material, procure enough Ormus (manna) for use during the entire year.

Once the Ormus (manna) begins to coalesce, it falls from solution as a precipitate faster than in the "Wet Process." It is the same material in a different form and yet it drops faster. The precipitate is lighter and fluffier than from the "Wet Process" and I have experienced the precipitate looking a bit like a "cloud" in the air or having a "cake-like" appearance.

The volume of manna collected during the "Dry Process" and any of *dry* processes is *less* than the amount of manna collected when performing a "Wet Process." Expect this and do not be surprised or dismayed. For example: I collected a ratio of 1:8 manna to source material when performing a "Dry Process (Cold Fire Process)" on magnetite and a ratio of 1:5 when performing a "Wet Process" on "drawn" seawater.

If the dry Ormus source material is "edible", (non-toxic) and having no toxic metals or toxic materials then there is nothing harmful in the manna collected during an Ormus collection process. If the ingredients in an Ormus source material are not known, it can be sent off for an assay. At the very least, assay the manna made from it. For more information, see "Resources and Supplies-Have a Source Analyzed." (Appendix I.)

A potential idea to filter the "living menstruum" after the soaking step is to buy a vacuum pump used to bleed car brakes. It is a thought that may prove helpful if performing the processes regularly on large batches of living menstruum. Buchner filter funnels are available with vacuum attachments that increase the filtration rate. However, Buchner filter funnels are expensive and with creative thought, inexpensive methods can be found instead of buying costly lab equipment.

Superconductivity of Ormus (manna) may be demonstrated. For more information, see "Basic Explanation-Final Thought." (Appendix VII.)

Note: the "Dry Process" (and all the *dry* processes) is based on a "salty solution" type of process. For more information, see "Basic Explanation-Final Thought." (Appendix VII.)

The filtered out Ormus source material sediment from the "living menstruum" can be saved and placed in a fresh batch of lye solution to prepare another batch of living menstruum. This can be done and more Ormus (manna) collected. You must know that the amount of Ormus (manna) that precipitates is not as high the second time around.

**Caution regarding silver:** If silver is the Ormus source material, (or in the Ormus source material to an appreciable degree), *hydrochloric acid* cannot be used to precipitate the Ormus (manna) or toxic silver chloride has been made. For more information regarding silver, see "Sources for the Ormus Processes-Metal." (Appendix VIII.)

"Living menstruum" (unless made from silver) can replace regular lye solution in a "Wet Process" with exceptional results. Since this lye solution is a living menstruum (it *contains* Ormus from the source material), a greater drop of Ormus (manna) is expected when performing a "Wet Process" (on "reconstituted" sea or drawn seawater). **Note:** "Living menstruum" created by soaking, boiling (or burning) a silver source is *never* saved for use. This is because you may *forget* the source material was silver and use the "living menstruum" in a *dry* process. All the dry processes include adding hydrochloric acid and once this has been added, toxic "silver chloride" is made. For more information, see "Sources for the Ormus Processes-Metal." (Appendix VIII.)

Another reason to save (a portion) of the "living menstruum" is in case the pH is brought a *little* too low during the "Dry Process" or any of the *dry* processes. The "living menstruum" can be used to raise the pH.

Do not work with lye or hydrochloric acid in "fear" as it is thought that feeling fear at the time of the "work" causes an "imprint" of "fear" onto the Ormus (manna). *Work with lye and hydrochloric acid in "respect" not "fear."* The emotions surrounding "fear" also cause a mind to "close off;" this results in making the steps of an Ormus collection process very difficult to absorb.

When washing containers and other equipment used, there may be observed a dried white ring in the container with dried white spots on it. These are easily removed with a solution of 3/4 part white vinegar and 1/4 part water.

A good organic source material for the "Dry Process" is Aloe Vera. David Hudson has said that this plant is high in the two most valued Ormus producing elements for the human being (rhodium and iridium). If you grow your own Aloe plants, it may be especially helpful to grow them in "volcanic soil" by adding Azomite® volcanic ash to the soil. Volcanic ash and volcanic soil are felt to contain high levels of Ormus.

NOTES:

> *"Ora, Lege, Lege, Lege, Relege,*
> *Labora et Invenies"*
> (Pray, Read, Read, Read, Read again,
> Labor, and Discover)
> Altus, Mutus Liber (1677)

#  SECTION FOUR

**Other Traditional Ormus Processes**

*dry* Lye Boil Proces

*dry* Lye Burn Process

*dry* Lye Burn and Boil Process

*dry* Sodium Burn Process (write-up by Don Nance)

*dry* Hydrogen Peroxide (Gold) Process (write-up by
Don Nance)

## DRY "LYE BOIL PROCESS"

Note: There are appendices that have cross-referencing information to that in this chapter.
These include:
"List of Ormus Resources and Supplies," "Common Measurement Conversions,"
"Best Practices Labware Choices," "pH Meter,"and "Sources for the Ormus Processes."
For "Lye Solution Preparation" and "Hydrochloric Acid Preparation"
see Section Three.

---

**CAUTION!!**
Note: Cautions are a form of education so that you may work with lye and hydrochloric acid in awareness and respect not fear.

Lye is a "caustic." Hydrochloric acid is an acid. Both lye and hydrochloric acid are strong chemicals and can damage eyes by rendering the cornea opaque, a form of irreparable eye damage. If lye or hydrochloric acid gets into eyes flush the eyeball with water immediately and seek medical attention if the burning persists.

If lye or hydrochloric acid contacts the skin it hurts and damages it. Lye or hydrochloric acid reacts with skin tissue and can cause permanent damage and scarring if severe. Even minor reactions can be painful. If lye or hydrochloric acid contacts clothes it damages them. If lye or hydrochloric acid gets onto your clothes or body, immediately flush the area with lots of water and seek medical attention if necessary.

It is very helpful to work near a sink, faucet or other source of wash water.

The area must be well ventilated as breathing fumes from lye or hydrochloric acid can damage air passages and lungs. Lye solution creates caustic fumes. Do not breathe in these fumes. Hydrochloric acid creates a pungent, corrosive "fog" when added to water. Do not breathe in this fog. Handle lye or hydrochloric acid with adequate ventilation such as a laboratory range hood vented outside or conduct the work outside. It is advisable to keep a bottle of baking soda solution handy to use against hydrochloric acid spills (baking soda powder can be sprinkled on if the spill is large) and a spray bottle of distilled white vinegar handy to use against lye spills.

For more information, see "The Chemicals of the Processes." (Appendix XIII.)

When working with lye or hydrochloric acid, (or any chemical) avoid touching your face or rubbing your eyes. Do not handle around food. Do not dump wastewater on the ground. Lye is generally safe to put down the drain, but first run water in the sink while slowly pouring the lye directly into the drain and don't mix it with any acid that may be in the drain as it can react explosively. Hydrochloric acid is generally safe to put down the drain, but first run water in the sink while slowly pouring the hydrochloric acid directly into the drain and don't mix it with any "pH alkaline" material that may be in the drain as it can react explosively.

When working with lye or hydrochloric acid, please wear goggles or a full-face visor (an industrial face protector), neoprene gloves and a PVC lab apron as well as protective clothing such as long sleeves and long pants.

Keep children and pets away from the work area and do not leave it unattended. Even if no one is around, an unsuspecting person could venture by and be at risk.

**Labware and Supplies to perform a dry "Lye Boil Process"**

Ormus source material, lye solution, hydrochloric acid, distilled water, pH meter, stainless steel pot for the "boil" (follow the stainless steel precautions in Appendix XIV), 5-lb flat weight (weight-trainer type) or a brick, heat source: propane turkey ring burner, borosilicate glass container (to perform the process), measuring cup, aluminum foil, barrel syringe or baster, funnel or flat strainer, filters (unbleached coffee filters), focus beam flashlight, plastic catch basin, stirrer of plastic or borosilicate glass, safety clothing and equipment. Hydrochloric acid used as the "reagent" in the process may be placed in an HDPE plastic bottle. Store the finished manna in HDPE plastic containers. For more information, see Appendix XIV.

As a safety measure, always place containers used in the process into a larger non-metallic "catch basin" (in case of leakage or breakage). For example: A (new) cat litter box or the bottom of an under-the-bed storage container. (Note: When adding the hydrochloric acid, a lot of heat is generated that could break the glass.)

To best ensure electromagnetic waves cause no interference on the stability of Ormus in source material or the manna (precipitate), it is prudent to keep the work and storage area six feet or more away from them. For more information, see "Labware Choices-Aluminum Foil." (Appendix XIV.)


**Definition**

This process mirrors the "Dry Process (Cold Fire Process)." The *only* difference is the addition of a "boil" with *external heat* applied to the one-gallon lye solution containing roughly one-cup (*dry*) Ormus source material.

Because of the "boil" added to this process, it is a *more* energetically active one than the "Dry Process" and can physically disaggregate (disintegrate or disassociate) to a *greater* degree, the molecules of Ormus source used in the "Dry Process."

Source materials for this process includes land-based minerals, sands and *less dense metal* such as finely shaved copper. (Note: This is not the most efficient process to make Ormus (manna) from gold.)


**Information**

Appearance: The collected Ormus is observed as a fluffy precipitate (not always a brilliant white color) in liquid.

Heat is added from an *external source* in this process to cause a "boil." Any Ormus process which uses external heat *especially when heat is applied to cause a boil*, is generally thought to place a slightly higher energy state (higher spin) on the Ormus material and this is felt to cause a bit more potency. It is also felt that more precipitate forms during a process that does not cause a boil. When boiling, some of the lighter Ormus boils off and therefore lost to the collection. For more information, see "Labware Choices-Heat." (Appendix XIV.)

All Ormus collection processes use the same lye solution concentration. For more information, see "Lye Solution Preparation." (Section Three). The pH of the lye solution is a little higher than pH 12.

The *"Living Menstruum:"* By placing the *dry* Ormus source material into lye solution then boiling the mixture, an "Ormus-containing lye medium" forms. This is termed "living menstruum" because Ormus is now *in* the lye liquid. The theory holds that this step allows Ormus to break free from the dry Ormus source material and "tie" to the lye solution. The Ormus is "tied" to the lye solution in one of two ways. The Ormus source material is *boiled* for four hours in the lye solution *or* it is soaked in it and the liquid stirred twice a day for several weeks (as done in the "Dry Process [Cold Fire Process].")

Because the lye solution containing the dry Ormus source material is *boiled* (external heat added), the preparation of the "living menstruum" (the Ormus-containing lye medium) occurs faster and is prepared in four hours rather than the several weeks required in the "Dry Process (Cold Fire Process)." The mechanism that causes the formation of a "living menstruum" is explained in "Dry Process (Cold Fire Process) - Information." (page 62)

After the boil, the "living menstruum" is cooled, filtered and used in the same way to collect Ormus as described in the "Dry Process (Cold Fire Process) - Perform the Process." (page 66)

Examples of sources for this process are minerals. For example: magnetite, pureganic minerals® or humic shale. Because *external heat* is added, the molecules of these source materials may be expected to physically disaggregate (disintegrate) *more* than in the "Dry Process (Cold Fire Process)." Disaggregating the molecules unlocks the Ormus and allows it to leach out and become available for collection. Other sources for this process include certain sands. (Copper, shaved very fine, is also expected to physically disaggregate its aggregation of molecules, called "breaking the metallic bonds" because it is a less dense metal, however if another Ormus process that utilizes higher heat is performed, the Ormus (manna) yield is higher. These processes are addressed in a later chapter. For more information, see "Sources for the Ormus Processes." (Appendix VIII.)

Any dry Ormus source material known to be edible (non-toxic) is a candidate for the *dry* "Lye Boil Process" (or any of the *dry* processes). If using an Ormus source material you do not know is "edible" and it makes a precipitate, at the very least send the *precipitate* off for an assay. For more information on assays see "Sources for the Processes-Information." (Appendix VIII.) (NOTE: There is an exception regarding *silver* as an Ormus source material and this is discussed in "Sources for the Processes-Metal." [Appendix VIII.])

## Preparing the Source Part 1

If using an *organic* source, prepare the Ormus source material as described in "Dry Process (Cold Fire Process)-Preparing the Source Part I." (page 64)

If using a *mineral* source (such as humic shale), it must be clean (rinse or wash the material if needed), in small particle size and completely drained of water *(being completely dry is better)*. The finer the particle size the better the chances that total disintegration occurs. Particle sizes may be seen ranging from as fine as talcum powder to a size smaller than 1/4 of an inch.

If using a *metal* source, it must be 99.9% *pure*, clean, in *small* particle size *(filed)* and fully drained of water *(being completely dry is better)*. The metal is to be shaved or otherwise in small particles. With some effort a clean "mill bastard file" can be used. (The file is stored clean and protected from rusting with a layer of edible oil.)

## Preparing the Source Part 2

### Boiling the Source

Because this step has *external* heat added, it *more energetically* tears the molecules of the Ormus source material apart allowing the Ormus to leach out of the source material and *into* the lye solution. Because heat energetically disaggregates the Ormus source material this boiling step is completed in four *hours*.

**Prepare one-gallon lye solution.** For more information, see "Lye Solution Preparation" (Section Three).

**Place the lye solution into a stainless steel pot that has a lid.** Choose a spot away from direct sunlight. Since this process adds *heat* to the lye solution, it is important to have a *stainless* steel pot. The stainless steel pot is to have no aluminum showing or in its construction (this can be checked with a magnet). This means there is to be no rivets where the handles meet the pot, *no* rusting, *no* flaking, *no* pitting, *no* chipping, *no* breeching of the stainless steel coating nor discoloration that can't be polished away with stainless steel cleansers. If the stainless steel pot has any rivets, they must be drilled out and replaced with stainless steel bolts. The lid including the knob is to have no aluminum and if aluminum is present, the knob, must be removed and replaced with a stainless steel bolt. For more information, see "Labware Choices-Stainless Steel." (Appendix XIV.)

**Add the fine dry particles of Ormus source material to the lye solution at a ratio of roughly one-cup dry Ormus source material to one-gallon lye solution.** Stir with a plastic stirrer while combining. The order of combining is specific and *it is important that the Ormus source material is always added to the lye solution.* If this order is not followed, the lye solution may sputter, boil and splatter onto you. (To make a smaller volume, use the same proportions, such as 1/2 cup dry Ormus source material to 1/2 gallon lye solution.) **Note:** 1/2 gallon is equal to eight cups or two quarts. For more information, see "Measurement Conversions." (Appendix XII.)

**Bring the lye solution containing the Ormus source material to a "rapid boil" in a covered stainless steel pot.** (Directly after the rapid boil the heat is reduced to high simmer.) *Boil the lye solution outside of the house as lye solution releases noxious fumes that are harmful if breathed.* A gas flame is generally preferred. For example, a propane turkey ring burner. For more information, see "Labware Choices-Heat Sources." (Appendix XIV.) Stir the contents when a rapid boil has been achieved.

Note: Lye solution isn't like water when it boils, it can *roll* when it boils. Lye solution doesn't bubble, as much as it *"burps"* and therefore it can roll up the sides of the stainless steel container (a bit like boiling oatmeal rolls up and out of the pot). Therefore it is wise to choose a pot deep enough to accommodate this "rolling" action. When applying high heat to reach a "rapid boil," it may be helpful to watch the pot closely or even bungee cord the lid down in the event the lye solution "overboils the pot" (rolling/bubbling up and out). For safety reasons, it is important to realize how lye doesn't boil like water and that once it does boil, it - like water - does so energetically.

Now you *may* choose to keep the pot "un-lidded" while observing for the "rapid boil" and *then* place the lid on at that time. However, one of the reasons the lid is left on the pot is because the lye solution can "explode off" any trapped gas that may be in the pieces of Ormus source material much like a log in a fireplace explodes (with a popping sound) sap trapped in the log.

**Lower the heat to an "energetic simmer" (a high simmer) such as seen in a gentle rolling boil, stir the liquid, cover the pot, add weight to the cover.** Simmer for four hours. To gauge the strength of the simmer, look for the amount of steam coming out from around the lid.

Heat is also *gassing* off Ormus (boiling into the air). Therefore, the pot is lidded (for safety reasons) and *weighted* down by placing a weight on top of the lid.

This set-up prepares the Ormus source material and includes a propane turkey ring burner (propane tank is outside the range of the picture), a stainless steel pot with lid and a 5-lb flat weight (weight-trainer type). Note: A heat diffuser such as the cast iron griddle shown here finds use if the heat is too high for an energetic simmer.

This weight on the lid helps to *maintain a tight seal*, and in this way, the amount of Ormus-containing steam leaving the pot is lessened. A 5-pound flat weight (weight-trainer type) can be used for this application. Position the center hole of the flat weight over the *stainless steel* "lid knob" of the stainless steel pot. (Many lid knobs are not stainless steel and must be changed to a stainless steel bolt.) A brick may be used to weigh down the lid in place of a 5-pound flat weight. This is an example of using something from around the house instead of purchasing specialized equipment. If a brick is used, position the center hole of the brick over the *stainless* steel "lid knob" of the stainless steel pot.

Note: If you choose to clamp the lid on (in place of putting a weight on the lid) make sure the lye liquid inside the stainless steel pot had already gotten hot before adding the clamp. A "bomb" has been made if the clamp is placed on the lid *before* the heat is applied to the stainless steel pot.

(Note: Conceptually, it is possible that a stainless steel pressure cooker may be used and in this manner both heat and pressure utilized to tear apart the molecules of the Ormus source material. This could be an experiment. However, make sure all stainless steel precautions have been met and study the heating requirements of a pressure cooker. It is possible pressure cookers may not safely accommodate *high* heat and therefore lower heat must be used. Finally, the pressure cookers I have seen incorporate plastic handles that may not withstand the rigors of a propane turkey ring burner and must be removed. For more information, see "Labware Choices-Stainless Steel." (Appendix XIV.)

**"Energetically simmer" four hours.**

(Alternative suggestions have been made which do not involve stainless steel precautions when boiling the lye solution containing the Ormus source material. The first suggestion is to place the lye solution/Ormus source material mixture into an uncapped HDPE bottle. Place the *uncapped* HDPE bottle into a pot of water and bring to a boil. (Perform this outside - never in the house.) When the water in the pot has started to boil, tighten the cap and continue boiling for four hours. As an experiment, a crock-pot could be used for the source of heat. Cap the HDPE bottle when the water in the crock-pot has gotten very hot. Replace the water in the crock-pot as needed (the lye water in the now capped HDPE bottle does not boil away so it does not need replenishing). (Source: *www.subtleenergies.com*.)

**Allow the "living menstruum" to cool with the lid on.** Keeping the lid on is speculated to hold Ormus (that rose up from the heat) inside the pot until it cools and lowers back down. (To best follow stainless steel precautions, remove the "living menstruum" from the stainless steel pot as soon as it has cooled and do not allow the living menstruum to remain in the stainless steel pot any longer than necessary.)

**Pour the cooled "living menstruum" off the top of the Ormus source material and filter the living menstruum.** The same filtering process is performed as described in the "Wet Process-Preparing the Source." (Section Three.) *Please note one difference:* a paper towel is never used because lye solution disintegrates the paper towel. The filtering process is repeated here, with modifications, for your convenience.

**Filter the "living menstruum" through a wetted coffee filter.** Always use distilled water to moisten the filter. One filter can be used at a time or two or three stacked together, if necessary. Pores of the filter *do* clog up so use a fresh dampened filter for each pour. Repeat the straining until the "living menstruum" runs through clear.

**Place a "candy/deep fry thermometer" on a thick cloth (to "seat" it) under a clean** *borosilicate glass* **container.** If the thermometer is constructed of all glass (containing no metal) it may be attached to the inside of the container. The thermometer allows us to monitor the temperature of the "living menstruum" as hydrochloric acid is added. The temperature during the process does rise and Ormus has been speculated to "boil off" (gassing) if it rises above 140 degrees farenheit. Consequently it is important not to exceed this temperature.

**Fill the** *borosilicate glass* **container less than 1/2 full of "living menstruum"** because the next step requires a *lot* of hydrochloric acid. (*High heat is generated when hydrochloric acid is added*, therefore *always* choose borosilicate glass containers and place a catch basin underneath. When a reaction releases heat, it is called an "exothermic reaction" and this heat causes the borosilicate glass container to become *very* hot.) For more information, see "Labware Choices-Borosilicate Glass." (Appendix XIV.)

*(What has been created is a filtered "living menstruum" that is central to the chemical reaction in all the dry Ormus collection processes.)*

## Perform the Process

**This is important:** The filtered living menstruum (Ormus-containing lye solution) must have *fully* cooled down after the boil and be at a *room temperature. If the solution is still warm the next step of the process will not work.*

Reminder: Because hydrochloric acid generates high heat when added to the lye solution, *always* choose a borosilicate glass container and place it in a "catch basin." For more information, see "Labware Choices-Borosilicate Glass." (Appendix XIV.)

**Hydrochloric acid is added to the cooled and filtered "living menstruum" to precipitate Ormus (manna) (if Ormus is present).** This is described in "Dry Process (Cold Fire Process)-Perform the Process." (page 66)

## Purifying (washing):

**The Ormus (manna) precipitate is washed with distilled water.** This is described in "Dry Process (Cold Fire Process)-Purifying (Washing)." (page 67)

## Storage

**Storage of the Ormus (manna) precipitate is the same as described in "Wet Process-Storage."** (page 52)

## Final Thought

When using copper metal as the source material, a stainless steel pot (or any utensil used in the process), is not suggested as *no* metal other than copper should touch the solutions. This is to ensure the end product is pure copper Ormus (manna). A suggestion that rids the use of stainless steel equipment is to use a Visions® glass/ceramic Dutch oven in a 5-quart size with lid and boil in this container as you would one made of stainless steel.

Different alchemists have different Recipes. For example: There are recipes that use *burned* Ormus source material - in this case, the *white* ash from burned *hardwood* trees (the ash must be *white* and contain *no* charred carbon containing pieces). The white ash is placed in a covered stainless steel pot with lots of distilled water, brought to a boil then simmered for four hours. The water is poured off the ash and filtered. If the pH of the water is high, perform "the drop" to the target pH 8.5 with *hydrochloric acid* and if the pH is low perform "the drop" to target pH 10.78 with *lye solution*. Often the pH of the water is high because lye (a high pH substance) is made from wood ash and water. (Old recipes for making lye include leaching metallic oxides from the burned ash of hardwood trees into water.) White ash from hardwood trees (an organic source material) is thought to be a good Ormus source because hardwood trees are *long-lived* and therefore may contain beneficial Ormus for longevity. This may be a basis behind this alchemist's recipe.

The filtered-out Ormus source material sediment from the "living menstruum" can be re-used by placing it in a fresh batch of lye solution that is re-boiled to prepare another batch of "living menstruum." This can be done and more Ormus (manna) collected. You must know that the amount of Ormus (manna) that precipitates is not as high the second time around.

**Caution regarding silver:** If silver is the Ormus source material, (or in the Ormus source material to an appreciable degree), *hydrochloric acid* cannot be used to precipitate the Ormus (manna) or toxic silver chloride has been made. For more information regarding silver, see "Sources for the Ormus Processes-Metal." (Appendix VIII.).

Remember that if no toxic metals or toxic materials are in the Ormus source material, the Ormus (manna) is not toxic and if you do not know what is in the source material, it and/or the Ormus (manna) collected from it can be sent off for an assay. For more information, see "Resources and Supplies-Have a Source Analyzed" (Appendix I) and "Sources for the Ormus Processes-Information." (Appendix VIII.)

*All additional final thought is the same as "Dry Process (Cold Fire Process)-Final Thought." (page 70)*

**NOTES:**

That the author is freely sharing from heart and soul the fruits of a caring mind that is ever active, never restful, these practical and thought-provoking pearls of hard-won knowledge; this should not be taken lightly.

and

Alchemical authors have said "many are called but few are chosen."  The chosen are the ones who are allowed to complete the Great Work--with the accompanying internal and external perfection of the individual.

## DRY "LYE BURN PROCESS"

Note: There are appendices that have cross-referencing information to that in this chapter. These include:
"List of Ormus Resources and Supplies," "Common Measurement Conversions,"
"Best Practices Labware Choices," "pH Meter,"
and "Sources for the Ormus Processes."
For "Lye Solution Preparation" and "Hydrochloric Acid Preparation" see Section Three.

---

**CAUTION!!**
Note: Cautions are a form of education so that you may work with lye and hydrochloric acid in awareness and respect not fear.

Lye is a "caustic." Hydrochloric acid is an acid. Both lye and hydrochloric acid are strong chemicals and can damage eyes by rendering the cornea opaque, a form of irreparable eye damage. If lye or hydrochloric acid gets into eyes flush the eyeball with water immediately and seek medical attention if the burning persists.

If lye or hydrochloric acid contacts the skin it hurts and damages it. Lye or hydrochloric acid reacts with skin tissue and can cause permanent damage and scarring if severe. Even minor reactions can be painful. If lye or hydrochloric acid contacts clothes it damages them. If lye or hydrochloric acid gets onto your clothes or body, immediately flush the area with lots of water and seek medical attention if necessary.

It is very helpful to work near a sink, faucet or other source of wash water.

When working with lye or hydrochloric acid, please wear goggles or a full-face visor (an industrial face protector), neoprene gloves and a PVC lab apron as well as protective clothing such as long sleeves and long pants.

Keep children and pets away from the work area and do not leave it unattended. Even if no one is around, an unsuspecting person could venture by and be at risk.

The area must be well ventilated as breathing fumes from lye or hydrochloric acid can damage air passages and lungs. Lye solution creates caustic fumes. Do not breathe in these fumes. Hydrochloric acid creates a pungent, corrosive "fog" when added to water. Do not breathe in this fog. Handle lye or hydrochloric acid with adequate ventilation such as a laboratory range hood vented outside or conduct the work outside. It is advisable to keep a bottle of baking soda solution handy to use against hydrochloric acid spills (baking soda powder can be sprinkled on if the spill is large) and a spray bottle of distilled white vinegar handy to use against lye spills.

For more information, see "The Chemicals of the Processes." (Appendix XIII.)

When working with lye or hydrochloric acid, (or any chemical) avoid touching your face or rubbing your eyes. Do not handle around food. Do not dump wastewater on the ground. Lye is generally safe to put down the drain, but first run water in the sink while slowly pouring the lye directly into the drain and don't mix it with any acid that may be in the drain as it can react explosively. Hydrochloric acid is generally safe to put down the drain, but first run water in the sink while slowly pouring the hydrochloric acid directly into the drain and don't mix it with any "pH alkaline" material that may be in the drain as it can react explosively.

**Labware and Supplies to perform a dry "Lye Burn Process"**

Ormus source material, both lye crystals and lye solution, hydrochloric acid, distilled water, pH meter, lidded stainless steel saucepan (follow the stainless steel precautions in Appendix XIV), 5-pound flat weight (weight-trainer type) or a brick, metal sleeve (to condense the heat in the area around the saucepan), a heat source: propane turkey ring burner with a *double* ring of flame (for the higher heat required for the "burn"), container made of HDPE plastic (to house the lye solution as it disaggregates the burned Ormus source material), container of *borosilicate glass* (to collect the precipitate), measuring cup, aluminum foil, barrel syringe or baster, funnel or flat strainer, filters (*unbleached* coffee filters), focus beam flashlight, plastic catch basin, stirrer of plastic or borosilicate glass, safety clothing and equipment. The hydrochloric acid used as the "reagent" in the process can be placed in an HDPE plastic bottle during the collection. Store the finished manna in HDPE plastic containers. For more information, see Appendix XIV.

As a safety measure, always place containers used in the process into a larger non-metallic "catch basin" (*in case of leakage or breakage*). For example: A (new) cat litter box or the bottom of an under-the-bed storage container. (Note: When adding the hydrochloric acid, a lot of heat is generated that could break the glass.)

To best ensure electromagnetic waves cause no interference on the stability of Ormus in source material or the manna (precipitate), it is prudent to keep the work and storage area six feet or more away from them. For more information, see "Labware Choices-Aluminum Foil." (Appendix XIV.)

## Definition

This is a less dangerous version of the "*dry* Sodium Burn Process."

The completely *dry* Ormus source material is first placed in a crucible (container) filled with *dry* lye crystals and "burned" with *high* heat. It is then placed in lye solution (the "secret fire") in the same manner described in the "Dry Process (Cold Fire Process)." To be specific, the lye solution is allowed to sit, covered, for weeks while being stirred regularly. The secret fire has been explained in "Lye Solution Preparation-Final Thought."

Because of the addition of a "burn" to this process, it is a more energetically active process than the *dry* "Lye Boil Process."

Source material for this process includes gold and copper filings as well as land based minerals like black sand. (Note: This is not the most efficient process to make Ormus (manna) from gold.)

## Information

Appearance: The collected Ormus is observed as a fluffy precipitate (not always a brilliant white color) in liquid.

The high heat needed to burn the Ormus source material in this process is greater than that used to boil the lye solution in the dry "Lye Boil Process." This is why a double ring of flame on the propane turkey ring burner is required. This higher heat burns the lye crystals, causing them to boil and physically disaggregate the aggregation of molecules in the Ormus source material to a greater degree. Therefore burning with this greater heat actually causes the molecules of metal to partially physically disaggregate ("break metallic bonds.")

This Ormus process can be used with "edible" (non-toxic) minerals, such as black sand (edible means there is nothing toxic in the sand). This process totally disaggregates the aggregation of molecules in edible minerals and partially disaggregates the aggregation of molecules in metal. This process can be used for fine copper shavings (as this is a less dense metal) or gold shavings although it is noted that the *dry* "Sodium Burn Process" and the *dry* "Hydrogen Peroxide (gold) Process" are more efficient for processing gold. For more information, see "Sources for the Ormus Processes." (Appendix VIII.)

Heat from an external source is utilized in this process to cause a "burn." It is generally thought that adding external heat during an Ormus process affects the Ormus (manna). This process uses external heat for a "burn" not a "boil." Some feel that a boil affects the Ormus (manna) more than a burn. This is described in "Labware Choices-Heat." (Appendix XIV.)

This Ormus collection process uses lye crystals and lye solution. All Ormus collection processes use the same lye solution concentration. For more information, see "Lye Solution Preparation." (Section Three.) The pH of the lye solution is a little higher than pH 12.

The source material must be washed and *completely* dry because lye crystals react violently in the presence of water. (NOTE: Lye crystals are reactive (volatile) with any form of water or moisture. Follow all lye precautions.)

The "Living Menstruum": By first burning the Ormus source material with lye crystals and then placing the burned Ormus source material into lye solution, an "Ormus-containing lye medium" (called a "living menstruum") forms. This is explained in "Dry Process (Cold Fire Process)-Information." (page 62) During a later step of the process, the "collection" step, hydrochloric acid is added to the living menstruum. A precipitate forms and falls to the bottom of the container where it is collected.

This is a more energetic process than the "Dry Process" because external heat is added and it is a more energetic process than the *dry* "Lye Boil Process" because even higher external heat is added (to burn lye crystals). However, this process is less energetic (dangerous) than the *dry* "Sodium Burn Process" because lye crystals are not as reactive (dangerous) as the pure sodium (metal) used in the *dry* "Sodium Burn Process." Therefore, this process is simpler and less dangerous than the *dry* "Sodium Burn Process," yet utilizes a higher heat to burn lye crystals (this is a higher heat than boiling lye solution). This higher heat causes metal to actually boil and partially disaggregate (break) metal bonds.

Note: If no toxic metals or toxic materials are in the Ormus source material, the Ormus (manna) is not toxic. If using an Ormus source material that makes a precipitate and it is not known if you can "eat" (non-toxic) the source, at the very least send the precipitate off for an assay. For more information, see "Sources for the Processes-Information." (Appendix VIII.)

## Preparing the Source Part 1

### Burning the Source

If using a *mineral* source (such as humic shale), it must be clean (rinse or wash the material if needed), in small particle size and completely dry. The finer the particle size the better the chances that total disintegration occurs. Particle sizes may be seen ranging from as fine as talcum powder to a size smaller than 1/4 of an inch.  The particles can be made smaller by placing the source in a plastic zip lock bag and then placing that bag into another zip lock bag.  Place the bag on a concrete floor and strike with a rubber mallet.

**If using a metal source, it must be 99.9%** *pure*, **clean (rinse or wash the material of needed), in** *small* **particle size (filed) and completely dry.**  The metal is to be shaved or otherwise in small particles.  With some effort a clean "mill bastard file" can be used.  (The file is stored clean and protected from rusting with a layer of edible oil.)

This process requires a one-quart crucible with cover.  (Basically, this is a one-quart lidded stainless steel saucepan.)  Titanium crucibles are made and can be purchased from labware companies however a lidded stainless steel container works and is less expensive.  Know that many lid knobs are not stainless steel and if so must be changed from the original knob to a stainless steel bolt.   Follow the stainless steel precautions in "Labware Choices-Stainless Steel." (Appendix XIV.)

A *double* ring of flame on the propane turkey ring burner is required for this process to achieve the heat necessary to burn the lye crystals and decompose the Ormus source material in the saucepan.  For more information, see "Labware Choices-Heat." (Appendix XIV.)

**Note the precautions regarding lye:**  Alternating layers of lye crystals and Ormus source material are added to the saucepan.  Make sure that more lye crystals are present than dry Ormus source material.  Use *twice* as much lye crystals as source material and using *three* times as much lye crystals is better *however do not fill the crucible more than 1/3 full of lye crystals and dry Ormus source material.*  Less full is better because it will boil over if too full.

**Place a layer of lye crystals on the bottom of a lidded stainless steel crucible (saucepan).**

**Next add a layer of completely** *dry* **Ormus source material.**  The Ormus source material must be *dry* and reduced to small/fine particles before starting the process.

It is imperative that the layers of lye crystals and Ormus source material are dry before adding heat because if any moisture is present, the lye crystals being reactive with any form of water or even moisture from the atmosphere would begin to dissolve and react with more volatility in the presence of heat.

**Follow with another layer of lye crystals.**

**Follow with another layer of completely dry Ormus source material.**

**Place the lid on top of the stainless steel saucepan and then place a 5-pound flat weight (weight-trainer type) on top of the lid.**  This holds the lid down and thereby maintains a tight seal with the saucepan.  In this way, Ormus may be deterred from floating away when heat is added. A suggestion is to hold the weight in place by positioning the center hole of the weight over the (stainless steel) lid knob of the stainless steel saucepan. (A brick has been used for this purpose.)

**Place a metal sleeve around the lidded stainless steel saucepan.** The sleeve holds the heat in the location of the pot. (An empty metal coffee container can make a great sleeve.)

**Turn the heat on** *high.* With the addition of high heat applied to the lye crystals, the molecules of metal actually boil and partially disaggregate (disintegrate) and the molecules of sand totally disaggregates. This takes about 20 minutes and is completed when you see the pot has its contents bubbling out. Know that if the bottom of the pot turns red when in the heat you have "good" heat. Red heat is 800 degrees. Gold has been said to go away from the source at 425 degrees Centigrade, but some have said that it stays in the saucepan because it is "lidded and sealed" (with the weight on top) and as the pot cools, it falls back down. (You may choose to heat the saucepan for four hours with less hot heat.)

**Turn the heat off.**

**Remove the stainless steel saucepan by picking it up along the sides with crucible tongs or big pliers.** (You may choose to leave it on the turkey ring burner [turned off] until it is cool. To best follow the stainless steel precautions, remove the burned material from the stainless steel pot as soon as it has cooled and do not allow the burned material to remain in the stainless steel saucepan any longer than necessary.) Note: The lid will be fused onto the saucepan.

**Allow the stainless steel saucepan to cool..**

**Remove the lid.** The lid is fused on therefore use a screwdriver to pry it open. (Note: Wear gloves, long sleeves and eye protection as dry lye coats the burned material and is also on the outside of the saucepan.)

**Place two baggies over the cooled lidless stainless steel saucepan and turn it upside down.** Two baggies are used in case one develops a tear. Now find a *rubber* mallet and a cement floor.
    Beat the bottom of the stainless steel saucepan (inside the two plastic baggies) with a rubber mallet on a concrete floor. The dried material caked on the bottom of the pan "pops out."
    Remove the stainless steel saucepan from the baggies.

**Beat the dried-out material (inside the 2 plastic baggies) on the concrete floor with a rubber mallet until the particles are smaller than 1/4 of an inch.** The material is soft enough that it does not poke holes in the plastic bags and having two plastic baggies acts as insurance in case one of the baggies does break. You may also choose to place a towel over the plastic baggies as additional cushioning. (Some have termed these crushed particles "crunchies" as they have the appearance of dried crunchy pieces.)

## Preparing the Source Part 2
### The "Secret Fire"
The crushed particles of burned Ormus source material (the "crunchies") are added to lye solution in the same way (with one exception) as in the "Dry Process (Cold Fire Process)." When adding the "crunchies" to the *lye solution* it "smokes" and this does not occur in the "Dry Process."

(Do not breathe in the lye fumes. For more information, see "Cautions" in the front of this chapter.)

**Prepare one-gallon lye solution.** For more information, see "Lye Solution Preparation." (Section Three.)

**Place the lye solution into a clean HDPE plastic container.** The container used to house the dry Ormus source and lye solution can be HDPE plastic or stainless steel. However, since external heat is not added in this process, HDPE plastic containers are more commonly used. (Not only is it easier to find them in various sizes but there are no precautions associated with their use as with stainless steel containers.) Glass is not recommended because the lye solution is in contact with the glass for a *long period of time and etches silica (a non-toxic contaminate) from the glass. For more information, see "Labware Choices." (Appendix XIV.)*

**Add the fine *dry* particles of burned Ormus source material to the lye solution at a ratio of roughly one cup of *dry* Ormus source material *to* one gallon of lye solution.** Stir with a plastic stirrer while combining. The order of combining is specific and it *is important that the Ormus source material is always added to the lye solution.* If this order is not followed, the lye solution may sputter, boil and splatter onto you. (To make a smaller volume, use the same proportions, such as 1/2 cup of dry Ormus source material to 1/2 gallon of lye solution.) **Note:** 1/2 gallon is equal to eight cups or two quarts. For more information, see "Measurement Conversions." (Appendix XII.)

**Continue the process by allowing time for Ormus to "tie" to the sodium in the lye solution.** This is described in "Dry Process (Cold Fire Process)-Preparing the Source part 2: Boiling the Source." (page 64)

**After several weeks, pour the "living menstruum" (Ormus-containing lye solution)** *off the* **top of the Ormus source material and filter it.** The same filtering process is performed as explained in the "Wet Process-Preparing the Source." (Section Three.) *Please note one difference:* a paper towel is never used because lye solution disintegrates the paper towel. The filtering process is repeated here, with modifications, for your convenience:

**(Filter the "***living menstruum***" through a wetted coffee filter.** Always use distilled water to moisten the filter. One filter can be used at a time or two or three stacked together if necessary. Pores of the filter *do* clog up so use a fresh dampened filter for each pour. Repeat the straining until the "menstruum" runs through clear.)

**Place a "candy/deep fry thermometer" on a thick cloth (to "seat" it) under a clean** *borosilicate glass* **container.** If the thermometer is constructed of all glass (containing no metal) it may be attached to the inside of the container. The thermometer allows us to monitor the temperature of the "living menstruum" as hydrochloric acid is added. The temperature during the process does rise and Ormus has been speculated to "boil off" (gassing) if it rises above 140 degrees. Consequently it is important not to exceed this temperature.

Fill the *borosilicate* **glass container less than 1/2 full of "living menstruum"** because the next step requires a lot of hydrochloric acid. (*High heat is generated when hydrochloric acid is added,* therefore *always* choose borosilicate glass containers and place a catch basin underneath. When a reaction releases heat, it is called an "exothermic reaction" and this heat causes the borosilicate glass container to become very hot). For more information, see "Labware Choices-Borosilicate Glass." (Appendix XIV.)

*(What has been created is a filtered "living menstruum" that is central to the chemical reaction in all the dry Ormus collection processes.)*

## Perform the Process
**This is important:** The filtered living menstruum (Ormus-containing lye solution) must be at a *room temperature. If the solution is still warm the next step of the process will not work.*

Reminder: Because hydrochloric acid generates high heat when added to the lye solution, *always* choose a borosilicate glass container and place it in a "catch basin." For more information, see "Labware Choices-Borosilicate Glass." (Appendix XIV.)

**Hydrochloric acid is added to the cooled and filtered "Living Menstruum" to precipitate Ormus (manna).** This is described in "Dry Process (Cold Fire Process)-Perform the Process." (page 66)

## Purifying (washing)
**The Ormus (manna) precipitate is washed with distilled water.** This is described in "Dry Process (Cold Fire Process)-Purifying (Washing)." (page 67)

## Storage
Storage of the Ormus (manna) precipitate is the same as described in "Dry Process (Cold Fire Process)-Storage." (page 69)

## Final Thought
The stainless steel crucible (saucepan) can be re-used if there is no pitting (pitting means lead in the pan is showing). We do not want lead around. Lead impurities are a challenge because lead is everywhere and effort is expended to keep it out of our labware. The stainless steel crucible (saucepan) can be re-used as long as the cover fits and the pot has no leaks (it holds water).

When using pure metal as the source material, a stainless steel pot (or any utensil used in the process), is generally not suggested as *no* other metal should touch the solutions. This is to ensure the Ormus (manna) forms from only the pure metal. It is understood that this process uses a stainless steel saucepan for the burn and therefore the Ormus (manna) is not pure Ormus from only the metal source.

The filtered out Ormus source material sediment from the "living menstruum" can be saved and placed in a fresh batch of lye solution to prepare another batch of "living menstruum." This can be done and more Ormus (manna) collected.  You must know that the amount of Ormus (manna) that precipitates is not as high the second time around.

**Caution regarding silver:**  If silver is used as the Ormus source material (or in the Ormus source material to an appreciable degree), *hydrochloric acid* cannot be used to precipitate the Ormus (manna) or toxic silver chloride has been made.  For more information regarding silver, see "Sources for the Ormus Processes-Metal." (Appendix VIII.)

Remember that if no toxic metals or toxic materials are in the Ormus source material, the Ormus (manna) is not toxic and if you do not know what is in the source material, either it and/or the Ormus (manna) collected from it can be sent off for an assay.  For more information, see "Resources and Supplies-Have a Source Analyzed." (Appendix I.) "Sources for the Ormus Processes-Information." (Appendix VIII.)

*All additional final thought is the same as mentioned in "Dry Process (Cold Fire Process)-Final Thought." (page 70)*

NOTES:

> "The secret of alchemy is this: there is a way of manipulating matter and energy so as to produce what modern scientists call a 'field of force.' The field acts on the observer and puts him in a privileged position *vis-a-vis* the Universe. From this position, he has access to the realities which are ordinarily hidden from us by time and space, matter and energy. This is what we call the Great Work"
>
> *Fulcanelli*

# DRY "LYE BURN AND BOIL PROCESS "

Note: There are appendices that have cross-referencing information to that in this chapter. These appendices include:
"List of Ormus Resources and Supplies,"
"Common Measurement Conversions,"
"Best Practices Labware Choices,"
"pH Meter," and
"Sources for the Ormus Processes."
For "Lye Solution Preparation" and "Hydrochloric Acid Preparation" see Section Three.

---

**CAUTION!!**

Note: Cautions are a form of education so that you may work with lye and hydrochloric acid in awareness and respect not fear.

Lye is a "caustic." Hydrochloric acid is an acid. Both lye and hydrochloric acid are strong chemicals and can damage eyes by rendering the cornea opaque, a form of irreparable eye damage. If lye or hydrochloric acid gets into eyes flush the eyeball with water immediately and seek medical attention if the burning persists.

If lye or hydrochloric acid contacts the skin it hurts and damages it. Lye or hydrochloric acid reacts with skin tissue and can cause permanent damage and scarring if severe. Even minor reactions can be painful. If lye or hydrochloric acid contacts clothes it damages them. If lye or hydrochloric acid gets onto your clothes or body, immediately flush the area with lots of water and seek medical attention if necessary.

When working with lye or hydrochloric acid, please wear goggles or a full-face visor (an industrial face protector), neoprene gloves and a PVC lab apron as well as protective clothing such as long sleeves and long pants.

Keep children and pets away from the work area and do not leave it unattended. Even if no one is around, an unsuspecting person could venture by and be at risk.

It is very helpful to work near a sink, faucet or other source of wash water.

The area must be well ventilated as breathing fumes from lye or hydrochloric acid can damage air passages and lungs. Lye solution creates caustic fumes. Do not breathe in these fumes. Hydrochloric acid creates a pungent, corrosive "fog" when added to water. Do not breathe in this fog. Handle lye or hydrochloric acid with adequate ventilation such as a laboratory range hood vented outside or conduct the work outside. It is advisable to keep a bottle of baking soda solution handy to use against hydrochloric acid spills (baking soda powder can be sprinkled on if the spill is large) and a spray bottle of distilled white vinegar handy to use against lye spills.

For more information, see "The Chemicals of the Processes." (Appendix XIII.)

When working with lye or hydrochloric acid, (or any chemical) avoid touching your face or rubbing your eyes. Do not handle around food. Do not dump wastewater on the ground. Lye is generally safe to put down the drain, but first run water in the sink while slowly pouring the lye directly into the drain and don't mix it with any acid that may be in the drain as it can react explosively. Hydrochloric acid is generally safe to put down the drain, but first run water in the sink while slowly pouring the hydrochloric acid directly into the drain and don't mix it with any "pH alkaline" material that may be in the drain as it can react explosively.

**Labware and Supplies to perform a dry "Lye Burn and Boil Process"**
Ormus source material, both lye crystals and lye solution, hydrochloric acid, distilled water, pH meter, stainless steel lidded saucepan for the "burn" (follow the stainless steel precautions in Appendix XIV), 5-lb flat weight (weight-trainer type) or a brick, metal sleeve (to condense the heat in the area around the saucepan), a heat source: propane turkey ring burner with a double ring of flame (for the higher heat required for the "burn"), stainless steel pot for the "boil" (follow the stainless steel precautions in Appendix XIV), container of *borosilicate glass* (to collect the precipitate), measuring cup, aluminum foil, barrel syringe or baster, funnel or flat strainer, filters (*unbleached* coffee filters), focus beam flashlight, plastic catch basin, stirrer of plastic or borosilicate glass, safety clothing and equipment. The hydrochloric acid used as the "reagent" in the process can be placed in an HDPE plastic bottle during the collection. Store the finished manna in HDPE plastic containers. For more information, see Appendix XIV.

As a safety measure, always place containers used in the process into a larger non-metallic "catch basin" (*in case of leakage or breakage*). For example: A (new) cat litter box or the bottom of an under-the-bed storage container. (Note: When adding the hydrochloric acid, a lot of heat is generated that could break the glass.)

To best ensure electromagnetic waves cause no interference on the stability of Ormus in source material or the manna (precipitate), it is prudent to keep the work and storage area six feet or more away from them. For more information, see "Labware Choices-Aluminum Foil." (Appendix XIV.)


## Definition

This process mirrors the *dry* "Lye Burn Process" as a "burn" is first performed on the Ormus source material and then it is placed in lye solution. The difference is the addition of *external* heat to the lye solution to cause a "boil." This boiling prepares the "living menstruum" (Ormus-containing lye solution) in four hours versus several weeks in the *dry* "Lye Burn Process." The additional heat from the boil also disaggregates (disintegrate or disassociate) the source material further. ("Living Menstruum" is explained in *dry* "Lye Boil Process-Information.")

Because of a "boil" added to this process, it is a more energetically active one than the *dry* "Lye Burn Process" and can physically disaggregate (disintegrate or disassociate) to a greater degree the molecules in Ormus source material used in the *dry* "Lye Burn Process."

Source material for this process includes gold and copper filings as well as land based minerals etc ... (Note: This is not the most efficient process to make Ormus (manna) from gold.)


## Information

Appearance: The collected Ormus is observed as a fluffy precipitate (not always a brilliant white color) in liquid.

Because of the boiling step, this process is both more energetically active and faster than the *dry* "Lye Burn Process" while being less energetic (dangerous) than the *dry* "Sodium Burn Process." Therefore, this process is simpler and less dangerous than the *dry* "Sodium Burn Process" yet generates *high* heat from both burning the lye crystals and then boiling the lye solution. This heat causes more physical disaggregation of the aggregation of molecules in Ormus source materials enabling more Ormus to be available for collection. (It is noted that the *dry* "Sodium Burn Process" and the *dry* "Hydrogen Peroxide (gold) Process" are more efficient for processing gold.)

Heat is added from an *external source* in this process to cause both a "burn" and a "boil." Any Ormus process which uses external heat *especially when heat is applied to cause a "boil"*, is generally thought to place a slightly higher energy state (higher spin) on the Ormus material and this is felt to cause a bit more potency. It is also felt that more precipitate forms during a process that does not cause a boil. When boiling, some of the lighter Ormus boils off and therefore lost to the collection. For more information, see "Labware Choices-Heat." (Appendix XIV.)

This Ormus collection process uses both lye crystals *and* lye solution. All Ormus collection processes use the same lye solution concentration. For more information, see "Lye Solution Preparation." (Section Three.) The pH of the lye solution is a little higher than pH 12.

The source material must be washed and completely *dry* because lye crystals react violently in the presence of water. (**NOTE:** Lye crystals are reactive (volatile) with any *form of water or moisture. Follow all lye precautions.*)

Note: If no toxic metals or toxic materials are in the Ormus source material, the Ormus (manna) is not toxic. If using an Ormus source material that makes a precipitate and it is not known if you can "eat" (non-toxic) the source, at the very least send the precipitate off for an assay. For more information, see "Sources for the Processes-Information." (Appendix VIII.)


## Preparing the Source Part 1
### Burning the Source

**Lye crystals are burned with dry Ormus source material.** This is described in dry "Lye Burn Process-Preparing the Source Part I." (page 85)


## Preparing the Source Part 2
### Boiling the Source

The crushed particles of burned Ormus source material (the "crunchies") are added to lye solution in the same way (with one exception) as in the "Dry Process (Cold Fire Process)." When adding the "crunchies" to the *lye solution it "smokes"* and this does not occur in the "Dry Process." (Do not breathe in the lye fumes. For more information, see "Cautions" in the front of this chapter.)

**Prepare one-gallon lye solution.** For more information, see "Lye Solution Preparation." (Section Three.)

**Place the lye solution into a stainless steel pot that has a lid**. Since this process adds *heat* to the lye solution, it is important to have a *stainless* steel pot. The stainless steel pot is to have no aluminum showing or in its construction (this can be checked with a magnet). This means there is to be no rivets holding the handles onto the pot, *no* rusting, *no* flaking, *no* pitting, *no* chipping, nor breeching of the stainless steel coating or discoloration that can't be polished away with stainless steel cleansers. The lid, including the knob is to have no aluminum and if aluminum is present the knob must be removed and replaced with a stainless steel bolt. For more information, see "Labware Choices-Stainless Steel." (Appendix XIV.)

**Add the fine dry particles of burned Ormus source material to the lye solution at a ratio of roughly one-cup dry Ormus source material to one-gallon lye solution.** Stir with a plastic stirrer while combining. The order of combining is specific and *it is important that the Ormus source material is always added to the lye solution.* If this order is not followed, the lye solution may sputter and boil and splatter onto you. (To make a smaller volume, use the same proportions, such as 1/2 cup dry Ormus source material to 1/2 gallon of lye solution.) *Note:* 1/2 gallon is equal to eight cups or two quarts. For more information, see "Measurement Conversions." (Appendix XII.)

**Boil, energetically simmer, cool and filter the "living menstruum" (Ormus-containing lye solution).** This is described in dry "Lye Boil Process-Preparing the Source Part 2: Boiling the Source." (page 77.)

**Place a "candy/deep fry thermometer" on a thick cloth (to "seat" it) under a clean** *borosilicate glass* **container.** If the thermometer is constructed of all glass (containing no metal) it may be attached to the inside of the container. The thermometer allows us to monitor the temperature of the "living menstruum" as hydrochloric acid is added. The temperature during the process does rise and Ormus has been speculated to "boil off" (gassing) if it rises above 140 degrees Farenheit. Consequently it is important not to exceed this temperature.

**Fill the** *borosilicate glass* **container less than 1/2 full of "living menstruum"** because the next step requires a lot of hydrochloric acid. *(High heat is generated when hydrochloric acid is added,* therefore *always* choose borosilicate glass containers and place a catch basin underneath. When a reaction releases heat, it is called an "exothermic reaction" and this heat causes the borosilicate glass container to become very hot). For more information, see "Labware Choices-Borosilicate Glass." (Appendix XIV.)

*(What has been created is a filtered "living menstruum" that is central to the chemical reaction in all the dry Ormus collection processes.)*

## Perform the Process

**This is important:** The filtered living menstruum (Ormus-containing lye solution) must have *fully* cooled down after the boil and be at a room temperature. *If the solution is still warm the next step of the process will not work.*

Reminder: Because hydrochloric acid generates high heat when added to the lye solution, *always* choose a borosilicate glass container and place it in a "catch basin." For more information, see "Labware Choices-Borosilicate Glass." (Appendix XIV.)

Hydrochloric acid is added to the cooled and filtered "Living Menstruum" to precipitate Ormus (manna). This is described in "Dry Process (Cold Fire Process)-Perform the Process." (page 66)

## Purifying (washing)

The Ormus (manna) precipitate is washed with distilled water. This is described in "Dry Process (Cold Fire Process)-Purifying (Washing)." (page 67)

## Storage

Storage of the Ormus (manna) precipitate. This is described in "Dry Process (Cold Fire Process)-Storage." (page 69)

## Final Thought

When using pure metal as the source material, a stainless steel pot (or any utensil used in the process), is generally not suggested as ideally no other metal should touch the solutions. This is to ensure the Ormus (manna) forms from only the pure metal. It is understood that this process uses a stainless steel saucepan for the burn and therefore the Ormus (manna) is not pure Ormus from only the metal source. A suggestion that rids one piece of stainless steel equipment is to use a Visions® glass/ceramic Dutch oven in a 5-quart size with lid for the "boil" part of the process. Boil in this container as you would one made of stainless steel.

The filtered out Ormus source material sediment from the "living menstruum" can be saved and placed in a fresh batch of lye solution and reboiled to prepare another batch of "living menstruum." This can be done and more Ormus (manna) collected. You must know that the amount of Ormus (manna) that precipitates is not as high the second time around.

**Caution regarding silver:** If silver is the Ormus source material, (or in the Ormus source material to an appreciable degree), *hydrochloric acid* cannot be used to precipitate the Ormus (manna) or toxic silver chloride has been made. For more information regarding silver, see "Sources for the Ormus Processes-Metal." (Appendix VIII.)

All "final thought" are the same as described in *dry* "Lye Burn Process-Final Thought." (page 89)

NOTES:

Alchemists agree that success in the Great Work is not achieved by human means alone, and that *spirit* is also present. Classical alchemy considers that matter is composed of spirit and soul, the former being masculine in nature and the latter feminine and that in addition to the source material, the alchemist also houses spirit (associated with thought) and soul (connecting him to the unconscious). When the two achieve a conscious and harmonious relationship it was considered that a *Royal Marriage* occurred, and the alchemist had become *whole*.

# DRY "SODIUM BURN PROCESS"

## Includes a Write-Up by Commercial Alchemist Don Nance

### Preface

This process is left to trained and seasoned alchemists and scientists because it requires sodium metal. **The reaction of sodium metal to moisture <u>in any form</u> is violently explosive (dangerous).**

The *dry* "Sodium Burn Process" is described so the reader may fully recognize how all the *dry* Ormus collection processes share the same basic chemistry. Now when the Ormus source material is very tightly aggregated (held together), as gold is, the energy required to initially dissociate it becomes so great that real danger exists to the alchemist or scientist at hand. Therefore, understand the *dry* "Sodium Burn Process;" however:

<u>DO NOT </u>perform it.

## WARNING

> Because sodium metal is so explosive even with the smallest amount of moisture, (even our breath) or water, I do not suggest or endorse performing the *dry* "Sodium Burn Process." <u>This process has been included for the purposes of information, historical posterity and so the reader may understand the similarity of the chemistry among all the dry Ormus processes.</u>

> In this process, the source material (gold) is so tightly aggregated (bound) that reactive, explosive and dangerous sodium metal is needed. Because a sodium explosion can cause great physical harm, do not perform the dry "Sodium Burn Process."

Note: There are appendices that have cross-referencing information to that in this chapter.
These appendices include:
"List of Ormus Resources and Supplies"
"Common Measurement Conversions"
"Best Practices Labware Choices"
"pH Meter"
"Sources for the Ormus Processes"
For "lye Solution Preparation" and "Hydrochloric Acid Preparation" see Section Three.

**CAUTION!!**

Note: Cautions are a form of education so that you may work with lye and hydrochloric acid in awareness and respect not fear.

Lye is a "caustic." Hydrochloric acid is an acid. Both lye and hydrochloric acid are strong chemicals and can damage eyes by rendering the cornea opaque, a form of irreparable eye damage. If lye or hydrochloric acid gets into eyes flush the eyeball with water immediately and seek medical attention if the burning persists.

If lye or hydrochloric acid contacts the skin it hurts and damages it. Lye or hydrochloric acid reacts with skin tissue and can cause permanent damage and scarring if severe. Even minor reactions can be painful. If lye or hydrochloric acid contacts clothes it damages them. If lye or hydrochloric acid gets onto your clothes or body, immediately flush the area with lots of water and seek medical attention if necessary.

It is very helpful to work near a sink, faucet or other source of wash water.

The area must be well ventilated as breathing fumes from lye or hydrochloric acid can damage air passages and lungs. Lye solution creates caustic fumes. Do not breathe in these fumes. Hydrochloric acid creates a pungent, corrosive "fog" when added to water. Do not breathe in this fog. Handle lye or hydrochloric acid with adequate ventilation such as a laboratory range hood vented outside or conduct the work outside. It is advisable to keep a bottle of baking soda solution handy to use against hydrochloric acid spills (baking soda powder can be sprinkled on if the spill is large) and a spray bottle of distilled white vinegar handy to use against lye spills.

For more information, see "The Chemicals of the Processes." (Appendix XIII.)

When working with lye or hydrochloric acid, (or any chemical) avoid touching your face or rubbing your eyes. Do not handle around food. Do not dump wastewater on the ground. Lye is generally safe to put down the drain, but first run water in the sink while slowly pouring the lye directly into the drain and don't mix it with any acid that may be in the drain as it can react explosively. Hydrochloric acid is generally safe to put down the drain, but first run water in the sink while slowly pouring the hydrochloric acid directly into the drain and don't mix it with any "pH alkaline" material that may be in the drain as it can react explosively.
When working with lye or hydrochloric acid, please wear goggles or a full-face visor (an industrial face protector), neoprene gloves and a PVC lab apron as well as protective clothing such as long sleeves and long pants.

Keep children and pets away from the work area and do not leave it unattended. Even if no one is around, an unsuspecting person could venture by and be at risk.

## Labware and Supplies to perform a *dry* "Sodium Burn Process"

(The author does not suggest you perform this dangerous process. This list is provided for informational, historical and posterity purposes.)

Ormus source material, pure sodium metal (explosive with even the smallest amount of moisture such as your breath vapor), face mask or respirator and a face shield, dry sodium carbonate, Ph meter, flock lined rubber gloves, meat cleaver, olive oil, lidded titanium crucible preferred or a good stainless steel saucepan (for the "burn.") If using stainless follow the stainless steel precautions in Appendix XIV, stainless steel pot (if performing a "boil") or container of HDPE plastic (if not performing a boil), heat source: propane turkey ring burner with a double ring of flame (for the higher heat required for the "burn"), metal sleeve (to condense the heat in the area around the crucible), mister bottle, distilled water, zip lock freezer bags, chisel, lye solution, hydrochloric acid, distilled water, 5-lb flat weight (weight-trainer type) or a brick, container of borosilicate glass (to collect the precipitate), measuring cup, aluminum foil, barrel syringe or baster, funnel or flat strainer, filters (unbleached coffee filters), focus beam flashlight, catch basin, stirrer of plastic or borosilicate glass, aluminum foil, safety clothing and equipment. The hydrochloric acid used as the "reagent" in the process can be placed in an HDPE plastic bottle during the collection. Store the finished manna in HDPE plastic containers. For more information, see Appendix XIV.

As a safety measure, always place containers used in the process into a larger non-metallic "catch basin" (in case of leakage or breakage). For example: A (new) cat litter box or the bottom of an under-the-bed storage container. (Note: When adding the hydrochloric acid, a lot of heat is generated that could break the glass.)

To best ensure electromagnetic waves cause no interference on the stability of Ormus in source material or the manna (precipitate), it is prudent to keep the work and storage area six feet or more away from them. For more information, see "Labware Choices-Aluminum Foil." (Appendix XIV.)

## Definition

(A very dangerous process.)

The metallic bonds of the gold source material are broken using very high heat. Pure sodium metal is used to reach this very high heat and causes a "burn." The disaggregated (disintegrated) molecules of the gold source material are then wetted with lye solution (as explained in all the *dry* Ormus collection processes). With time or external heat added to perform a "boil" (and less time), the Ormus it thought to move out of the burned source material and into the lye solution. A precipitate is dropped using hydrochloric acid (as explained in all the *dry* Ormus collection processes).

Because of a "burn" caused by sodium metal, this process is more energetically active than the *dry* "Lye Burn Process."

Source material for this process includes tightly bound ones such as pure metals and ores of metals such as gold ores, silver ores, and copper ores. (Ores are not usually used).

This is a faster and more energetic way of extracting Ormus from metals.

(**Note:** This process is beyond the scope of the average Ormus collector and this manual.)

## Information

Appearance: The collected Ormus is observed as a fluffy white precipitate.

As a service to the Ormus community, commercial alchemist Don Nance has provided a description of the *dry* "Sodium Burn Process." This follows "Final Thought."

Heat is added from an external source in this process to cause a "burn" of the source material and heat may also be chosen to "boil" the lye solution. Any Ormus process which uses external heat *especially when heat is applied to cause a "boil"*, is generally thought to place a slightly higher energy state (higher spin) on the Ormus material and this is felt to cause a bit more potency. It is also felt that more precipitate forms during a process that does not cause a boil. When boiling, some of the lighter Ormus boils off and therefore lost to the collection. For more information, see "Labware Choices-Heat" (Appendix XIV).

Gold is a diatom. Its chemical signature is Au2. It is a two-atom cluster and its two atoms do not like to split apart. The two-atom cluster resists spitting apart in a major way. In order to have the two atoms split, very energetic (explosive) reactions are required and therefore this is a volatile and dangerous reaction. A real fight is ensuing at the atomic level for relinquishment of one of the two atoms in the cluster. It may be said in a simple analogy that "gold loves itself." This is probably why gold is classified as the most "noble" of all the elements on the periodic table. (Noble elements are inert and it is very difficult for them to be attracted to or react chemically with another substance.)

> Pure sodium metal is chosen because it is highly energetically active (volatile, explosive) to the point of being able to split apart the two atom gold cluster. There is a very real danger in working with sodium metal and unless you are a trained and seasoned alchemist or scientist with a proper laboratory set up, the dry "Sodium Burn Process" is not to be performed.

The *dry* "Sodium Burn Process" burns the sodium metal at about 800 degrees C. along with the cleaned, dry and shaved gold metal. The sodium causes very <u>high</u> heat that disaggregates (disintegrates) both itself and the Ormus source material (the gold).

Pure sodium is very reactive and explodes when in contact with water. Even the water in the <u>humidity of the air or of our breath or from a drop of sweat off our nose can cause a violent (explosive) reaction.</u> For this reason the Ormus source material must be dry, having no water on it.

> In addition to proper laboratory conditions, safety glasses and a mask MUST be worn since even the higher humidity resulting from our breath can cause an explosion.

This is a process used when the Ormus source is a pure metal or the ores of metals such as gold ore, silver ore or copper ore. (Gold, silver or copper ores are seldom used.) For more information, see "Sources for the Ormus Processes-Metal" (Appendix VIII).

This method works with silver although hydrochloric acid is not used when making silver Ormus manna as silver chloride has been precipitated. **"Silver chloride" is a toxic material.** For more information regarding silver, see "Sources for the Ormus Processes-Silver" (Appendix VIII).

## Preparing the Source Part 1

**Burning the Source**

> Because sodium metal is so explosive even with the smallest amount of moisture, (even our breath) or water, I do not suggest or endorse performing the *dry* "Sodium Burn Process."

Place the source material in the lidded stainless steel (saucepan) or titanium crucible. See stainless steel precautions in "Labware Choices-Stainless Steel." (Appendix XIV.) Titanium crucibles are the best (although very expensive) and can be purchased from labware companies. Stainless Steel saucepans do work.

In the *dry* "Sodium Burn Process", pure sodium metal is burned (not lye crystals as are burned in the *dry* "Lye Burn Process"). Sodium metal provides the very high heat required. (Pure sodium is a soft metal that is so soft it can be sliced with a knife.) The completely dry Ormus source material and the pure sodium are layered one above the other

Burn the source material for 20 minutes in a closed crucible at hot heat. This is described in *dry* "Lye Burn-Preparing the Source." A 140,000 BTU propane turkey burner with a double ring of flame is required to provide this high heat. For more information, see "Labware Choices-Heat." (Appendix XIV.)

**NOTE: Be aware of all the hazards of very volatile and very reactive (explosive) sodium metal described in this chapter under "Preface" and "Information."** The Ormus source material disaggregates with the addition of the high heat and lines the sides and bottom of the crucible (saucepan).

## Preparing the Source Part 2

**The "Secret Fire" *or* Boiling the Source**

As a safety measure, always place containers used in the process into a larger non-metallic "catch basin" (in case of leakage or breakage).

Complete the preparation of the Ormus source material by chiseling out the cooled and annealed (burned) source material, reducing to fine particles and adding to lye solution (in that order). This is described in *dry* "Lye Burn Process-Preparing the Source Part 1."

This mixture is allowed to sit, covered for weeks, with routine periodic stirring and then filtered. This is described in *dry* "Lye Burn Process-Preparing the Source Part 2: Boiling the Source."

OR

This mixture can be boiled, allowed to cool and filtered. This is described in *dry* "Lye Boil Process-Preparing the Source Part 2: Boiling the Source."

**Be aware of the hazards of working with lye.** For more information, see "The Chemicals of the Processes." (Appendix XIII.)

*(What has been created is a filtered "living menstruum" that is central to the chemical reaction in all the dry Ormus collection processes.)*

## Perform the Process

**This is important:** The filtered living menstruum (Ormus-containing lye solution) must have fully cooled down after the boil and be at a room temperature. *If the solution is still warm the next step of the process will not work.*

Reminder: Because hydrochloric acid generates high heat when added to the lye solution, *always* choose a borosilicate glass container and place it in a "catch basin." For more information, see "Labware Choices-Borosilicate Glass." (Appendix XIV.)

Place a "candy/deep fry thermometer" on a thick cloth (to "seat" it) under a clean *borosilicate glass* container. If the thermometer is constructed of all glass (containing no metal) it may be attached to the inside of the container. The thermometer allows us to monitor the temperature of the "living menstruum" as hydrochloric acid is added. The temperature during the process does rise and Ormus has been speculated to "boil off" (gassing) if it rises above 140 degrees Fahrenheit. Consequently it is important not to exceed this temperature.

Hydrochloric acid is added to the filtered "living Menstruum" (it must be room temperature not hot) to precipitate the Ormus (manna). This is described in "Dry Process (Cold Fire Process)-Perform the Process."

## Purifying (washing)

The precipitate is washed with distilled water. This is described in "Dry Process (Cold Fire Process)-Purifying (Washing)."

## Storage

Storing the Ormus (manna) is the same as described in "Dry Process (Cold Fire Process)-Storage."

## Final Thought

Don Nance has said that gold fights the process during the summer months and that gold Ormus is best collected during the winter months.

When using pure metal (gold) as the source material, a stainless steel pot (or any utensil used in the process) or titanium, is generally not suggested as ideally no other metal should touch the solutions. This is to ensure the Ormus (manna) forms from only the pure metal. It is understood that this process uses a stainless steel saucepan (or a titanium crucible) for the burn and therefore the Ormus (manna) is not pure Ormus from only the metal source. If a "boil" is performed after the "burn", a suggestion that rids one piece of stainless steel equipment is to use a Visions® glass/ceramic Dutch oven in a 5-quart size with lid for the "boil" step. Boil in this container as you would one made of stainless steel.

The filtered out Ormus source material sediment from the "living menstruum" can be saved and placed in a fresh batch of lye solution to prepare another batch of "living menstruum." This can be done and more Ormus (manna) collected.  Be aware that the amount of Ormus (manna) that precipitates is not as high the second time around.

**Caution regarding silver:**  If silver is the Ormus source material, (or in the Ormus source material to an appreciable degree), hydrochloric acid cannot be used to precipitate the Ormus (manna) or toxic silver chloride has been made.  For more information regarding silver, see "Sources for the Ormus Processes-Metal." (Appendix VIII.)

The "Living menstruum" (unless made from silver) can be used in place of regular lye solution in a "Wet Process" with exceptional results.  Since this lye solution is a "living menstruum" that contains Ormus (from the source material), a greater drop of Ormus (manna) is expected when performing a "Wet Process" on "reconstituted" sea or "drawn" seawater.  **Note:** "Living menstruum" created by soaking, boiling (or burning) a silver source is never saved for use.  This is because you may forget the source material was silver and use the "living menstruum" in a dry process.  All the dry processes include adding hydrochloric acid and once this has been added, toxic "silver chloride is made.  For more information, see "Sources for the Ormus Processes-Metal." (Appendix VIII.)

Do not work with lye or hydrochloric acid in "fear" as it is thought that feeling fear at the time of the "work" causes an "imprint" of "fear" onto the Ormus (manna).  Work with lye and hydrochloric acid in "respect" - not "fear."  The emotions surrounding "fear" also cause a mind to "close off;" this results in making the steps of an Ormus collection process very difficult to absorb.

When washing containers and other equipment that were used there may be observed a dried white ring in the container and dried white spots on it.  These are easily removed with a solution of 3/4 part white vinegar and 1/4 part water.

All additional final thought is the same as *dry* "Lye Burn Process-Final Thought."

---

Since this process is unstable and the smallest amount of water causes pure sodium metal to explode, it is most dangerous.

---

Therefore, this process is only done when it is worth the work and is only used when the source is gold or silver.  Be aware that there are other methods to disaggregate gold such as the *dry* "Hydrogen Peroxide (gold) Process" described in a later chapter.

Remember that a "less" energetic (dangerous) alternative process, to the *dry* "Sodium Burn Process" is the *dry* "Lye Burn Process" (which partially disaggregates gold molecules).

---

Note: The *dry* "Sodium Burn Process" uses very destructively reactive chemicals that are outside the scope of most Ormus collectors.  Therefore, this process is not encouraged or suggested and it has been included in the manual for informational, historical and posterity purposes.

---

The *dry* "Sodium Burn Process" described by commercial alchemist Don Nance follows:

# THE SODIUM BURN PROCESS

By Don Nance

## PART ONE: Preparation of the Metal

One ounce, by weight, of the metal of choice is to be prepared.

The pure gold, silver or copper metal must be processed into very thin leaves either by hammering it on an anvil or by rolling it with a jewelers' roller mill and then either hammering it into very thin leaves or filing it into fine particles using a hardened steel Mill Bastard file.

Hammering it into thin leaves is the preferred form because it gives the maximum contact area with the sodium metal to be used.

Next the crucible is to be prepared. It needs to be dried over heat until there is no moisture associated with it whatsoever.

While the crucible is cooling, the prepared metal or black sand samples are to be thoroughly dried over heat to be certain that there is no moisture associated with them whatsoever.

Once the crucible has cooled the pure sodium metal must be prepared. The ONLY form of pure sodium metal that will work with this process is Fisher part number S-135. It comes as a one-pound block vacuum packed in a can, similar to a canned ham. This must be opened and the block of sodium removed (Authors note: Wear rubber gloves, face mask or respirator and a face shield). It will resemble a pound of butter in shape and size.

For cutting the sodium, the very best utensil is a very sharp meat clever which has been coated with a very light coating of extra-virgin olive oil. This oil coating helps to prevent moisture from condensing on the clever. The extra weight of a clever cuts the sodium metal much easier than other knives.

The sodium metal must be very quickly cut into four equal parts resembling sticks of butter. Three of these must be immediately placed into a glass jar and sealed with a plastic lid. The fourth stick is to be cut in half and one half placed into the jar with the other longer sticks and sealed tightly.

The remaining two-ounce piece of sodium must be cut into pieces resembling patties of butter that are about 1/8th inch thick: With the final slice being cut front-wise by making an "X" on it so that it makes four pieces that are triangular in shape.

The bottom of the crucible is now lined with these pieces of sodium and the triangular shaped pieces help to fill out any voids or gaps that would leave large openings between the gold and the bottom of the crucible.

The now dried and cooled pieces of gold are placed over the cut sodium metal as evenly as is possible. However, you must remember to work quickly!

Place a lid over the crucible and place it onto your 140,000 BTU gas burner and adjust it for centering over your burner/flame. Place a weight onto the lid of the crucible and fire the burner for as much heat as you can get.

If the bottom of the crucible turns cherry red within a minute or two you have good heat for the process.

A few minutes after the bottom turns cherry red the lid of the crucible will attempt to rise and you may see light and fire come out from around the edges of the lid. This is an indication that the gold is being disaggregated and is going into the high-spin state.

In order to react as much of the sodium as possible the burn should continue for another 20 minutes or until you see another episode of fire shoot out of the lid. After that time, turn the burner off and allow the crucible to cool completely.

Realize now that if you were working with a pure metal, such as gold, silver or copper that you still have unreacted sodium metal in your crucible and it is dangerous.

If you remember reading about the OUROBOROS then you may understand that in a coming part of this process your burned materials will need to be boiled in a lye solution. This is all a part of the Great Work and what is now dry must soon become wet. It is safest to react any unreacted sodium now so that it can be handled safely.

If you were working with a metallic ore, such as black sand gold ore, etc. all of the sodium usually has reacted at this stage.

After it is completely cool you may now carefully remove the lid and begin a very slow wet-down of the contents and lid. This is accomplished using a spray mister bottle and pure distilled water. You want to spray a very small, light mist one squirt at a time.

You will observe fire and sparking and some possibly violent reactions from this mist. You must proceed very slowly. Allow each reaction to burn itself completely out before misting again. Realize that with each of these reactions your M-state/ORMUS gold is being vaporized and it will not come back to you.

Once all reactions are completed, including the lid, you will wish to save all of this water and add it into the lye boil stage that follows after you have removed all of the solids from the crucible.

Once you have collected and saved all of the liquid (remember that it is very strong lye now) you will want to hammer and chisel the solids out from the bottom of the crucible. I place the crucible into a large, heavy duty, Ziploc® freezer bag and then place that inside of another one. I make a hole through the side and insert my chisel through it. I then hammer the solids and chisel them into pieces that are all smaller than 1/4 inch.

## PART TWO: Doing the Process

Once this is accomplished you will finish processing it all by following the steps necessary to perform the dry "Lye Boil Process" as is outlined in another section of this manual. Remember to add the liquid that you previously saved into the boil.

## Additional information:

We normally use two-ounces of the sodium and one-ounce of the metal of choice. This allows a more complete conversion than using a different ratio. There is always unreacted sodium leftover.

Although there is always unreacted sodium left over there is also always unreacted precious metal leftover that can be cleaned, dried and reburned.

During the mist down phase, gold forms a coating that one of my teachers, Avi Zamites, named the "skin of the rhino" and that is what it resembles. There will often be unreacted sodium metal beneath it and this sodium must also be reacted. Tread carefully!

If we were using black sand gold ore we would use 1/4 cup of it with the same two-ounces of sodium. This always reacts all of the sodium metal and leaves some black sand unreacted.

We normally use a one-quart size stainless steel sauce pan with a tight fitting lid as the crucible. A titanium crucible of the same size is better but is not really necessary. It will simply last much longer. The stainless steel is only going to survive a few burns. We never want to fill it more than 1/3rd full, by the way.

Never use any source material that has a sulfurous smell associated with it. It will not precipitate after the boil but will instead yield an ugly yellow solution and all of your efforts have been in vain.

Some gold coins and many black sand gold ores contain sulfur and this will also ruin your work. The best coin that I have used is a one-ounce U.S. Liberty Trade coin. It is pure gold and is without any filler/hardeners that accompany many of the "collectible" coins. (Authors note: The formula used to make gold coins does change. Therefore confirm the ingredients in a gold coin with a coin broker before using.)

While cutting and handling your sodium metal you must wear a face mask or respirator and a face shield. Any of your breath vapor is enough to cause a violent reaction with the sodium metal. Should something happen, you must have a large quantity of dry sodium carbonate available and use it to extinguish the flames and smother the vaporous reactions. You will have ruined your materials but your house will not have burned down.

A pair of flock-lined rubber gloves that have been coated with a very light coating of extra-virgin olive oil are useful for handling the pieces of sodium metal. The dishwashing variety is perfect because they are thick enough to protect your hands while allowing a high degree of manual dexterity.

I hope that you have found this information interesting if not useful. Please work safely.

Don Nance
October 2008

A Sodium Burn with Copper
Notice the flames that are shooting outward from the lid.
The five-pound weight prevents the lid from escaping.

FLAME ON!
Complete with flying fireballs. My student added too much water
too soon

**A Flare-up During Misting**
This should be allowed to grow completely cold again before more misting.

White Powder of Gold
Made by Don Nance.

## *DRY* "HYDROGEN PEROXIDE (Gold) PROCESS"

### Includes a Write-Up by Commercial Alchemist Don Nance

Note: There are appendices that have cross-referencing information to that in this chapter. These include:

"List of Ormus Resources and Supplies," "Common Measurement Conversions," "Best Practices Labware Choices," "pH Meter," and "Sources for the Ormus Processes." For "Lye Solution Preparation" and "Hydrochloric Acid Preparation" see Section Three.

---

**CAUTION!!**

Note: Cautions are a form of education so that you may work with these chemicals in awareness and respect not fear.

Lye is a "caustic", hydrochloric acid is an acid and 35% hydrogen peroxide is a strong oxidizer. All are strong chemicals that can damage eyes by rendering the cornea opaque, a form of eye damage that is irreparable. If lye, hydrochloric acid or 35% hydrogen peroxide get into eyes flush the eyeball with water immediately and seek medical attention if the burning persists. (continued on next page)

Lye, hydrochloric acid and 35% hydrogen peroxide can burn skin, clothes and eyes. Lye, hydrochloric acid and 35% hydrogen peroxide reacts with skin tissue and can cause permanent damage and scarring if severe. Even minor reactions can be painful. If you spill lye, hydrochloric acid or 35% hydrogen peroxide onto clothes or body, immediately flush the area with lots of water and seek medical attention if necessary.

The area must be well ventilated as breathing fumes from lye or hydrochloric acid can damage air passages and lungs. Both Lye solution and hydrochloric acid create caustic fumes. Do not breathe in these fumes. Hydrochloric acid creates a pungent, corrosive "fog" when added to water. Do not breathe in this fog. Handle lye or hydrochloric acid with adequate ventilation such as a laboratory range hood vented outside or conduct the work outside. It is advisable to keep a bottle of baking soda solution handy to use against hydrochloric acid spills (baking soda powder can be sprinkled on if the spill is large) and a spray bottle of distilled white vinegar handy to use against lye spills. It is advisable to be near a water source to use against 35% hydrogen peroxide spills,

It is very helpful to work near a sink, faucet or other source of wash water.

For information see "The Chemicals of the Processes." (Appendix XIII.)

Lye solution creates caustic fumes. Do not breathe in these fumes. Hydrochloric acid creates corrosive fumes and a pungent corrosive "fog" when added to water. Do not breathe fumes or fog.

When working with lye, hydrochloric acid or 35% hydrogen peroxide, please wear goggles or a full-face visor (an industrial face protector), neoprene gloves, a PVC lab apron as well as protective clothing such as long sleeves and long pants.

Keep children and pets away from the work area and do not leave it unattended. Even if no one is is around, any unsuspecting person could venture by and be at risk.

When working with lye, hydrochloric acid, 35% hydrogen peroxide or any chemical, avoid touching your face or rubbing your eyes. Do not handle around food. Do not dump wastewater on the ground. Lye is generally safe to put down the drain, but first run water in the sink while slowly pouring the lye directly into the drain and don't mix it with any acid that may be in the drain as it can react explosively. Hydrochloric acid is generally safe to put down the drain, but first run water in the sink while slowly pouring the hydrochloric acid directly into the drain and don't mix it with any "pH basic" material that may be in the drain as it can react explosively. 35% hydrogen peroxide should be diluted with water before pouring down drain as in that concentration it can react explosively with any organic matter that may be in the drain.

## Preface

This process is generally for Ormus researchers and trained alchemists because while it can be performed, it requires laboratory expertise beyond those of the average Ormus collector.

### Labware and Supplies to perform a dry "Hydrogen Peroxide (Gold) Process"

Pure gold, jewelers roller mill, hammer and anvil, 35% hydrogen peroxide, both lye crystals and lye solution, hydrochloric acid, one-liter borosilicate glass filtering flask with tubulation attachment and solid stopper, polypropylene tubing, glass container with stopper, one-liter flask, distilled water, Morton® canning/pickling salt, stirrer of plastic or borosilicate, Visions® glass/ceramic Dutch oven with lid, propane turkey ring burner, 5l-b flat weight (weight-trainer type) or a brick, non-metallic funnel or flat strainer, filters (*unbleached* coffee filters), container made of borosilicate glass (to collect the precipitate), sand, thermometer, focus beam flashlight, plastic bucket, steel can, cardboard box, saran wrap, aluminum foil. For more information, see Appendix XIV.

As a safety measure, always place container(s) used in the process into a larger non-metallic "catch basin" (in case of leakage or breakage). For example: A (new) cat litter box or the bottom of an under-the-bed storage container. (Note: When adding the hydrochloric acid, a lot of heat is generated that could break the glass.)

To best ensure electromagnetic waves cause no interference on the stability of the Ormus in the source material or the manna (precipitate), it is prudent to keep the work and storage area six feet or more away from them. For more information, see "Labware Choices-Aluminum." (Appendix XIV.)

### Definition

This is a process to disaggregate gold bonds by using, among other chemicals, hydrogen peroxide. The core reaction revolves around thin leaves of 99.9 pure gold disaggregated using salt, hydrochloric acid and then 35% hydrogen peroxide, precipitated with lye solution, and re-dissolved with hydrochloric acid. (The wide pH swings break the metallic bonds of the gold metal.) There are further steps in the process.

So long as you have a way to capture the chlorine gas fumes created and observe the precautions while working with acids and caustics described in this book, it is a "relatively" safe process. Please note: It may be beyond the scope of most average Ormus collectors.

### Information

Appearance: The collected Ormus is observed as a fluffy white precipitate in liquid.

As a service to the Ormus community, commercial alchemist Don Nance has provided a description of the dry "Hydrogen Peroxide (gold) Process." This follows "Final Thought."

When using pure metal (gold) as the source material, a stainless steel pot (or any utensil used in the process), should *not* be used as *no* other metal should touch the solutions. This ensures the Ormus (manna) forms from only pure metal. In this process a Visions® glass/ceramic Dutch oven in a 5-quart size with lid is used for the "boil" step and therefore no metal is used. Boil in this container as you would one made of stainless steel.

Hydrochloric acid doesn't break the metallic clusters of gold but hydrogen peroxide in small incremental amounts does. (In *low* concentrations, hydrogen peroxide (35% food grade) can dissolve gold however when the concentrations are higher, it precipitates gold.) This is an unexpected energetic phenomenon seen in the Ormus reaction.

"As little as one part per million of hydrogen peroxide is sufficient to initiate electrolyzing (dissolving) of the gold. No advantage has been found for concentrations of hydrogen peroxide above about 0.5% ..."    (wo/1986/007046 method and apparatus for purification of gold http://www.wipo.int/pctdb/en/wo.jsp?IA=WO1986007046&wo=1986007046&DISPLAY=DESC)

The gold source must be in fine thin leaves. These leaves are placed into a salty, acidic solution and hydrogen peroxide added. Thus begins the work of a multi-step process.

This work should be done in a well-ventilated space. Outside of the house is recommended. See the precautions for lye and hydrochloric acid and also Appendix XIII.

A properly chosen gold source has 99.9 gold content and is washed thoroughly so as to be clean before using. For more information, see "Sources for the Ormus Processes -Metal" (Appendix VIII). Gold wire is also available from precious metals companies. For more information, see "Resources and Supplies-Precious Metal." (Appendix I.)


## Preparing the Source

The gold metal is first reduced to fine thin leaves. This can be accomplished by rolling through a "Jeweler's Roller Mill" and then hammering the gold on an anvil into very thin leaves.

The metallic bonds of the gold are disaggregated using salt, hydrochloric acid and then 35% food grade hydrogen peroxide ($H_2O_2$).

*The solution of disaggregated gold is a yellow colored solution of gold chloride. It is still a metal. Monoatomic gold solution as a chloride has a forest green color and alchemists call it the "Green Lion."*

Lye solution is added to a pH of 12.5 then hydrochloric acid is added to a pH of less than 1. This raising and lowering of the pH is repeated and causes wide pH swings which break the metallic bonds of the gold metal. Note: The concentration of lye solution and hydrochloric acid are the same used in all the Ormus collection processes.

Lye crystals are then added to facilitate the process as they tie Ormus into the solution (by adding more sodium from the lye crystals). The liquid is boiled. This step mirrors the reaction in the *dry* "Lye Boil Process-Preparing the Source Part 2."

In a later step of the process, hydrochloric acid is added to form a precipitate. This step mirrors the "Dry Process-Perform the Process."


## Perform the Process

Always choose *borosilicate glass* containers and place in a "catch basin." For more information, see "Labware Choices-Borosilicate Glass." (Appendix XIV.) (A focused beam flashlight can be used to view the Ormus (manna) "cloud" that forms in the liquid.)

## Purifying (washing)

The precipitate is washed with distilled water. This is described in "Dry Process (Cold Fire Process)-Purifying (Washing)." (page 67)

## Storage

Storage of the Ormus (manna) is the same as described in "Dry Process (Cold Fire Process)-Storage." (page 69)

## Final Thought

Don Nance has said that gold fights the process during the summer months and gold Ormus is best collected during the winter months.

The filtered out Ormus source material sediment from the "living menstruum" can be saved and placed in a fresh batch of lye solution to prepare another batch of "living menstruum." This can be done and more Ormus (manna) collected. Be aware that the amount of Ormus (manna) that precipitates is not as high the second time around.

"Living menstruum" (unless made from silver) can be used in place of regular lye solution in a "Wet Process" with exceptional results. Since this lye solution is a "living menstruum" that contains Ormus (from the source material), a greater drop of Ormus (manna) is expected when performing a "Wet Process" on "reconstituted" sea or "drawn" seawater. **Note:** "Living menstruum" created by soaking, boiling (or burning) a silver source is never saved for use. This is because you may forget the source material was silver and use the "living menstruum" in a *dry* process. All the *dry* processes include adding hydrochloric acid and once this has been added, toxic "silver chloride is made. For more information, see "Sources for the Ormus Processes-Metal." (Appendix VIII.)

Do not work with lye or hydrochloric acid in "fear" as it is thought that feeling fear at the time of the "work" causes an "imprint" of "fear" onto the Ormus (manna). *Work with lye and hydrochloric acid in "respect" - not "fear."* The emotions surrounding "fear" also cause a mind to "close off;" this results in making the steps of an Ormus collection process very difficult to absorb.

When washing containers and other equipment that were used, there may be observed a dried white ring in the container and dried white spots on it. These are easily removed with a solution of 3/4 part white vinegar and 1/4 part water.

The *dry* "Hydrogen Peroxide (gold) Process" described by alchemist Don Nance follows:

# HOW TO MAKE WHITE GOLD ELIXER
**By Don Nance**
Date: 19 October 2008

Since I first wrote of this process in 2002 I have made much progress regarding its efficiency and results so I thought it best to write an update and in that way make a significant contribution to Chris' efforts with this manual.

The most direct way to the white powder of gold is to perform the Sodium Burn Process as previously described. However, this HCl/H2O2 Process is much less violent. So long as you have a way to capture the chlorine gas fumes and observe the stated precautions while working with acids and bases as described in this book, this is a relatively safe process.

Be advised that there is certain amount of art involved here. But, be heartened that your gold would never be wasted because it will always remain in one form or another.

One of the most important factors regarding this work is the initial preparation of the gold metal itself. Instead of reducing it to filings I have found that by taking the gold to a very thin leaf, the initial disaggregation stages are better accomplished. Specifically, hammering it into a very thin leaf changes the actual crystalline arrangement on the atomic level. This change in atomic structure is described as the alchemical "opening of the metal" which is referenced in many alchemical treatises.

If you are beginning with a coin and have access to a jewelers' roller mill then the coin can be rolled to a paper-thin form and then it should be beaten with a hammer on an anvil. Just rolling it in the mill will not accomplish your goal but it can greatly reduce the amount of labor involved.

Get whatever quantity of pure (at least 99.95% pure) gold that you can afford. Then process it into leaves which are thin enough to tear apart by hand. You will only need to actually use a few grams at a time as you learn what you are doing. (Authors note: There are exactly 31.1035 grams/ounce and this is generally rounded to 30 grams/ounce.)

I will list the process step-by-step. You will need to be aware of the fact that some of these steps will need to be repeated several (if not many) times.

You will want to be certain that you have 35% Hydrogen peroxide solution. For various reasons, a more dilute strength is not optimum. The main reason being that you will find yourself with an overabundance of liquid before you finish the process. You will also need to keep it in a cool place and handle it with the respect that you would give to any concentrated acid or oxidizer.

There is a time for every purpose and making edible gold is certainly no exception. Several astrological influences play strongly in your theatre. Beginning in late September there is a cosmic window which opens and, speaking for the element gold specifically, this window remains open through late May. This is an exceptionally long window duration because of the specific influence of the stars Sirius A and B.

You will want to begin your work a few days after a full moon. As it usually takes approximately one lunar month to complete this process you should find yourself completing it on or around the following full moon.

You will need to have a way to contain the chlorine gas fumes which evolve from the gold digestion. You may wish to acquire a one-liter borosilicate glass filtering flask with a tubulation attachment and a solid stopper or an Erlinmeyer flask with a one-hole stopper. Use some polypropylene or polyethylene tubing to vent the gasses into a container which is 2/3rd filled with water and stoppered. If you can smell chlorine during this process then you may want to improve upon your gas containment system.

### To dissolve 1/10th ounce of gold, I use the following recipe, step-by-step.

1) Into a one-liter flask I place 100 ml. of distilled water.

2) I stir in one-heaping teaspoonful of pure salt. Good to use Morton® canning and pickling salt. Be CERTAIN that all of the salt is dissolved and the solution is clear of particulates. This is important. Don't use iodized salt and do not use a salt with anti-caking chemicals in it. Using pure NaCl. Morton® Kosher salt works well.

3) Add two or three grams by weight of your gold leaves.

4) Stir in, VERY SLOWLY, 140 ml. of full strength muriatic (HCl) acid. I use ACS quality, but Buckman's Laboratories makes a very pure muriatic acid, which is available from quality pool/spa dealers. Smart brand also works. The muriatic acid must be clear/colorless, as the yellow variety contains sulfur and will NOT work. The acid must be added VERY slowly. If you go too fast, the salt will precipitate back out of your solution. This will work, but seriously slows down the dissolution of your gold. When this happens, the salt will slowly go back into solution as your gold dissolves. If this occurs, just go on with the recipe, realizing that it slowed down your process considerably.

5) Add some 35% H2O2 (hydrogen peroxide) food grade (great) or technical grade (minimum). Add it about one-teaspoon at a time and wait 20 minutes. A "fire" will begin inside of your flask. You want to have a good steady stream of bubbles coming from all of your gold. You also want to build your fire slowly. If you add too much H2O2 you run the risk of having it boil on you and it will come out of your flask and the gassing will be extreme and acid will go everywhere and life on our planet, as we know it, will have changed :-)

6) Place this inside of a shield (nest) and check it three times a day. Add H2O2 as needed until your gold goes away. This takes as long as it takes. The Philosophers had many ways of marking time. The two that we are concerned with here are the lunar phases and the "elastic" time...that which is marked by a reaction taking as long as it takes. The variable being that you will never have exactly the same particle size for your gold and the same exact phase of the moon during your next dissolution.

7)    Once all of your gold is dissolved, add more H2O2 and keep the fire going for a while longer. This will help to break up the metallic clusters.

Once this is complete, you will have a very pretty yellow colored gold chloride. Its pH will be MINUS 2.0 (on my well calibrated meter). It is still metal.

8)    Once your gold solution has stopped bubbling from the H2O2, stir in yet another teaspoonful of Morton salt. If there is any unreacted H2O2 your mix will again begin to form bubbles. If it does, then let it continue until it stops. If it doesn't begin to bubble again then pour your solution into a beaker and begin dripping a 1/8 lye menstruum into it at a rate of about 2 drops per second while stirring briskly. You ARE wearing gloves and eye protection, aren't you? Bring the pH up but not too quickly! If you go too fast then it will boil on you...if you see some steam collecting on the sides of your beaker then it is getting too hot. Slow down with your lye addition and keep stirring. This reaction takes a WHILE.

Your solution may become clear and colorless when near neutral pH. If you are going too fast, the solution may clear and then very quickly change color and a precipitate will form. That's fine, no worries. It may precipitate as a shining black (the "sign of the crow," the "Blackness of Black") or as a deep royal blue or even as a brownish-brick red. Either way, you will want to bring the pH up to 12.5 pH.

(NOTE) At this point you are still mostly working with gold metal. Whatever amount of it that has already converted to M-state is now in the solution and the metallic content has precipitated as oxides/hydroxides of gold. You can rest for a while at this point and let your solution cool to room temperature.

9)    Start stirring your gold solution and slowly drip in some 18-20% HCl (acid) solution. Stop adding acid solution when your gold precipitate disappears. The pH will be less than pH 1 (Around pH 0.7 is good.) The color of the solution will likely be gold but not as concentrated looking as before. It may also be another color. No worries again, just look at it to see that there are no particles. Place the solution back into your flask and attach the gas trap after adding some more H2O2 just as before and break this gold up some more. Continue as before until it stops bubbling and there are no visible particles.

10)   Once all of the bubbling has stopped again then transfer the solution to your beaker again and begin stirring your gold acid solution and start dropping in your LYE menstruum to again raise the pH of your solution. You want to go on up to pH 12.5 again. Don't be surprised if this is yet a different color from the last time you did this.

11)   Repeat steps 9 and 10 until during step 9 the color of your acid solution has become decidedly green. It is a "grass green" and how dark it appears is determined by the amount of gold that you began with. This is known alchemically as the "Green Lion."

Congratulations! You now have monatomic gold. Of course, it isn't edible yet. It is concentrated acid. Please note that at this point there is an alternative method of proceeding that I will include at the end of this process.

12) Now, place it into your beaker and bring the pH of your solution up to about pH 12.5 by stirring quickly and adding your lye menstruum slowly by drops as before. If it changes to a color that you have seen before during your work then you may have to repeat steps 9 and 10 yet again. If it changes to a grayish white or stays green then proceed to step 13.

What we have accomplished with all of these pH swings is the breaking of the metallic bonds of your gold metal. Next we need to tie the M-state gold into solution so that we can precipitate the white powder of gold separately from any of the gold which may still prefer to remain metallic or re-tie its metal bonds.

13) You will need a large boiling pot. I use a Visions glass/ceramic Dutch oven in 5-quart size WITH LID. Take it out of doors, on a moonlit night, before the full moon, and place your pH 12.5 solution (including any precipitate and top water all together as was the end result of step 12) inside of it. Adjust the volume of solution so that the Dutch oven is approximately 1/2 to 2/3 full by adding some distilled water.

14) Stir into this some dry lye crystals (or powder) to approximate a one-pound per gallon solution. (IE: If you guess the total amount of solution to be 3 quarts then add 3/4 pound of dry lye)

15) Bring this to a full rolling boil over a gas flame and reduce the heat, while stirring, then cover tightly and place a brick or some other inflammable weight on the lid to reduce steam losses. THIS BOILING LYE IS VERY DANGEROUS!!! Let it boil, at a gentle rolling boil, for at least 3 hours. If you do not have an appreciable amount of precipitate in your mix then there is no need to stir.

16) When done, let it cool for a while (until all of the steaming has ceased) and then add some distilled water to bring the level up to one-gallon. Let it finish cooling and settling.

17) Carefully separate your liquid M-gold lye solution from whatever solids may remain in your Dutch oven. Filter your solution through unbleached filters until it is clear of any particulates. I use a one-micron filtering system with a Buckner funnel and a cross-coupled, dual manifold vacuum pump. But you can filter it by hand. Save any solids (dregs) that may be in the bottom of your Dutch oven and reprocess them beginning with step #1.

18) While stirring your filtered solution rapidly, drip in some 20% HCl solution (acid solution) to reduce the pH to around 8.0 slowly. Don't let it get too hot.

19) Let your white precipitate settle and separate the top water from it and save the top water for use as described elsewhere in this book. This white precipitate of gold is known as the White Lion.

20) Wash the precipitate as previously described in this book with distilled water. Let it settle and separate. Save this top water as also described elsewhere in this book.

After washing the white M-gold is ready to eat. I am careful to leave it sufficiently salty such that it is "decidedly salty" to taste. When this is done its shelf life is extended. I have kept samples for over two years with no apparent degradation in efficacy.

## Alternative process steps as mentioned after step # 11.

In order to obtain a more complete conversion of our gold to the M-state/ORMUS form we may wish to proceed as follows after completion of Step 11.

12a) Now, place it into your beaker and bring the pH of your solution up to about pH 8.5 by stirring quickly and adding your lye menstruum slowly by drops as before.

Let this settle for 24 hours and check the pH to be certain that it has not drifted downward towards an acid pH. It needs to remain in the pH 8.0 to 8.5 range for 24 hours. This shows us that all previous reactions are complete.

13a) Now, partially fill a boiling pot with clean sand. You are making a "river bath" which will help you to control the temperature of this step. Insert your beaker into this sand but do not allow it to contact the bottom of your sand bath pot. You want this sand to buffer against the heat of the gas flame.

14a) Next, place a thermometer into the sand and in contact with the bottom of your beaker and place the pot onto a gas burner that is set for a very low temperature.

15a) We will now slowly evaporate all of the liquids to a "just dry" state. Your temperature should approximate "the temperature of the setting sun (in the desert)" and should be near 121 degrees F. but never exceed 140 degrees F. There should be no steaming. This will take a while to accomplish however; the river bath has a flywheel effect of maintaining temperature even if the flame goes out. So, you can relight it and continue until your M-gold is just dry. Be certain to not bake or scorch it.

16a) Next, proceed to perform the dry "Lye Burn and Boil Process" that is outlined elsewhere in this manual to its completion.


## A few further explanations:

If you do not get a white precipitate from step 19 you may simply have to wait for it to actually precipitate and fall. I have seen M-gold take three (or more) days to precipitate.

If you get to the white during any of the pre-boil steps then simply adjust it to pH 8.5 and wash the precipitate as previously described. However, it needs to stay white and not keep changing colors.

Don't eat the green gold. It is not "ripe" yet, at any pH.

Shielding is needed ... The "Nest" (as mentioned in step # 6)

I do my Work by placing my flask inside of a plastic bucket, which is placed inside of a steel can, which is placed inside of a cardboard box. I line the steel can with saran wrap. If you don't, the steel will not last very long. The tubing going to your gas containment flask needs to be long enough to accommodate this but the containment flask need not be shielded at all.

I sincerely wish you love and abundance on your magical ORMUS journey.

Don Nance

NOTES:

The ancient Alchemist's laboratory was a sacred place, situated 'between worlds,' and a key to success in the ancient art included an ability to work simultaneously on the different levels of reality.  These included the psychological and spiritual levels, as well as the physical level.
Images showing laboratories of ancient alchemists display a draped meditation area for reflection, contemplation, and focusing.

# SECTION FIVE

**Procuring Ormus  from a Fresh Water Source**

Magnet Vortex Water Trap

# MAGNET VORTEX WATER TRAP

### Labware and Supplies to perform a "Magnet Vortex Water Trap" process

Good drinking water, "Magnet Vortex Water Trap" (or "Vortex Water Trap"), glass storage container away from light or electromagnetic wave (EMF) producing appliances, aluminum foil.

To best ensure electromagnetic waves cause no interference on the stability of the Ormus in the source material or the Ormus product, it is prudent to keep the work and storage area six feet or more away from them.    For more information, see "Labware Choices-Aluminum Foil." (Appendix XIV.)

### Definition

This process uses centrifugal force to separate some of the Ormus from (good) drinking water as it is runs through a faucet or a hose into and through a "Magnet Vortex Water Trap." The collected Ormus in the water is directed out of the trap via thin plastic aquarium tubing and this water is the "trap water" (containing Ormus) that is drunk. Most traps have strong magnets placed on the outside of the housing to help with separating some of the Ormus from the drinking water, this is why they are called "Magnet Vortex Water Traps."

(A "Vortex Water Trap" does not have magnets placed on the outside of the housing.)

Magnet Vortex Water Trap

### Information

Appearance: The Ormus in trap water cannot be seen and the trap water product looks like water. If Ormus is present in the trap water it can be felt while drinking as the water has a thicker, softer and smoother texture. (I have termed this "creamy water.")

There is a specific energy in water that makes water a "liquid" versus a solid or a vapor and this is beyond simple temperature. Water is an anomaly and to demonstrate this lets consider ice. Ice is "frozen" water and it floats. Ice really should sink because cold temperatures usually cause molecules to become denser and heavier. Instead, ice floats and the fish and marine life are safe under winter's frozen lake tops. However, if ice sank instead (as it should), the fish and marine life would die. Pause a moment to realize how life on this world would not exist if ice sank. Water is an anomaly and its truly unique properties are what enable life to be on this earth. Many feel that a portion of this specific unique energy found in water is collected by the actions of a "Magnet Vortex Water Trap" (or "Vortex Water Trap").

Ormus is thought to "hide out in tight places" and the theory holds that the water molecule offers a tight place to hide.

In the "icosahedral cluster model" of water, tetrahedral (plural of tetrahedron) water clusters may combine to form an icosahedral network

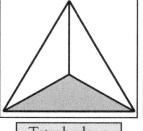

Tetrahedron

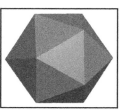

Icosahedron

cluster that forms a curved surface when bound together. The icosahedral water cluster is a packing of the tetrahedral units and contains large interstitial cavities that may allow suitable materials to occupy them. These may include the Ormus materials. Therefore good drinking water is the Ormus source material in this process. (Web search: *Water Structure and Science* by Martin Chaplin.)

There may be less Ormus in city water because municipal water is "daylighted." Many have said that daylighting reduces the quantity of Ormus in the water. Daylighted water is water that has been exposed to daylight and this can occur as it is stored in reservoirs or carried by canals to central distribution systems. Sunlight is also used to cleanse water of organic material. (When using the "Magnet Vortex Water Trap" (or "Vortex Water Trap") it is generally thought best to obtain source water directly from underground via a well or spring.) Ormus is found in some municipal water and I have experienced the taste of Ormus in trap water made from city water. (My own concern is the fluoride and chlorine additives in the municipal water.) Most that use water traps collect Ormus from well water.

A few words regarding chlorine in the drinking water: We usually do not worry about chlorine in the water as we can let the water sit out and the chlorine dissipates. An "under the sink filter" will also remove chlorine. It may be nice to know that sodium thiosulfate is a de-chlorinator usually found in pet shops for owners of fish aquariums to de-chlorinate the water. Add one drop of 10% sodium thiosulfate solution to about a liter (approximately 1 quart) or so of water. (Sodium thiosulfate may be considered as an additive for bath water as it is said by some that bathing with municipal water causes more damage than drinking it.)

A few words about fluoride in the drinking water: Some say that the form of fluoride placed in municipal water supplies is not healthy. Fluorine, a trace element, is a nonmetallic halogen element that combines with other elements to make fluorides. Fluorine in the form of the natural fluorides is found in the body (most notably in bones and teeth) and beneficial to health. The natural fluorides found in nature are "Sodium Fluoride" and "Calcium Fluoride." Fluorosilicic acid, which is not naturally occurring, is placed in many municipal drinking water supplies. Once added, this material is difficult to remove from the water.

(Fluoride waste is a by-product of aluminum manufacturing. The late 1940's plan of disposing fluoride into municipal water supplies was a boon for the aluminum industry. Huge legal liability suits may ensue if the government admitted to negative health effects from "fluoridation." *(John R. Lee M.D. "Medical Letter." February 1999) and ("Acres U.S.A." June 2008.))*

(Chemically, a pinch of borax to about one-quart of water causes fluoride to complex and become deactivated. Borax is sodium borate, sodium tetra borate and is what 20 mule team borax is. "20 Mule Team Borax" is in the laundry section of the grocery store. (Mellor's Comprehensive Treatise on inorganic and theoretical Chemistry 1980 Volume V, p294 says Borax/Boric acid can form complexes with fluoride.) This is mentioned for informational purposes and the makers of 20 Mule Team Borax (The Dial Corporation) discourage any consumer from using TMT Borax for food and in drinking water). (A small amount of borax may be considered as an additive for bath water as it is said by some that bathing with municipal water causes more damage than drinking it.)

The Ormus content of different municipal water treatment plants varies and some contain no Ormus. The question to ask first is if the source water supply comes from a deep layer. If it does, the water may have percolated through a sand or limestone layer and these place more Ormus in the water. Other considerations include: How much "daylighting" has been performed on the water and what type of water filtering system does the water treatment plant use. If charcoal filters are used, many feel that charcoal holds onto Ormus and this may impede Ormus going through the filters. However, the plant may not have changed the charcoal filter for a long time and, therefore, Ormus materials are getting through.

Now, carbon filters may also be in your home (under the kitchen sink) for water filtration. Some feel that the stream of water going through a carbon filter may not be in contact with it long enough to make a significant difference in the Ormus content of the drinking water. Currently, there is no consensus.

## Perform the Process

Theory holds that the "Magnet Vortex Water Trap" has two actions on the source drinking water. The first action is the creation of a "magnetic field" caused by the presence of magnets that have been placed around the trap and this helps break down hydrogen bonds in the water molecule (water is $H_2O$). This is said to make the extracted water more bio-available in our body as the water molecules are smaller and not as "clustered" (clumped).

The magnets are also thought to cause the release of Ormus held within the hydrogen bonds of the water clusters. As the water passes by each of the many magnets, it is subjected to sudden increases and then decreases of the magnetic field. This is called "hammering" the water and the overall effect of this occurrence is that it helps free Ormus that is bound to the water molecules (the clusters of water).

(Note: The magnets used in the "Magnet Vortex Water Trap" are the "neodymium" (NIB) type rated at 12,000 gauss. These magnets are powerful magnets and *it is suggested to remove mechanical watches or jewelry containing iron when you are around the water trap. If you have a pacemaker or a hearing aid, avoid using this process or being around when this process is performed as any exposure could be extremely unsafe. If this is the case, it would not be wise for you to be around the "Magnet Vortex Water Trap" at all.*)

("Neodymium" (NIB) magnets are about 100 times stronger than "ceramic" magnets. Ceramic magnets contain iron locked into ceramic, which is then fired, to melt the iron, followed by a cooling period. The magnet created is as strong as the iron in it and is usually about 800-900 gauss. "Neodymium" (NIB) magnets are made from alloys of rare earth elements (neodymium/ iron/boron) and are the most affordable variety of "rare earth" magnets. They are also substantially stronger than magnets made with iron.)

The second action of the "Magnet Vortex Water Trap" (and the "Vortex Water Trap") is "centrifugal force." Centrifugal force causes heavier particles to move (be forced) to the outside of the vortex while lighter substances such as the oily Ormus stay more in the center. This lighter Ormus substance in the center of the vortex works its way up the trap. This action is facilitated by a property of Ormus that causes it not to want to move within a "magnet field." Once the Ormus has reached the top of the trap, a small piece of polyester rope housed inside a PVC tube carries it through the top and then connects to thin plastic aquarium hosing.

The polyester rope at the top of the trap is housed inside a PVC tube and serves as a surface for the Ormus type oils to collect and slowly rise towards the aquarium hosing and then out through the hosing and into a bottle or pitcher. The spaces between the strands of the rope are "quiet" areas, away from the vortexing action of the water, where the Ormus can collect. Once on the rope cord, the pressure pushing up from the vortexing water below slowly raises the Ormus up and then out via the attached aquarium tubing. Without the rope cord, the Ormus material we seek continues to be moving quite quickly in the center of the vortex. (The trap works without the rope cord but tests indicate an increased performance with it in place.)

It takes about 17 minutes to fill a gallon container with trap water. Three things determine the rate. The first two include the speed the water is entering the trap from the water source and the speed water is allowed to leave from an opening in the bottom of the trap. The third variable is the speed the "trap water" is allowed to leave from the top of the trap through the polyester rope (then through the aquarium tubing). Regulation of the amount of "trap water" exiting via the aquarium tube occurs by how high the tubing is manually held in the air. When the "trap water" exits the aquarium tubing at a slower rate (controlled by holding the plastic tube higher in the air) there is a higher amount of Ormus in the trap water. (Some have said that allowing the "trap water" to exit through the tubing with a force that pushes the water out one inch before the water flow "breaks" and then falls into the pitcher is generally a proper flow to collect good trap water.)

The amount of Ormus in the extracted water is variable and depends on the source of the fresh water and on the subtle energetics involving the earth, sun and moon and the cosmos. This may also involve the energetics surrounding a full moon or an equinox. For more information see "Moon Chart." (Appendix X.) I have noticed that some days my well water produced smooth, creamy tasting "Magnet Vortex Water Trap" water and some days the texture was not noticeable.

When drinking Ormus trap water it tastes creamy because (and one theory holds that) Ormus is a type of oil (and can actually taste a little bit sweet). The "Magnet Vortex Trap" (and "Vortex Water Trap") concentrates this oil in water as a thin emulsion and this is one reason the water becomes creamy feeling. In fact, you may remember being in nature and drinking water that was sweet and felt creamy. If this has happened, some say the experience is from the presence of Ormus in the "good" drinking water.

A "Magnet Vortex Water Trap" can include, but does not have to include, a second stage. While the second stage is not necessary, some add it to further concentrate the Ormus that has been collected from the source water in the first stage "Magnet Vortex Water Trap." Exposing the water to a second trap is thought to raise the vibrational energy of the "trap water" and should make the trap water more potent. The second stage trap attaches to the aquarium hose containing the trap water from the "first stage" water trap. In this way, the water source for the second stage trap comes from the first stage trap. The second stage is a little smaller in height and diameter and runs the trap water in a magnet vortex just as the first stage did. The resultant trap water exits via thin plastic aquarium hosing located near the top of the "Second Stage Magnet Vortex Water Trap." The second stage trap is open at the top (the first stage trap is closed at the top) and a pressure may be felt rising up against the palm of a hand held over the opening. Some feel this is plasma M-state (Ormus), and it rises. There may also be an odor like or similar to semen emanating from the top of the second stage water trap. This may be what the ancients called the "Semen of God." This is discussed in "Getting Started" (Section Two).

A "Magnet Vortex Water Trap" researcher has made a third stage trap and it attaches to aquarium hose containing the trap water from the second stage water trap. In this way, the water source for the third stage trap comes from the second stage trap. Theory holds that when exposing the water to a third "Magnet Vortex Water Trap" the vibrational energy of the trap water raises even higher and should make the water even more potent. Few people use a second stage and it is very rare that a third stage is used. (Some have said that a seven-stage trap has been made.)

## Purifying

**The purifying process begins with the initial choice made regarding the source water used in a "Magnet Vortex Water Trap" (or "Vortex Water Trap.")**

Always choose good drinking water to make "trap water." (The trap water's volume of collected Ormus corresponds to the amount of Ormus that was in the initial drinking water and this amount may fluctuate with subtle energetics as mentioned earlier.)

## Storage

**Store the trap water in a** *glass* **container.** This is preferred because the Ormus in trap water is considered to be in its "free state." This collected Ormus is not in "boxes" (observed as a precipitate) as with many other Ormus processes and therefore it is "free to roam." Because pores of plastic are larger, Ormus is thought to more easily tunnel out of containers made of that material.

(Sources of glass bottles could be clean Ball canning jars, mayonnaise jars and glass milk bottle jars-yes glass milk bottle jars are still made.) For more information, see "Resources and Supplies." (Appendix I.)

**Wrap the container in aluminum foil.** Aluminum foil may help the Ormus in some way to "stay put." For more information, see "Labware Choices-Aluminum." (Appendix XIV.)

**Store the trap water at room temperature, away from light and covered** to further shield it from ambient light rays in the room. Refrigerator storage may be acceptable as some say the cold refrigerated Ormus then gravitates to your body heat. Wrap the container in aluminum foil because if the container is refrigerated without the aluminum foil covering, the Ormus is felt to seek warmer temperatures and escape when the door is open.

**Drink as much "trap water" as you wish.** For example: Six to eight glasses a day. Trap water Ormus is in free form, right there and ready to be used by the body. It can be drunk or used on sores (in addition to proper first aid care) and to smooth the skin.

**Use the trap water within 7-30 days.** The aluminum foil wrap may be overlooked if you are making and drinking it daily.

## Final Thought

Many have said that water sources with lots of sulfur in it have less available Ormus.

Checking for Ormus in the trap water is an experiment you can perform by doing a "Wet Process" on the trap water to see if you get Ormus (manna) precipitate. Ormus researchers have done this on "trap water" obtained from a well. A precipitate formed but not enough to make it worthwhile. (In this experiment, the speculation holds that the "Wet Process" has put the Ormus collected from the "Magnet Vortex Water Trap" back "in a box" (Ormus moves back into a "hiding place.") A white precipitate forms and then falls to the bottom of the container. The precipitate is this "hiding place" and it is considered the same type of precipitate that is collected from "reconstituted" seawater or "drawn" seawater during a "Wet Process.")

As another experiment, the Ormus in "Magnet Vortex Water Trap" (or "Vortex Water Trap") trap water can be concentrated by reducing the volume of water in it. Do this by almost fully freezing the trap water *making sure there is ice on the top and bottom and sides of the water* and then remove the liquid in the middle of the ice. (Using a glass container is best for this.) Ormus stays in the middle area that is still liquid water because it is thought by some that Ormus prefers warmth and that space is the "warmest" area. Remove the liquid by poking a hole in the ice and drain the trap water out and into another container. Repeat the freezing making sure that with each freeze there is ice all the way around the water. (You can end up with a 75% reduction.) Taste the ice from each frozen batch. If you taste Ormus in the ice you know that you have reduced enough.

Visual signs of Ormus may be observed in "trap water" by pouring some of it into a clear dark drinking glass and letting it sit in the dark for about half an hour. Shine a focused beam flashlight on the top of the water at an angle. There may be seen a thin oil slick when looking at the surface of the trap water. Next, shine the focused beam flashlight downward through the sides of the glass and bubbles may also be observed. These are not regular bubbles - they may hang on the side, they may rise to the surface or they may float downward. If the bubble(s) are defying gravity, for example going down instead of up, you may be experiencing the effects of superconductivity. (The size of the bubble has been said by some to tell the M-state.) Sometimes the particles must be watched for a long period and Ormus researchers have videotaped the container and then reviewed the tape on high speed.

These traps can be made at home and blueprints for the "Vortex Water Trap" and "Magnet Vortex Water Trap" are found at *www.subtleenergies.com*.

NOTES:

There are two forms of magic: a Devil's magic that seeks to harm others by illicit means, and a holy magic which rediscovers the secrets of nature.

#  SECTION SIX

**Miscellaneous Ormus Processes**

Dried-Out Wet Precipitate

Concord Grape Process

Cold Extraction Process on Stones

Dew Collection Process

Over-the-Hem Process (A Refining Process)

# DRIED-OUT WET PRECIPITATE

## Labware and Supplies to make "Dried-Out Wet Precipitate"

*Washed*, undiluted Ormus (manna), container made of plastic or glass, filters, aluminum foil.

To best ensure electromagnetic waves cause no interference on the stability of Ormus in the source material or the Ormus (manna), it is prudent to keep the work and storage area six feet or more away from them. For more information, see "Labware Choices-Aluminum Foil." (Appendix XIV.)

## Definition

This process involves drying out Ormus (the precipitate) collected during a "Wet Process" or any *dry* process. (Most often the Ormus (manna) collected from the "Wet Process" is used.)

## Information

Appearance: The dried-out Ormus (manna) precipitate looks like small dried pieces that are the color of the precipitate.

In antiquity, alchemists were often travelers without access to storage and they had no refrigeration. Drying out the Ormus precipitate may have been the only option and, if so, was better than nothing. Some have said that an effect is observed from dried Ormus (manna), just not as much of an effect as when it was wet. (An Ormus collector has mentioned how there was an effect from his dried precipitate, and a researcher has annealed the dried precipitate from the "Wet Process" and reported that it was exceptional.) It is also known that alchemists collect Ormus in both a "wet" and "dry" form.

When the precipitate is dried, some feel the body does not as easily assimilate the crystals and therefore they feel it is best to take the Ormus (manna) as a liquid (diluted wet precipitate). It may be that taking dried-out precipitate with aloe juice may be helpful and is a thought that some have expressed. For more information, see "Aloe Vera." (Appendix XIX.)

"Higher end" alchemical work performed by alchemists and Ormus researchers may require drying out the Ormus (manna) however drying it out *is* not necessary for the purposes of the average Ormus collector. This process is not part of our focus. However, it is of interest to know of its existence.

## Perform the Process

**Prepare Ormus (manna).** The Ormus is "dropped" from the "Wet Process" or any of the dry processes then collected and purified (washed). Do *not* dilute the manna.

**Dry out the Ormus (manna).** Dry by removing as much water as possible from over the Ormus (manna) precipitated. Keep airborne debris out by covering the container of Ormus (manna) with an unbleached coffee filter or several layers of food grade cheesecloth. While the Ormus is drying, keep it away from sunlight and EMF (electromagnetic field) producing appliances such as electric stoves, microwaves, dishwashers and refrigerators.

## Storage

**Place a lid on the container holding the Ormus (manna).** A glass or (appropriate) plastic container is acceptable. Cover the container with aluminum foil and leave at room temperature and away from EMF wave producing appliances such as electric stoves, microwaves TVs and refrigerators. For more information, see "Labware Choices-Aluminum." (Appendix XIV.)

## Final Thought

An observation regarding the dried precipitate is that, once dried, the Ormus (manna) does **not** re-dissolve. The pH can be dropped to a pH of 2 with hydrochloric acid and it still won't re-dissolve. (I held the dried precipitate under my tongue for 15 minutes. Initially it was salty tasting and the pieces became slightly smaller. After 30 minutes their size had hardly diminished so I chewed them. The dried precipitate had no taste beyond the initial salty one.)

Superconductivity of the dried-out Ormus (manna) may be demonstrated. For more information, see "Basic Explanation-Final Thought." (Appendix VII.)

One theory holds that by drying out the precipitate, you are ridding it of one good hiding place for the Ormus material and that is in the liquid. Unless there is another place for the Ormus to go, that portion of it is lost. It is also not known if there is another location - or even if there were, would the Ormus material from the liquid move to it?

# CONCORD GRAPE PROCESS

## Labware and Supplies to perform a "Concord Grape Process"

Welch's® frozen Concord grape juice, glass container, good water, measuring cup and measuring spoon, plastic stirrer, baking soda and aluminum foil.

To best ensure electromagnetic waves cause no interference on the stability of Ormus in source material or the finished Ormus product, it is prudent to keep the work and storage area six feet or more away from them. For more information, see "Labware Choices-Aluminum Foil." (Appendix XIV.)

## Definition

This process frees Ormus from its bond with sugar molecules in purple Concord grape juice so it is available as an activated Ormus Concord grape juice.

## Information

Appearance: The Ormus in the Concord grape juice cannot be seen and the Ormus product looks like grape juice that has turned a darker shade of purple.

Purple Concord grapes have been said to contain Ormus - and Ormus concentrates in the *seeds* of Concord grapes. (Therefore, when eating purple grapes, it may make sense to include chewing the seeds.)

A theory holds that the Ormus in Concord grape juice utilizes the crystalline structure of sugar to form a "shielding" that protects it from "magnetic fields" of the earth. The "tight" spaces provided by the sugar and salt molecule provide these spaces. A problem with the presence of sugar is that it is thought by some to compete for Ormus with our body to a greater degree than salt does. (Note: This is one of the reasons that carrots used as an Ormus source material in the "Dry Process" are juiced twice. Running the carrots through a juicer two times removes a lot of the sugar in addition to the water.)

Adding baking soda breaks down sugar bonds in reconstituted grape juice and the Ormus within freed; making it available. (**NOTE:** This process is not suggested if you are on a sodium-restricted diet as there is a high sodium content in baking soda. Baking soda is sodium bicarbonate and is also called "Bicarbonate of Soda.")

### Perform the Process
Buy frozen Concord grape juice. Bottled grape juice has been pasteurized and therefore not acceptable for this process. (Seneca® was a brand the Ormus community used however Seneca sold the grape juice line to Northland who later went out of business.) Welch's™ sells a frozen Concord grape juice and this is chosen as the Ormus source material in this process. Read the label as some containers read: Made from "Concord" and some do not. (Check with health food stores for organic frozen Concord grape juice. Perhaps at some time an organic food supplier will bring a frozen Concord grape juice to the marketplace.)

**Choose a clean glass container.** 1/2 gallon size is more than large enough.

**Reconstitute the grape juice.** Add 1/4 to 1/3 gallon of "good" water (4 cups to 5.5 cups of water) to the can of frozen "Concord" grape juice.

**Add one HEAPING teaspoonful of baking soda to the reconstituted Concord grape juice.** (This is baking soda such as the Arm & Hammer® brand not baking powder.) Foam will form on top of the grape juice and the color of the grape juice will darken. Taste test for sweetness. Baking soda breaks sugar bonds and if the Concord grape juice is still sweet add more baking soda; one teaspoon is usually enough and two teaspoon generally thought to be the most you should use. **Use no more than one heaping tablespoon (three teaspoons) of baking soda.**
(To make half the can of frozen Concord grape concentrate, use 1/8 to 1/6 gallon of good water (two cups to three cups) of water. Place 1/2 HEAPING teaspoon ofbaking soda into the reconstituted Concord grape juice. Taste test for sweetness. If it is still sweet use more baking soda. 1/2 teaspoon is usually enough and one teaspoon generally thought to be the most you should use. **Use no more than two heaping teaspoons.**

### Storage
It is thought that the "activated Ormus Concord grape juice" contains Ormus in a "free" state. Ormus has moved out of sugar bonds that have been broken in the Ormus source material. (Other Ormus collection processes postulated to contain Ormus in a "free" state are the "Magnet Vortex Water Trap" (or "Vortex Water Trap"), "Live Oil" and "Dew Collection Process.") Because

the Ormus in the grape juice is in a "free" state it is easier for it to "wander off" and it is suggested that "activated Ormus Concord grape juice" is stored away from sunlight and electromagnetic waves such as those associated with refrigerators or TVs. Because the Ormus is in a "free to roam" state, the length of storage time is lessened and I have heard to use the juice within about four days eight hours. Depending on how quickly you plan to drink it, you may wish to keep it in a cooler packed in ice or at room temperature.

**Store the "activated Ormus Concord grape juice" in a glass container with a tight fitting non-metallic lid.** If the lid *is* metal, first place a layer of plastic wrap over the top of the glass container. This acts as a barrier between the metal lid and the grape juice. Plastic containers are *not* suggested for storage as pores of plastic are larger and some feel the Ormus material will tunnel out more easily.

**Wrap the "activated Ormus Concord grape juice" container in aluminum foil.** For more information, see "Labware Choices-Aluminum." (Appendix XIV.)

**Final Thought**

I have heard that "activated Ormus Concord grape juice" is best taken on an empty stomach. Some consider one ounce a good amount to take.

The presence of sugars in the Concord grape juice offset the benefit of the Ormus within. Because sugar is thought by some to have an even higher affinity for Ormus than salt, the body fights sugar to release the Ormus. Therefore, when comparing "Concord grape juice" to the "carrots" used as a source material in the "Dry Process," the *carrots* having been juiced and sugar removed prior to use probably makes them a better source material and the "Dry Process" a better process.

NOTES:

Many believe that Ormus processes involve transmutations
and this belief follows ancient Hermetic teachings.  To
these ancient practitioners the operations of alchemy
included transmutation and the steps during the operations
were stages among the eternal pattern of transformation
that is part of the fabric of time and space occurring
naturally on every level in the world.  In modern days
Ernest Rutherford (1905) showed that one element
becomes another element through the process of naturally
occurring transmutation where particles are given off as
radiation.

## COLD EXTRACTION PROCESS ON STONES

Note: There are appendices that have cross-referencing information to that in this chapter. These include:
"List of Ormus Resources and Supplies,"
"Common Measurement Conversions,"
"Best Practices Labware Choices,"
"pH Meter," and "Sources for the Ormus Processes."
For "Lye Solution Preparation" and "Hydrochloric Acid Preparation" see Section Three.

---

**CAUTION!!**

Note: Cautions are a form of education so that you may work with lye and hydrochloric acid in awareness and respect not fear.

Lye is a "caustic." Hydrochloric acid is an acid. Both lye and hydrochloric acid are strong chemicals and can damage eyes by rendering the cornea opaque, a form of irreparable eye damage. If lye or hydrochloric acid gets into eyes flush the eyeball with water immediately and seek medical attention if the burning persists.

If lye or hydrochloric acid contacts the skin it hurts and damages it. Lye or hydrochloric acid reacts with skin tissue and can cause permanent damage and scarring if severe. Even minor reactions can be painful. If lye or hydrochloric acid contacts clothes it damages them. If lye or hydrochloric acid gets onto your clothes or body, immediately flush the area with lots of water and seek medical attention if necessary.

It is very helpful to work near a sink, faucet or other source of wash water.

The area must be well ventilated as breathing fumes from lye or hydrochloric acid can damage air passages and lungs. Lye solution creates caustic fumes. Do not breathe in these fumes. Hydrochloric acid creates a pungent, corrosive "fog" when added to water.

Do not breathe in this fog. Handle lye or hydrochloric acid with adequate ventilation such as a laboratory range hood vented outside or conduct the work outside. It is advisable to keep a bottle of baking soda solution handy to use against hydrochloric acid spills (baking soda powder can be sprinkled on if the spill is large) and a spray bottle of distilled white vinegar handy to use against lye spills.

For more information, see "The Chemicals of the Processes." (Appendix XIII.)

When working with lye or hydrochloric acid, (or any chemical) avoid touching your face or rubbing your eyes. Do not handle around food. Do not dump wastewater on the ground. Lye is generally safe to put down the drain, but first run water in the sink while slowly pouring the lye directly into the drain and don't mix it with any acid that may be in the drain as it can react explosively. Hydrochloric acid is generally safe to put down the drain, but first run water in the sink while slowly pouring the hydrochloric acid directly into the drain and don't mix it with any "pH alkaline" material that may be in the drain as it can react explosively.

When working with lye or hydrochloric acid, please wear goggles or a full-face visor (an industrial face protector), neoprene gloves and a PVC lab apron as well as protective clothing such as long sleeves and long pants.

Keep children and pets away from the work area and do not leave it unattended. Even if no one is around, an unsuspecting person could venture by and be at risk.

---

**Labware and Supplies to perform a "Cold Extraction Process on Stones"**

Ormus source material, lye solution, hydrochloric acid, distilled water, pH meter, stainless steel pot (follow the stainless steel precautions in Appendix XIV), 5-lb flat weight (weight-trainer type) or a brick, heat source: propane turkey ring burner, container of borosilicate glass (to collect the precipitate), measuring cup, aluminum foil, barrel syringe or baster, funnel or flat strainer, filters, focus beam flashlight, plastic catch basin, plastic or borosilicate glass stirrers, safety clothing and equipment. The hydrochloric acid used as the "reagent" in the process can be placed in an HDPE plastic bottle during the collection. Store the finished manna in HDPE plastic containers. For more information, see Appendix XIV.

As a safety measure, always place containers used in the process into a larger non-metallic "catch basin" (in case of leakage or breakage). For example: A (new) cat litter box or the bottom of an under-the-bed storage container. (Note: When adding the hydrochloric acid, a lot of heat is generated that could break the glass.)

To best ensure electromagnetic waves cause no interference on the stability of Ormus in source material or the Ormus precipitate (manna), it is prudent to keep the work and storage area 6 feet or more away from them. For more information, see "Labware Choices-Aluminum Foil." (Appendix XIV.)


## Definition

This process extracts Ormus from stones. Research the stone source as we do not want aluminum in the Ormus (manna). Stones to consider are Opal, Agate, and Moldevite.


## Information

Appearance: The collected Ormus is observed as a fluffy precipitate (not always a brilliant white) in liquid.

This process is interesting to know although not usually performed because the stones are ruined for any other use after soaking in lye solution. This is the same process as the "Dry Process (Cold Fire Process)." The Ormus source materials in this process are stones.

Heat from an *external source* may be chosen in this process to cause a "boil." Any Ormus process which uses external heat, especially when heat is applied to cause a "boil", is generally thought to place a slightly higher energy state (higher spin) on the Ormus material and this is felt to cause a bit more potency. It is also felt that more precipitate forms during a process that does not cause a boil. When boiling, some of the lighter Ormus material boils off and therefore lost to the collection. For more information, see "Labware Choices-Heat." (Appendix XIV.)

Ormus (manna) can be precipitated any time or day of the year. To alchemists, there *is* an ideal time for the collection of Ormus (manna) and this is three days before a full moon or an equinox. These are energetically active times during the year and it has been said by some that Ormus (manna) collected during these time frames is exceptional. For more information, see "Moon Chart." (Appendix X.)


## Preparing the Source

It is best for the process if the stones are reduced to granules. Make the granules as fine as possible (less than 1/4 inch). Wash and then dry the stones.

## Preparing the Source Part 2
### Boiling the Source

Soak the granules of stone in lye solution to create the "living menstruum" (Ormus-containing lye medium) required for the Ormus collection process. This is described in "Dry Process (Cold Fire Process)-Preparing the Source Part 2." (page 64)

OR

External heat may be added by boiling the lye solution that contains the granules of stone. This is described in dry "Lye Boil Process-Preparing the Source Part 2." (page 77)

## Perform the Process

Filter out the granules of stone from the lye solution. Adding hydrochloric acid to the lye solution precipitates the Ormus (manna). This is described in "Dry Process (Cold Fire Process)-Perform the Process." (page 66)

## Purifying

Wash the Ormus (manna) precipitate with distilled water. This is described in "Dry Process (Cold Fire Process)-Purifying (Washing)." (page 67)

## Storage

Storage of the Ormus (manna) is the same as described in "Dry Process (Cold Fire Process)-Storage." (pages 69)

## Final Thought

All final thought is the same as "Dry Process (Cold Fire Process)-Final Thought." (page 70)

# DEW COLLECTION PROCESS

To best ensure electromagnetic waves cause no interference on the finished product, it is prudent to keep the work and storage area six feet or more away from them. For more information, see "Labware Choices-Aluminum Foil." (Appendix XIV.)

## Definition

Dew is collected during the night air because dew has been said to contain Ormus. There are two basic dew collection processes and one that is more unconventional.

## Information

Appearance: Ormus in "Collected Dew" cannot be seen and the Ormus product looks like clear water. The "Collected Dew" may taste "earthy" and have characteristics pointing to the presence of the Ormus material such as tasting thicker, being creamy or oily tasting and smoothly slick.

The best time frame to perform a "Dew Collection Process" is said to be during the night of a "Full" moon. The energetics of the Full moon appears to draw Ormus up from the ground. Consequently, there may be more Ormus in the air and, hence, in the dew when there is a "Full" moon. It has been said by some that there is actually more dew on the night of a full moon.

The "Full" moon also causes the Earth to receive a particular and special light occurring from the reflected rays of the sun off the "Full" moon. Some have said that the Ormus (manna) benefits from this light. The best season for the "Dew Collection Process" is springtime as this is when the Earth's magnetic field is the most active. For more information, see Appendix X.

## Perform the Process
## Dew Collection Process 1

This is the most commonly performed "Dew Collection Process."

### Labware and Supplies to perform "Dew Collection Process 1"

Ice, large "regular glass" container and something plastic or glass to hold it up a bit, non-metallic catch basin and aluminum foil. Store dew in a glass container.

**Fill a glass container with water or rainwater.** Alchemically, rainwater is considered better however regular water also works. (Rainwater is high in Ormus and it is felt this may transfer to the dew that is collected.) I use a two-gallon round glass jar found at Wal-Mart®. An appropriate plastic container can be used in place of glass, although many would prefer glass.

**Freeze the water solid in the container or fill it with ice cubes.** Instead of freezing the water solid in the container (which has cracked my container) it can be filled with ice cubes. The rest of the space in the container is then filled with cold water. (If you want to increase the yield of the collected dew, add more ice during the night as the ice in the container melts.) The larger the container, the more dew can be collected as there is more surface area for condensation to form. (A small amount of "rock salt" (an inexpensive salt such as road salt-also called Halite) or sea salt (the dry natural sea salt must have no anti-caking or coloring agents) can be added to lower the temperature of the water in the container and this can increase the yield of dew collected. This can be performed as an experiment however know that the yield of the dew may not be increased over the course of the night such that it is worth the expense of the salt.)

**Place this (ice or ice and water) filled container in a (clean) non-metallic catch basin larger than itself and raise the container two to three inches off the bottom of the catch basin.**

**Place the catch basin (containing the raised ice or ice and water filled container) into the** *night* **air.** Dew will collect on the outside of the glass container by the process of *condensation* and slide down, off the bottom and into the catch basin.

**Bring the "Collected Dew" inside before the sun hits it.** Sunlight is thought to "burn" the Ormus off of the dew because the Ormus is in a "free" state and "runs" from the sun.

Once the dew is collected, drink it as you would water.

## Perform the Process
## Dew Collection Process 2
## Labware and Supplies to perform "Dew Collection Process 2"
Plastic sheeting and container to catch the dew.

**Lay plastic sheets on the ground at night.** After the dew sets on the ground, lift up the sheets and collect the dew beaded on the bottom side of the plastic sheet. Collect the dew before the sun rises.

Once the dew is collected, drink it as you would water.

## Perform the Process
## Dew Collection Process 3
The usefulness of this process in collecting Ormus is based on salts characteristic trait of being "hygroscopic." This means that it has an affinity for atmospheric moisture (water) - it draws it to itself and hence into the bowl containing the salt. (**NOTE**: This process is not suggested if you are on a sodium-restricted diet. The process utilizes pure natural salt to collect the dew and the dew product contains this salt.)

## Labware and Supplies to perform "Dew Collection Process 3"
Natural sea salt, lidded glass bowl

**Place a glass bowl filled with natural sea salt outdoors overnight.** The dry natural sea salt must have no anti-caking agent or coloring added. Remove any visual impurities by hand from the sea salt.

**Bring the collected dew inside before the sun hits it.** Do not allow morning sunlight to strike the bowl containing sea salt. Drain the bowl of the collected dew and cover the bowl with a sealed lid.

**Place the bowl in a dark place for the day and away from electromagnetic fields.** Examples of electromagnetic fields include refrigerators, stoves, microwaves, TVs, electric clocks and lit lamps. For more information, see "Labware Choices-Aluminum." (Appendix XIV.)

**Repeat every night until the sea salt has dissolved - or you don't wish to continue.**
This dew can be taken orally. (There has been no consensus on the amount of dew to take.) A suggestion has been made to take drops of the dew either as it is or diluted in some water.

As an experiment, the dew collected from "Dew Collection Process 3" can be used to make Ormus (manna) precipitate by performing a "Wet Process" and using the collected dew in place of distilled water.

## Purifying

The process of "condensation" is itself a "purifying" process. The dew collected is pure and ready for use.

## Storage

Because of the small amount of dew collected in a night, it may be preferable to drink the dew from collection processes 1 and 2, right away and not store it at all.

It is thought that "Collected Dew" contains Ormus in its "free" state. Ormus is thought to "hide in tight places" and the water molecule with its tetrahedral shaped units that contain large interstitial cavities provides such places for Ormus to "hide." This is explained in "Magnet Vortex Water Trap-Introduction." (Other Ormus collection processes believed to contain Ormus in the "free" state are the "Magnet Vortex Water Trap" (or "Vortex Water Trap"), "Concord Grape Process" and "Live Oil Process.") Because the Ormus in "Collected Dew" is in a "free" state it is easier for it to "wander off" and it is suggested that "Collected Dew" should be stored away from sunlight and electromagnetic waves such as those associated with refrigerators or TVs. Because the Ormus is in a "free to roam" state, the "collected dew" should be used within 30 days.

**Store the "Collected Dew" in a** *glass* **container with a** tight fitting non-metallic lid. If the lid is metal, place a layer of plastic wrap over the top of the glass container before capping with the lid. This acts as a barrier between the metal lid and the "Collected Dew." Plastic containers are not suggested for storage as pores of plastic are larger and the Ormus material can more easily tunnel out.

A small amount of natural sea salt (no additives) can be added to "Collected Dew" from "Dew Collection Process 1 or 2" to encourage the Ormus to "stay put" and in this way can better retain its potency.

**Wrap the "Collected Dew" container in aluminum foil.** For more information, see "Labware Choices-Aluminum." (Appendix XIV.)

## Final Thought

Alchemical texts termed collected dew "white dew," the "white condensate," "the white dove" or it is depicted as a white feather. This is because the dew was purified as a "volatile" material: a material that could wander off. The Ormus is free to travel off. All symbols of being fed by a dove, or receiving the white dove are alchemical symbols.

# OVER-THE-HEM PROCESS (a Refining Process)

Note: There are appendices that have cross-referencing information to that in this chapter. These include: "List of Ormus Resources and Supplies," "Best Practices Labware Choices"

## Labware and Supplies to perform the "Over-the-Hem" Process
Washed, undiluted Ormus (manna), retort, condensing pot, ice and gas flame with diffuser.

To best ensure electromagnetic waves cause no interference on the stability of Ormus in source material or the manna (precipitate), it is prudent to keep the work and storage area six feet or more away from them. For more information, see "Labware Choices-Aluminum Foil." (Appendix XIV.)

## Definition
Once the Ormus (manna) precipitate from any process is obtained, it can be put "over-the-hem." This process is felt to draw out the higher frequencies of Ormus from the rest of the manna. The purpose is to "purify" the manna product. In today's vernacular we are "refining" the manna.

The historical significance of the "over-the-hem" process may be that ancient alchemists did not have "pure" Ormus source material as we have available today. The source material they had may have contained impurities and this process could have been a way to remove the impurities from the Ormus (manna). The process may also raise the vibration frequency of the Ormus material and this is generally thought to increase its potency.

## Information
Appearance: The Ormus product looks like a white powder.

Heat is added from an external source during this process. Adding external heat affects the Ormus (manna). This is described in "Labware Choices-Heat." (Appendix XIV.)

The Ormus (manna) used is manna (from any Ormus process) that has first been dried-out. For more information, see "Dried-Out Wet Precipitate." (page 130.) A retort is then used to send the dried Ormus (manna) "over-the-hem."

This process purifies or refines the Ormus (manna) - making it pure and pulling the best of the best from itself. (A part of the dried-out manna rises and then goes "over-the-hem" to the other side of the retort.) Whatever part of the manna rises and falls to the other side of the retort is what you want. Whatever part has gone "over-the-hem" (to the other side) is also thought to be a higher frequency material (more potent).

(Note: Do not refine using this process more than twice as I have heard that the manna can become unstable [lose potency].)

The guidelines of ancient alchemy considered an Ormus (manna) "drop" (precipitation) to have been prepared most properly when performed during the full moon period, during the springtime and then put "over-the-hem." Doing the work during a full moon was especially important.

## Perform the Process

Place the dried Ormus (manna) in a stainless steel pot or borosilicate glass container. (If using a stainless steel pot there is to be no rusting, no flaking, no pitting, no chipping, no breeching of the stainless steel coating nor discoloration that can't be polished away with stainless steel cleansers. For more information, see "Labware Choices-Stainless Steel." (Appendix XIV.) The cover of this container is to have a hole through the lid. Glass tubing is put in the hole of the cover and rises up and over - to and down through a hole in the lid of another similar container continuing till it is close to the bottom of the second container. This second container (called the "cooling pot" or "condensing pot") sits in an ice water bath.

The cooling pot (condensing pot) also has a small short vent tube through the top. This vent releases excess pressure that may build up.

Place the first pot on a diffuser that sits over the flame heat source (or use a double boiler as explained below). A gentle heat is required therefore diffuse the heat. Generally, a diffuser is a piece of metal that raises the pot up higher off the flame. Another method of obtaining a gentler heat is to use a "double boiler." This is a stacked double pot. The bottom pot contains water and it sits directly on the flame. The top pot receives its heat from steam that rises from the boiling water in the bottom pot. This double boiler set up is termed a "Blaine Marie" after its inventor. The gentler the heat source, the better the "Over-The-Hem Process" works. A white cloud or fog lifts up from the first container and floats "over the hem" to the other side where it condenses into the second container sitting in the ice water. Once the process is completed, discard the contents of the first pot.

## Storage

Keep the powder that has gone over the hem dry or re-wet it with water

## Final Thought

Some M-state gas is lost in the process because this is not an airtight sealed system. Keep in mind that the Ormus material doesn't have to be sent "over-the-hem" to be active. This process is included for informational and Ormus-related historical purposes as well as for those Ormus collectors who wish to experiment.

NOTES:

*Enhance the Ormus collection workspace with carefully selected music. Music creates order out of chaos and thus leads to a greater universal order. In the presence of music, direction and even purpose is supplied to mere repetitious time.*

#  SECTION SEVEN

**Other Substances that Attract Life Force**

These substances have been included as their presence may augment benefits attributed to Ormus.

Ocean Plasma

Dowsing

Diet

Colloidal Silver

Colloidal Gold

Vedic Alchemy

Essiac Tea

Air

Pyramid

Magnetite Effect on Ormus Water (aka MEOW Kettle)

Salt Crystal Lamp

## OCEAN PLASMA

### Definition

Diluted seawater is similar to mammalian lymph and blood plasma systems. In other words, diluted seawater and the blood in our body are similar and Ocean Plasma has been used successfully in animal tests as a blood transfusion substitute (diluted seawater has been substituted for saline solutions in blood transfusions). Diluted seawater is compatible with living organisms, and people who were dying said they regained vigor after the use of ocean plasma.

### Information *

Seawater is an organic colloidal solution (a colloidal system) and differs from artificial saline solution. The artificial saline solution used intravenously (IV) is "Lactated Ringers Solution" and contains water with electrolytes added. The "electrolytes" are calcium chloride, potassium chloride, and sodium chloride. Electrolytes are substances that become "ions" when in solution and, therefore, acquire the capacity to conduct electricity. Consequently, the balance of electrolytes in our body is essential to the normal functioning of cells and organs.

Seawater provides cellular nourishment. It is regenerating, re-mineralizing and contains the life-giving essence (ancient alchemists would say spirit) of all the minerals and trace elements which work together for optimum functioning of the body. There are said to be 83 bio-available elements in natural seawater including calcium, potassium and sodium.

Other names given to diluted seawater may include: "Marine Plasma or Serum," Quinton Plasma or Serum" and "Marine Matrix."

"Ocean Plasma" (diluted seawater) has found use orally as well as by injection or in a transfusion. The seawater is extracted from the ocean at a particular geographical location and depth. The depth is 10 meters (about 32 feet) from the bottom and 30 meters (about 96 feet) from the top. A meter is approximately 3.2 feet.

*Sources for much of the information on "Ocean Plasma" include: *oceanplasma.org, truthquest2.com* and *originalquinton.com.*

### Final Thought

Seawater is the Ormus source material used to collect the Ormus material during the "Wet Process" and diluted seawater is also the ingredient in a product called "Ocean Plasma." Both Ormus (manna) and "Ocean Plasma" are believed to help regain "vigor."

It is my postulation that traits attributed to "Ocean Plasma" and Ormus (manna) may have a causal link between one another. The presence of Ormus *in* seawater may be at least one of the links and, if this is so, could explain the positive results recorded and observed from both Ormus (manna) and "Ocean Plasma."

Original Quinton™ offers Ocean Plasma (marine plasma) in the United States, Canada, the Caribbean and parts of Northern Mexico.

# DOWSING

## Definition

Dowsing is an exercise of a human faculty that allows one to obtain information in a manner beyond the scope and the power of standard physical senses such as sight, sound and touch.

## Information *

"I know very well that many scientists consider dowsing as they do astrology, as a type of ancient superstition. According to my conviction this is, however, unjustified. The dowsing rod is a simple instrument which shows the reaction of the human nervous system to certain factors which are unknown to us at this time."- *Albert Einstein*

Everyone can dowse; it is an innate intuitive skill that anyone can use. Dowsing is a learned thing (like learning to play the piano). First, there is a desire to learn and this is followed by "dedication," "determination," "balance of mind/body/soul" and, with time, "confidence." During the dedication step know that it is while "doing" it wrong you are actually learning to "do it right." There are books and organizations available that can help teach how to dowse. The "American Society of Dowsers" has local chapters and a web bookstore. A book that teaches us how to dowse is called: *Letter to Robin-A mini-course in Pendulum Dowsing.*

Dowsing can be done with a tool such as the "famed" forked stick, an L-rod or a pendulum. The tool is the visual display; the primary instrument is the mind of the dowser. The belief is the subconscious has the answers and since it can't articulate or speak, it utilizes the muscles of the body to "speak" through the tool. The mind is to be clear and free of your own conscious intervention and the process works best when you are in the alpha or meditative state. The meditative state is a very receptive one and is the same state used when praying. The focus is to be on the question without being involved with the answer.

Historically, dowsing has been used to locate underground water or oil sources. When looking for water, it is called "water-witching." A "witching" stick was traditionally made from a willow tree although any tree should work. Dowsing has also been used to find other objects such as missing children and adults, lost possessions, and buried treasure. The government has used dowsing to locate the enemy in wartime. All are examples of "physical dowsing."

When dowsing is used to seek information only, it is called "non physical" physical dowsing. Some examples include: checking on physical health, checking which vitamins or minerals are needed and inquiring about the best decision to choose among various choices. (A local medical doctor uses a pendulum as a part of the medical practice.)

Some have suggested the less dominant hand be used when dowsing. Are you left or right handed? That is the dominant side and it has been said to choose the other hand when dowsing so the weakest side of the brain is accessed. In this manner, the response is said to be more noticeable and maybe less conscious.

Dowsing can be performed using the muscles of the body. This is called "manual muscle testing," "muscle dowsing" or "kinesiology."

Dowsing can also be performed using the inner senses and this goes by the name: "intuition" or "paranormal abilities."

*The source for much of the information on "Dowsing" is the "American Society of Dowsers."

## Perform the Process

When dowsing a question it is to be a very specific question that is answerable with a "yes" or "no." (Record the questions asked and answers received in a journal.) The answers from dowsing are only as good as the questions asked. Therefore ask specific concise "yes" or "no" questions. Be specific. For example, the question: "Should I move to Dearborn, Michigan?" is a more specific one than "Should I move?"

There are a few questions to ask first. These include: "Are you ready for a question?" and "May I ask a question?" These inquire if you have permission to be involved in the question. Then ask, "Can I ask a question?" This inquires if you have the ability to dowse this question. Finally ask, "Should I ask?" This addresses if it would be appropriate and proper to ask this question. In short, these inquiries are the "should I, could I, may I" questions and if the answers received are "yes," it is known that you may comfortably proceed.

## Final Thought

Dowsing can answer questions we ask ourselves as we perform an Ormus collection process. For example: "Would this sacred geometric shape placed near my Ormus (manna) collection site draw more Ormus gold out of the source?" (The answer was no.)

Because Ormus is considered a bridging material between "spirit" and "matter," it is possible that results observed from dowsing may be enhanced.

# DIET

## Definition

Ormus is postulated to cause an increase in "cellular communication" and "rebuilding." Therefore, it becomes common sense to supplement the body with the minerals (both major and trace) needed to rebuild cells.

## Information *

Without minerals, life would not be possible and minerals can be considered the "spark plugs of life," acting as catalysts for every bodily function. The body uses the mineral (calcium) to maintain a balanced pH in the body and all nutrients (sugars, proteins, enzymes etc.) require minerals to metabolize. Many vitamins also require minerals be present in order to be active. There are over 70 minerals (more continue to be discovered) and our body needs a whole range of them. If you currently use a multivitamin/mineral supplement count the number of minerals listed as ingredients. (How many of the over 70 possible minerals are listed?)

An easily assimilable natural source of minerals is the best form to look for. Food is the most basic form. Therefore, make conscious meal choices keeping the mineral content of the foods in mind. Minerals are found in a variety of food such as meat, cereals (including breads), fish, milk, and foods from dairy as well as vegetables, fruit (especially dried fruit) and nuts. Trace minerals are found in small amounts in foods such as meat, fish, cereals, milk and dairy foods, vegetables and nuts.

Another natural source of minerals is seaweed. It contains, in addition to other nutrients, almost every mineral and trace mineral necessary for human existence. Seaweeds are broadly divided into the "kelps" (brown, red and green) and "dulse." The mineral content of kelp ranges from 8 to 10% and the mineral content of dulse ranges from 28 to 35%. (Dulse can be purchased as granules for use as a table salt replacement.)

Another natural source of minerals is "algae" such as blue green algae. There are those who say that wild alga is a better source than spirulina algae and some say algae have "anti-aging" properties.

Another natural source of minerals is seawater and therefore Ormus (manna) collected during the "Wet Process" is expected to contain the minerals from the "reconstituted" sea or "drawn" seawater. The Ormus (manna), unless filtered (and the manna is not filtered), does not contain less mineral content than the seawater (drawn or reconstituted) from which it is made. "Drawn" seawater generally contains over 80 minerals in detectable quantities and it is expected that "reconstituted" sea made by dissolving natural sea salt in distilled water would yield the same results.

"Ocean Plasma" (diluted seawater) is another natural source of minerals and has been discussed earlier.

An intriguing natural source of minerals is "Humic Shale" because it is a plant derived mineral source. This material is made up of the remains of prehistoric plants and therefore is an organic based form of minerals. Humic shale is found in specific geographical climates. The most potent sources come from areas with little rainfall because, over time, rainfall leaches the minerals out of the humic shale. Rich Earth™ humic shale offers "liquid minerals with Fulvic acid" and "Fulvic powder with minerals" and they are available for human supplementation. The "liquid minerals with Fulvic acid" is obtained by reverse osmosis, of the humic shale, with water. The water is allowed to evaporate and the resultant powder is the "Fulvic powder with minerals." For more information, see "Resources and Supplies-Mineral Source." (Appendix I.)

(Note: It has been said by some that when supplementing with minerals, those that come from inorganic sources (rocks and clays) are poorly absorbed (roughly 20-40%). Chelated minerals are absorbed a bit better (roughly 50-60%) while organic colloidal minerals are naturally chelated and remain in an electro-magnetic state. This allows the body chemistry to more easily utilize them. Therefore absorption of "organic colloidal minerals" is considered very high (organic colloidal minerals consist of water containing plant derived minerals). The "inorganic colloidal minerals" contain a combination of soils and clays in water).

* The source for much of this information on "Diet" is "*richearth.net*" and Internet searches.

## Final Thought

Other "nutrients," besides minerals, often missing from the diet or not present in proper amounts are the B Vitamins (including B12), pro-biotics and digestive enzymes. The result of their lack is a draining of the "vital energy" in the body.

Conversely, when the body is properly "fed" more physical vibrancy is experienced and, when this is the case, a greater effect from the Ormus (manna) may be expected.

The proper process of eating causes it to be a "conscious act." In this society, digestion is not a conscious act. Consider adding a level of consciousness to the process of eating by appreciatively looking at the food item. Imagine it and the ground it grew from, the harvest and all those who worked together to bring it to you. In doing so, a subtle, deeper connection with "life" while performing daily routines may be experienced.

## COLLOIDAL SILVER

### Definition

According to verified reports: "Colloidal Silver" kills pathogenic organisms and there is no known microbe not destroyed by colloidal silver. (The primary method of action is blocking the microbe's ability to take in oxygen.)

### Information *

Appearance: Colloidal silver looks like clear water.

Colloidal silver is non-toxic and non-addictive. Argyria has been linked to long-term use of colloidal silver or *large* particle size in the silver preparation and causes the skin to turn a grayish color. *Particles* in properly prepared colloidal silver contain about 15 atoms each and are hundreds of times smaller than a red blood cell. This is why some have said the body easily absorbs properly-sized particles.

It has been said that "Colloidal Silver" fights bacterial and viral infections and therefore taking it is likened to having a boosted immune system. Ask the manufacturer of the colloidal silver product to direct you on how to take it.

It may be preferable to hold "Colloidal Silver" under the tongue for 15 seconds before swallowing. By holding it under the tongue, where the Lingual vein is located, "Colloidal Silver" can be directly absorbed into the bloodstream and thus bypass the filtering action of the stomach and especially the liver. It makes sense to rinse the mouth *before* so there is minimal interference in absorption.

Now, colloidal silver also kills the friendly bacteria that reside in the gastrointestinal tract. Therefore, a suggestion made is that the gut be "re-seeded," with friendly bacteria, three hours after colloidal silver. Re-seeding occurs by ingesting "pro-biotic" supplements that contain microbes specific to the human gastrointestinal tract.

With pro-biotics, the object is to get the friendly bacteria to the lower intestines and the colon. To do this, they must pass through the stomach and small intestines; therefore enteric-coated pro-biotic formulations may be preferred. The special enteric coating protects the pro-biotic as it travels through the stomach and small intestines. It has been suggested that two important friendly microbes are contained in a pro-biotic formula: Acidophilus and Bifidobacteria. Other beneficial bacteria are "L. Salivarius", "L. Rhamnosus", and "L. Plantarum." Frutooligosaccharides(FOS) may be included as a nutrient to promote the growth of the beneficial bacteria once they arrive "on site." Often the "better" pro-biotic formulas must be refrigerated. Pb8Pro-Biotic Acidophilus and primal Defense with HSOs are said to be good pro-biotic formulas
* The source for much of this information on "Colloidal Silver" is "The Micro Silver Bullet" by Farber.

## Perform the Process
There are many "Colloidal Silver" products and generators on the market. For more information, search the Internet.

Note: An important note regarding the purity of the silver used in making colloidal silver. The silver is to be 0.999 fine (99.9 percent pure) and is sold as silver wire, 1oz solid silver bars or round coin shaped silver pieces. Do not under any circumstance use sterling silver or any other alloy of silver, as these are not 99.9 percent pure.

Ancient alchemists associated the moon with silver and some have said that the phases of the moon affect colloidal silver production. For example, the week surrounding a full moon may be a good time to make colloidal silver and the week surrounding a new moon not as good a time. For more information, see "Moon Chart." (Appendix XX.) The colloidal silver is observed by shining a focused light beam through the liquid. When the light beam streams straight through the side of the glass container you will observe a "Tyndal Effect" as the tiny silver particles in the water scatter the light. A red-beamed laser pointer is one such focused light source however, a small "focused beam" flashlight also works. Mini-Maglite® is an example of a focused beam light.

## Storage
Store the container of colloidal silver in dark brown or colored *glass* bottles in a cool dark place.

**Do not store in plastic bottles.** Plastic containers can hold a static charge and a static charge causes the silver particles to collect on the sides of the plastic container. If a plastic container is used it has been said the shelf life is reduced to less than seven days. (*www.globallight.net*)

Store at room temperature in a cupboard or cabinet. Do *not* store in the sun. Store the colloidal silver away from all forms of light as the presence of light, the most offending of which is UV rays (sunlight), darkens and degrades the silver.

## Final Thought
It is said that kidneys, lymph and bowel eliminate "Colloidal Silver" after three weeks. Therefore, some say that a regular daily intake can make sense as a protection against unwanted pathogens.

Others say that colloidal silver should not be taken every day because silver can build up in the body. At this time, there is no consensus.

Some have said that silver particles may be affected by intent. If this is so, it may be beneficial to visualize the state of perfect health when taking "Colloidal Silver." (*www.globallight.net*)

"Colloidal Silver" can be used topically to promote healing and prevent infection (with proper first-aid care) for cuts, scrapes and rashes.

"Colloidal Silver" can be sprayed on kitchen countertops, used to sterilize canning jars and lids as well as added to laundry and bath water. Colloidal silver can be sprayed on chicken, meats, fruits and vegetables to kill germs (Salmonella and E.Coli).

Colloidal silver can be added to pets' water dishes to retard pathogen growth.

The size of the never-ending attack on our bodies by microscopic pathogens (microbes) is huge and some have said that we would be dead in minutes if our immune system was not functioning. Therefore, if "Colloidal Silver" decreases the pathogen count in the body, our immune system expends less energy combating pockets of pathogens. The conserved energy may be observed as better health with a feeling of more vim and vigor and if this occurs, our ability to interact with Ormus may be enhanced.

**Note:** This may be important. No reference has been made regarding taking Ormus (manna) with colloidal silver. It has been suggested to space each by one hour (or two hours if food has been eaten) and to not take them at the same time. This is a suggestion in the event the two products interact with each other. It has been reported that adding colloidal silver to Ormus (manna) caused the Ormus to separate and a white precipitate (the color of the Ormus) to settle to the bottom of the container.

Perform research to determine if "Colloidal Silver" is for you.


## COLLOIDIAL GOLD

### Definition

It has been said that "Colloidal Gold" enhances the body's *electric circuitry* at the brain level and throughout the body by its extraordinary *conductive* properties.


### Information *

Appearance: Colloidal gold looks like a red or reddish liquid.

A result of "enhanced electric conduction" may be an acceleration of the thought processes and memory improvement. In addition colloidal gold is thought to increase neurotransmissions in both lobes of the brain, thereby balancing creative and logical thoughts and to promote communication between the conscious and subconscious. Therefore it may be possible that enhanced consciousness is experienced from taking "Colloidal Gold."

"Colloidal Gold" is sold in various concentrations measured in ppm (parts per million.) A 200ppm liquid contains 200mg of gold per liter. Ask the manufacturer of the colloidal gold product to direct you on how to take it.

It may be preferable to hold "Colloidal Gold" under the tongue for 15 seconds before swallowing. By holding it under the tongue, where the Lingual vein is located, "Colloidal Gold" can be directly absorbed into the bloodstream and thus bypass the filtering action of the stomach and especially the liver. It makes sense to rinse the mouth before so there is minimal interference in absorption.

*The source for much of this information on "Colloidal Gold" is www.metosphericplasmaproducts.com and www.colloidalgoldmachines-central.com

## Perform the Process

The "Colloidal Gold" process requires a large amount of electrical current and affordable home generators, at this point in time, are not offered.

## Storage

Plastic storage containers may be used.

Do *not* store in the sun. The presence of light, the most offending of which is UV rays (sunlight), can degrade the gold.

Store at room temperature in a cupboard or cabinet.

## Final Thought

The Central Nervous System network in the body involves electric impulse transmissions between neurons and supplementing with "Colloidal Gold" is thought to *enhance* the electric circuitry in the body. One theory holds that increased impulse transmissions in the brain results in "mental clarity" and "enhanced consciousness." Since the Ormus material is theorized to be a part of the "matrix of consciousness," which acts as a type of bridging material between "spirit" and "matter," it is possible that better functioning circuitry in the brain may result in a greater effect from the Ormus (manna).

**Note:** This may be important. No reference has been made regarding taking Ormus (manna) with colloidal gold. It has been suggested to space each by one hour (or two hours if food has been eaten) and to not take them at the same time. This is a suggestion in the event the two products interact with each other. It has been reported that adding "Colloidal Gold" to Ormus (manna) caused the Ormus (manna) to separate and a colored precipitate (similar in color to that of colloidal gold) to settle to the bottom of the container.

Perform research to determine if "Colloidal Gold" is for you.

# VEDIC ALCHEMY

### Definition
"Vedic Alchemy" is part of Ayruveda which comes from East India. Ayruveda is India's traditional, natural system of medicine thousands of years old. Vedic Alchemy offers a treatise (a recipe) said to make water containing the "vibrational resonance" of copper, silver or gold.

### Information *
Appearance: The finished product looks like water.

This process does not give Ormus or the benefit of Ormus. Instead, it utilizes boiling to transfer a type of energy - the "vibrational resonance" of the source material (copper, silver or gold) - into the water. By drinking this water, which now contains the vibrational resonance of the source material, the vibrational resonance in the body is felt by some to be raised. The effect might be small, however it is to be remembered that the vibrational resonance of the body has been affected by adding this new vibrational resonance. The effect seen is individualized and if the person is sensitive, it is believed that they will feel it.

Throughout history, the "vibrational resonance" of each metal has found a specific use. For example: "Copper" has been attributed to healing, rejuvenation, softening of tissues, anti-aging and an ability to promote harmony and balance in associating with others. It is also said to increase a person's magnetism to others. "Gold" has been attributed to leading to clarity of thought, enlightenment, improving mental attitude, stimulating the nerves, increasing the life force, increasing mental acuity and the ability to concentrate. "Silver" has been attributed to being an anti-infective - being bactericidal and also acting as a mental purifier that enables us to see the past clearly and remove fears and blockages.
  * The source for much of this information on *Vedic Alchemy* originated with Don Nance, searches on the Internet and *Sorcerer's Stone* by Dennis Hauck.

### Perform the Process
Place the pure metal source in a stainless steel pot. (Follow the stainless steel precautions in Appendix XIV.) Use a pure 99.9% metal source (copper, silver or gold). No alloys are to be in the metal. The source metal must be thoroughly cleaned.
  Add a quart of distilled water.
  Boil gently (gas flame preferred), open to the air until 1/2 of the liquid is removed from the container.
  The water is ready (after cooling) to drink.

### Storage
Ayruveda states that the vibrational frequency lasts three days. To be on the conservative side, some suggest drinking the water within two days. There is no suggested amount to drink. Drink as often as you would any water and then make more. Store the liquid in HDPE plastic.

## Final Thought
When an Ormus process cannot be performed, this process is better than having nothing at all.

## ESSIAC TEA

### Definition
"Essiac Tea" is attributed to the Ojibwa Indians who used it for illnesses. A patient who was using the tea gave the formula to a nurse named Rene Caisse. This story was initially told in the (out of print) book *Calling of an Angel* by Gary Glum. A current book on the subject is available and titled *Essiac Essentials* by Sheila Snow and Mali Klein. Caisse pioneered the idea of an injectable form of the herbs which she felt would be more potent and faster acting. After years of research, doctors developed an injectable version of the formula and it did prove to work even better. They requested authorization from the government to perform studies on the injectable form and were denied. The oral form of "Essiac Tea" is available.

### Information*
Appearance: The finished Essiac tea looks like muddy colored tea.

David Hudson has commented in his lectures that "Essiac Tea" is high in rhodium and iridium and these may be helpful in cancers of soft tissue. The content of many of these lectures can be found on the Internet. One site is *subtleenergies.com*.

The original "Essiac Tea" formula contained four *main* herbs: "Burdock root," "sheep sorrel herb," "slippery elm bark" and "Turkish Indian rhubarb root." Other herbs said to have been in the original formula are: "blessed thistle," "kelp," "red clover" and "watercress."

An "Essiac Tea" powder containing these eight ingredients is available. For more information, see "Resources and Supplies." (Appendix I.)

"Essiac Tea" is designed to deplete the body of the toxins causing illness and to boost the immune system. By becoming stronger, the immune system is more able to fight or ward off disease.

*The source for much of this information on "Essiac Tea" is *www.magnetitewater.com* and transcripts of David Hudson's lectures.

### Perform the Process
**Add one ounce of the powdered tea to one quart spring water or well water or four ounces of tea to one gallon of the water.** (Distilled water is not used as the water should have some minerals in it.) Steep the tea and simmer in a stainless steel pot. (Follow the stainless steel precautions in Appendix XIV.)

**Leave out overnight, uncovered, for 12 hours.** Do not strain the herbs.

### Storage

**Store prepared "Essiac Tea" under refrigeration, preferably in a glass container.** Plastic is also acceptable as a storage container. Prepared "Essiac Tea" is said to last two weeks.

Stir or shake the tea before drinking to help mix the herb sediment. The herbs are important to the function of the tea in the body and, therefore, best results have been said to occur when the herb sediment from the bottom of the tea's container is also ingested. (Many do not realize this and throw out the herbs that made the tea.)

Drink three ounces of tea twice a day on an empty stomach, first thing in the morning and in the evening before going to sleep. Drink the tea quickly as it does not have a pleasant taste and follow it with some water to rinse the taste away. If you wish to be aggressive, for example when having a health challenge, drink three ounces of tea three times a day.

### Final Thought

There are some who feel that "Vitali-Tea" is better. The ingredients of "Vitali-Tea" are said to be grown in Ormus enriched soil.

# AIR

### Definition

Ormus is postulated to be in air. Air contains the highest vibrations of the Ormus material and that is why the Ormus floats. Ormus is hypothesized to be a superconductor and, as such, it levitates in the presence of magnetic fields. The earth generates a magnetic field and this is how it is presumed that Ormus enters the air. Therefore, while breathing air the body can be receiving Ormus for the "light body" as well as oxygen for the "physical body." This is the reasoning thought to explain why drawing in air deeply is better than shallowly breathing. (The Ormus material is in the air as well as our food and our water.)

### Information

Body Flex™ is a physical exercise routine for the body that may be collecting the Ormus in the air. This exercise is all about breathing in a certain distinct and forceful way while concurrently employing isometric exercises felt to move "life force energy" to specific areas in the body.

Other cultures speak of "life force energy." Hindu tradition speaks of "Prana" that can be collected from air by using breathing techniques. "Prana" is "life force energy" and specific breathing practices are said to collect more of it. Chinese tradition speak similarly of "Chi" or "qi," Hawaiian tradition speaks of "Manna," the Japanese call it "Ki" and the Southern African Bushmen, who are an ancient indigenous peoples, call it "Boiling Energy."

## Doing the Process

The Body Flex™ exercise routine utilizes a specific manner of breathing. It takes *work* to breathe in this way - the breath is drawn in and out through *pursed* lips.

Because sunlight is postulated to disturb the state of the Ormus material, it may make sense to perform this exercise routine when it is dark outside.

## PYRAMID

### Definition
There is said to be great energy located in a pyramid shape at the level of the "King's Chamber." (This is explained next.)

### Information
There is an energy emitted by the pyramid shape termed the "secret fire." The translation of the word pyramid is "fire in the middle." The location of the "King's Chamber" is approximately the horizontal meeting point inside the pyramid roughly 1/2 way down from the top of the pyramid and 1/2 way up one side of the pyramid. For more information, see "Resources and Supplies." (Appendix I.)

### Perform the Process
An experiment with a pyramid shape and a piece of gold was performed. An oily sheen formed on the piece of gold. The oil sheen was felt to be gold Ormus. (Note: Use only a clean 0.999 pure gold or copper source.)

**Align a pyramid shape with one side facing "Celestial North" (Polaris North Star).** This north side facing is also called "true north" or "astronomical north" and is preferred over that of magnetic north which is determined by compass reading. "Celestial North" is a bearing in the night sky that lies within 0.5 degrees of Polaris (the "North Star").

**Hang a piece of 99.9% pure copper or gold in the pyramid at the "King's Chamber" height.** The metal must be thoroughly cleaned. To hang the piece of metal, use material like thread or fishing line.

**Place a glass of water under the hanging copper or gold.** Allow no light to enter the pyramid shape. Oil may form over time on the copper or the gold and this may be the Ormus form of the gold metal.

If there is a lot of oil, you may not want to use your finger because it is thought that Ormus will go through the skin, and the amount taken in could be too much. Therefore use a popsicle stick to remove some of the oil from the oil coated metal and add it to drinking water.

## Final Thought

It is said by some that Ormus (manna) stored in a pyramid has displayed enhancements in its effect. This may be worth further experimentation.

For additional information, search the Internet. Some sites include "God's Recipe for the Elixir of Life" and the Russians "Phi Pyramid" also known as the "Sharp Pyramid" which is the "Golden Mean Pyramid." Joshua Gulick performed the pyramid experiment and Dr. Fred Bell has done work with the pyramid shape.

## MAGNETITE EFFECT ON ORMUS WATER (MEOW Kettle)

## Definition

A "MEOW Kettle" uses the earth's magnetic field to concentrate Ormus around a bottle of drinkable "well" water or "spring" water. This is thought to occur because the bottle of water is sitting within a container filled with natural magnetite and, thus, has a magnetic field around it. This is called a "MEOW Kettle." The bottle of water sitting in this field forms "Magnetite Effect Ormus Water" (MEOW) sometimes called "magnetic water." (Some consider the term magnetic water inaccurate.) The water is said to have Ormus-like subtle energy effects and others say this is all about the Ormus material.

## Information *

Appearance: Magnetite water looks like water.

Natural magnetite can be used to create a "field-effect" treatment on a bottle of water because its presence causes a localized magnetic field. This treatment has been said by some to induce "Ormus-like properties" in the water.

There are two grades of magnetite available: "Ormus-Like Minerals Magnetite" and "Wild Harvest Magnetite." "Ormus-Like Minerals Magnetite" contains the sand that is co-mingled with the magnetite. The sand may carry transition elements. Transition elements are Ormus producing elements and therefore are collectable (as Ormus material) during an Ormus collection process. "Wild harvest magnetite" contains only the magnetite granules that were co-mingled with the sand in "Ormus-Like Minerals Magnetite." For more information, see "Sources for the Processes-Minerals" (Appendix VIII) and "Resources and Supplies-Magnetite" (Appendix I).

When making a "MEOW Kettle" the "Ormus-Like Minerals Magnetite" and "Wild Harvest Magnetite" are mixed in a 50-50 ratio. The action of the magnetite is to create the "field of energy" and the sandy material found around the magnetite is the "Ormus source material."

"Magnetite Water" - water that has been charged by the presence of magnetite and its co-mingling sand has been said to speed up the delivery of whatever is taken with the water. Some suggest spacing medication and magnetite water, perhaps by two hours, so neither is in the system at the same time. It makes sense to monitor the effects of medicine taken and include your physician in on the results. This is part of a suggestion made by some to exercise caution and use judgment if taking medications or other supplements.

"Magnetite Water" is said by some to prevent clogging of arteries, cause strengthening of the immune system, decrease addiction to chemicals (such as caffeine, alcohol, cigarettes) and is electrically attracted to cells in the body resulting in an overall feeling of more energy. Included is the thought that magnetite water may reduce acid in the body - in other words, help the body to achieve a more "alkaline" (basic) state. (Reams "Biological Theory of Ionization" states that the body is healthier when in an alkaline condition.)

*The source for much of this information on the "MEOW Kettle" is "http://www.ormuslike.info/index.html."

## Perform the Process
**Place a plastic or glass bottle of drinkable well or spring water in a plastic bucket and then add the magnetite mixture to the bucket.** My personal preference for the material that houses the well or spring water is glass. Voss® sells "artesian" water at the grocery store packaged in a tall glass container. (One bottle containing 16oz of water fits in a one-gallon plastic bucket. Two to four bottles each containing 16oz of water fits in a two-gallon bucket.)

Do not use a metal container as metal upsets the action of the magnetite. The presence of metal interferes with the magnetic field of the earth that keeps these magnetite minerals charged.

The magnetite mixture added to a "MEOW Kettle" is a 50-50 mixture of "Ormus-Like Minerals Magnetite" and "Wild Harvest Magnetite." (Ten pounds of the magnetite mixture is a good quantity for a one-gallon plastic bucket that houses one bottle containing 16oz of water.)

(Note: There is a different "MEOW Kettle" configuration that incorporates a "nest" for the bottle of drinkable well or spring water. To make the nest, place the bottle of water in a cardboard sleeve and then place the bottle and the sleeve within a larger plastic container. Next, pour the magnetite mixture between the outer container and the inner sleeve. For a drinking size bottle of water, there is to be no less than one-inch thickness of magnetite mixture between the outer and inner container and the water level is to be below the level of the magnetite mixture. Suggestions for materials to use for the cardboard sleeve and plastic can are an empty cardboard oatmeal sleeve packaging and a plastic 1.32 gallon sized empty vinegar container. Anything can be used, with the exception of metal.)

(Note: It has been said by some that six to eight small grains of pure natural sea salt added per 20oz bottle of water may be helpful to the process. Others say they do not use salt in the water and have excellent results. If sea salt is used, there are to be no anti-caking agents or coloring added to the sea salt. Do not add salt if you are on a sodium restrictive diet.)

It has been said that it is best to have the "MEOW Kettle" close to the earth and that ground level floors are the best location. Keep the "MEOW Kettle" away from electronic equipment as much as possible.

Whenever possible, place the "MEOW Kettle" in an area where the sun can shine on the magnetite and if using a dark storage location, one day every month or two, take the kettle outside and place it in the sun. The sun will permeate the magnetite as it sits in the "MEOW Kettle."

This is said to maintain the magnetite at its fullest charging potential. (Perhaps this works because the magnetic field of the earth combined with the power of the sun has a positive effect on the magnetite.)

**Store the bottle of water inside the "MEOW Kettle" three to five days.** The water is now ready to drink.

The time frame for the bottles left in the "MEOW Kettle" (called the "charger") is very broad. Bottles left from three days to seven days gave good results. It is felt by some that water intended for children seems to need less time in the kettle and that being charged for four hours or less was enough. One report said that a bottle left in the kettle for one month was good and gave a lot of energy.

It has been said by some that three days is enough time to form the "magnetite water" in the "MEOW Kettle" and additional days spent in the kettle isn't worth the difference in the water. The purists of magnetite water feel that five days in the kettle makes optimal water.

When the bottle of "magnetite water" is removed from the "MEOW Kettle," place another bottle of well water or spring water in the kettle.

If the "magnetite water" is ingested on a regular basis, three (or five) kettles are required for constant cycling and daily availability of magnetic water.

Natural juices can be placed in a "MEOW Kettle." Use bottled juice or if fresh juice is used place the "MEOW Kettle" inside a covered cooler filled with ice so it does not spoil.

For more information, see "Resources and Supplies." (Appendix I.)

## Storage
Use "Magnetite Water" within 8-10 weeks for optimal retention of the "field effect." If you live in a rural area and are away from most electrical disturbances, the water storage parameter is said by some to increase to as high as 16 to 18 months.

## Final Thought
"Magnetite Water" has been said to aid in strong bone formation and if so it is advisable to take extra calcium and magnesium when drinking the water.

An experiment that can be performed with "reconstituted" sea or "drawn" seawater intended for use in the "Wet Process" is to first place it in a "MEOW Kettle" (to induce the "field effect" treatment). Perform the "Wet Process" on the seawater five days later. Compare the precipitate volume with seawater (drawn or reconstituted) that was not placed in a "MEOW Kettle."

Another experiment is to put the Ormus (manna) collected from an Ormus collection process in the "MEOW Kettle" (away from sunlight) for five days to see if the "field effect" treatment enhances the action of the Ormus (manna).

A "MEOW Kettle" may be better than putting a bottle of water on a "magnet pad." "Magnet Water" is a container of drinking water that has been placed on top of a *magnet* pad for 8 hours or so. The magnet breaks down the size of the water molecules and it has been said this makes the water easier to absorb in the body and in addition, the "magnetic field" (generated from the *magnet*) pumps Ormus through the air to the water to induce Ormus-like properties in the water. (In a "MEOW Kettle" the bottle of water is *surrounded* with natural "magnetic field" generating magnetite.)

(Another way to collect Ormus in good drinking water is to use a "Magnet Vortex Water Trap" or "Vortex Water Trap." For more information, see "Magnet Vortex Water Trap." (page 122) The trap concentrates Ormus in drinking water and some have said may retrieve more Ormus than the "MEOW Kettle.")

# LAMINAR CRYSTALS

## Definition
The term "Laminar Crystal" is *not* a generic term. "Laminar Crystal," is used to describe mica that has been transformed via the work of a *specific* process called a "Laminar Crystal Process." The "Laminar Crystal Process" contains a multitude of steps performed in a specific order and includes *"imprinting"* and *"charging."* This imprinting and charging step is said by some to add *power* to the piece. Because of the imprinting/ charging that is performed, it may be wise to choose a "Laminar Crystal" manufacturer who is living a "wholesome" life. If the "Laminar Crystal Process" is not strictly followed, then the product is best described as a ceramic piece that contains some mica. Therefore, it has been said by some that mica alone does not contain the same healing powers as a "Laminar Crystal." To make matters more interesting, there are some 2,000 forms of mica to choose from when performing a "Laminar Crystal Process."

## Information *
Appearance: A "Laminar Crystal" looks like a baked ceramic piece. Most are non-glazed.

Like collecting Ormus, the work of making "Laminar Crystal" is process driven. Specific steps are performed in a specific order that utilizes the physical, psychological and spiritual levels simultaneously. Similar to the Ormus processes, if the work is not done on all levels, the effort is more akin to traditional chemistry.

A "Laminar Crystal" has been said to absorb "life-force energy" from the universe and then radiate that energy to all in its presence.

For more information, see "Resources and Supplies." (Appendix I.)

*The source for much of the information on "Laminar Crystals" is *www.giftsfromthestars.com.*

## Perform the Process
A "Laminar Crystal" treats all water sources - and human beings are at least 70% water. The crystal is said by some to increase water's hydration delivery and this allows cells to absorb the "life force energy" which the crystal has imparted to the water.

**Use the "Laminar Crystal" (often in sets of three) for drinking water, cooking water, bath, spa or pool and also place externally on areas of the body that need restoring.** Initial results can

Image, courtesy www.giftsfromthestars.com

be seen or felt quickly and five days has been said to be enough time to form the basis of an anti-aging regimen. "Laminar Crystals" are made in many sizes and shapes from small round marbles to long pyramid shaped bars. The ceramic and mica material is also fashioned into plates and cups and various sized pads containing granular laminar crystals that range in size from small to large. Large pads are placed under bedding and slept on.


## Final Thought

Ormus is postulated to utilize a type of "scalar energy" (scalar electromagnetics) and "Laminar Crystals" are postulated to utilize the same energy. In this important way, the two are related. (In the simplest most direct terms, scalar electromagnetics (scalar energy) is the notion of a vast, unseen background of scalar energies which underlay all physical reality. Therefore, this energy may be able to change physical reality.)

The concentration of Ormus in the body has been said to directly relate to the amount of cellular coherence (cellular communication) that occurs. This cellular coherence is thought to allow for activities of the cell such as healing. If the presence of "Laminar Crystals" also increase the concentration of Ormus in the water we use, as some feel occurs, the benefits of the Ormus (manna) collected in Ormus collection processes may be increased. Because of this line of reasoning, "Laminar Crystals" may be worth exploring.

The use of "Laminar Crystals" may augment Ormus (manna) or as some have said, make Ormus collections unneeded.

(Note: As an experiment, during the fall equinox, I used "Laminar Crystals" during the purifying (rinsing) step of a "Wet Process." A large three-inch diameter round "Laminar Crystal" was added to the Ormus precipitate after the second rinse of the Ormus (manna). The "Laminar Crystal" remained in the Ormus (manna) through the third rinse and then was removed. I noticed the finished Ormus (manna) tasted better, exhibited a more "salty" flavor and felt smoother. This experiment may warrant further research.)

(Note: As an experiment I used "Laminar Crystal" water when mixing concrete for a house project. The water used to mix the concrete came from a swimming pool that contains several "Laminar Crystals" of varying sizes and shapes. One batch of concrete was made with water from the hose and a second batch of concrete was made with "Laminar Crystal" pool water. It was noted by two observers that the powdered concrete hydrated more quickly and was easier to thoroughly blend with no lumps when combined with "Laminar Crystal" water.)

# SALT CRYSTAL LAMP

## Definition

A "Salt Crystal Lamp" is fashioned from a chunk of "Natural Salt Crystal" taken from deep within the earth. It is made into a colored glowing lamp by placing a 7-25 watt bulb inside the piece of natural rock salt. The colors of a *lit* "Salt Crystal Lamp" range from light apricot to dark orange with every shade of pink and peach in between.

## Information

Appearance: A lit up salt crystal lamp looks like a chunk of salt emanating the colors of light apricot to dark orange and all the way to brownish red.

The proponents of the "Salt Crystal Lamp" report that computers, televisions, printers, faxes, microwaves, air conditioners and dehumidifiers, emit *positive* ions that, when breathed in, can result in mental and physical exhaustion. In addition, pollution from exhaust fumes in cities creates Ozone and some say this causes challenges to health when Ozone mixes with positive ions emitted from electronic equipment. A "Salt Crystal Lamp" is said to emit *negative* ions that cause the positive ions in the air particles to reach an electrical or ionic balance. For more information, see "Resources and Supplies." (Appendix I.)

A "Salt Crystal Lamp" is available in four sizes ranging from small to very large. A small "Salt Crystal Lamp" is between 6-8 pounds, a medium lamp 9-11 pounds, a large lamp 12-15 pounds and an extra large lamp 18-21 pounds. (When 20 pounds are exceeded, a *fully* lit lamp is often prevented because of the thickness and turbidity of the chunk of rock salt.)

The results of using a "Salt Crystal Lamp" are said to include: improved concentration, a feeling of refreshment, enhanced immunity, improved sleep and relief of migraines. Some have called the "Salt Crystal Lamp" the "vitamins of the air."

The lamp also utilizes color therapy. The colorization of the lamp is from infusions of minerals within the salt crystals. The most common colors are a medium peach or pink. Some have a reddish glow (the redder the salt, the higher the iron content) and some are a deep red-almost brown. (The deep red lamps are hard to light up even with a higher wattage bulb.) When a "Salt Crystal Lamp" is lit, it radiates the shades of reds, pinks, whites and browns. Some say these colors have beneficial effects termed "color therapy" (light wave frequency therapy). It has been said that the red color activates the heart and circulation, pink opens the emotional body, white has an emotionally cleansing and detoxifying effect while brown helps to find ones own balance as well as supporting a feeling of being grounded.

## Perform the Process

The lamp is a *passive* system and is *not* fan driven. A large "Salt Crystal Lamp" is said to reach out about 10 feet and a medium lamp about five feet. It is suggested that a "Salt Crystal Lamp" be placed on the nightstand next to the bed, near the monitor of a computer and next to the television.

## Final Thought

If a "Salt Crystal Lamp" supports the physical body through positive and negative ion balancing as well a color therapy then the experience with Ormus may be enhanced.

NOTES:

A common belief is that entering the Ormus collection processes emotionally upset or focused on one's ego and not the greater universal workings that allow the Ormus material to be revealed destroys the delicate connection with the subtle level of reality on which the collector of Ormus hopes to work.

# SECTION EIGHT

**Closing**

Final Remarks

Postscript

## Final Remarks

Many Ormus collection processes have been detailed. After all is said, indications point to a few processes that may be *better* for the average Ormus collector. These include processes that extract Ormus using "oil" or "salty solutions."

The oil process is called a "Live Oil Process" and the most useful salty solution type processes are the "Wet Process" and (once you feel comfortable with that process) the "Dry Process."

You will hear of other Ormus collection processes during your Ormus journey and must judge their merit for yourself. Some guidelines are necessary for this work as it is easy to become excited about a "new" process when instead the time has come to begin "investigative thinking." Current Ormus collection theory includes the following thoughts: First, we are on the learning curve right now and it is understood how much there is yet to learn about Ormus and its collection. Therefore, these guidelines contain some of the current opinions and thoughts of present-day alchemists and Ormus researchers. As the science of the study of Ormus evolves, these guidelines may alter.

1) Using appliances with high electromagnetic frequencies (EMF) has been said by some to place a "pressure" on Ormus (drives it away). Therefore, it may be advisable that processes avoid the use of electric ovens or stoves. Most agree that one should not use an electric stove or oven. There is not a consensus of opinion at this time regarding the use of a refrigerator and it is recommended that the Ormus product may be shielded from spin disturbing waves by enclosing the container in aluminum foil if placing in the refrigerator.

2) Lye is a chemical that is central in Ormus collection processes. To be more specific, in one theory of Ormus chemistry, the *sodium* in the lye is important to the processes. Ancient alchemical treatises also include sodium's presence in what they termed the "secret fire." Therefore many processes are expected to use lye (to disintegrate the Ormus source material) rather than sulfuric acid or sulfur-containing compounds. David Hudson has said carbon, (including carbon monoxide) sulfites, nitrogen oxide and shortwave length waves (such as UV light) are the four main things that "kill" this material in the body. These may be said to "kill the light" and is a reference to the "Meissner field" that surrounds a superconductor (such as Ormus). This is explained in the beginning of the book.

3) Processes that include pH swings up and down (i.e.; lye solution is added then hydrochloric acid is added) are believed to induce "energetics" beneficial to the collection. The pH swings are thought to free Ormus bound in the molecules of source material. Therefore all processes designed to induce (increase) energetics are considered better ones if the pH is fluctuated up and down rather than relying on factors such as boiling. (The energetics of boiling is based on faster movement of molecules versus the energetics of pH swings, which is based on interaction at the molecular level.)

4) A "wet" Ormus product is considered by some to be more bioavailable to the body than a "dry" form and therefore processes are often expected to collect Ormus in a wet form. It is felt by some that grittiness remaining in the mouth when taking a dry powder form indicates a (non-toxic) impurity in the Ormus powder and that a "good" Ormus powder completely

dissolves when held under the tongue. However, there is not a clear consensus on this point and most alchemists make both "wet" and "dry" Ormus products. Ormus collectors have reported that dry Ormus worked well and a researcher has annealed (heated) the precipitate collected from the "Wet Process" and reported that it was exceptional. We are again reminded how there is much to learn about the Ormus material.

5) Sugar, with its crystalline structure like that of salt, is thought to protect Ormus from "magnetic fields" on the earth. Some believe that the sugar molecule competes for Ormus more than the salt molecule and therefore collection processes are generally not expected to include "sweet" sources. However, there is no consensus of opinion on "sweet" versus "non-sweet" materials used as an Ormus source at this time.

6) Heat is thought to affect Ormus. It may cause the Ormus to become more energetically active by increasing the spin on the Ormus material and it may cause some of the lighter Ormus to float away. There is no consensus of opinion at this time or complete agreement regarding the use of heat in an Ormus collection process. Many do generally agree on three areas. First, it may be beneficial to be near the heated pot to allow the Ormus material that does leave to possibly come to you (and personally align with you). Next, the use of external heat is to be at the lowest temperature possible and practical (to reduce the amount of Ormus material that "boils" off). Finally, heat is applied for no longer than necessary to ensure a minimal amount of the lighter Ormus substance floats off.

Now, the "Wet Process" is a process that revolves around Ormus collection from seawater. It is felt by many that seawater *naturally contains more* Ormus to begin with than other Ormus source materials. In addition seawater's form (wet) of Ormus is easier to collect than land-based (dry) source materials form of Ormus. The collection is more akin to "harvesting" or "concentrating" Ormus in the form of a precipitate. (Recall that the precipitate is casually observed, handled and called "Ormus" and when the Ormus source material is a pure metal element, it does form a "single source" precipitate that contains the Ormus form of only that metal. However, the vast majority of Ormus collectors do not use pure metals as the Ormus source material and consequently there are other constituents in the precipitate.)

Your work is complete. You are able to perform Ormus collection! Have fun and along the way develop a rapport with fellow seekers who have found Ormus. Share the news about the ease with which Ormus may be collected - and the processes that are fairly easy and straightforward. Remember a message from long-past alchemists:
"Let it be observed, then, that all who have written on the art, from undoubted principles, assert that the genuine process is not expensive; time and fuel, with manual labour, being all allowed for." (*Collectanea Chemica* by Eirenaeus Philalethes and others 1893)

The *Primer of Ormus Collection Processes* closes now on the high vibrational notes of appreciation, love, joy, gratitude and peace.

Chris Emmons RPh.

## Postscript

I have heard Ormus seekers comment on how they understand an Ormus collection process and yet don't feel their Ormus product will "work." There is little need for this feeling.

When preparing to perform an Ormus process know how you hold a place within a large "Life Force" that does exist and is everywhere. Once you have a full conscious "awareness" of this "life force" it becomes easy to leave "ego" behind.

Consequently, your mind is full with the thought of the "life force" that is everywhere-including here with you-as the Ormus process begins. The result of this directed thinking is that you have brought the "Life Force" with you, through you and into the Ormus extraction and collection work.

This acknowledgment of the presence and involvement of "spirit" in the work is an important point and the key difference between an alchemist and a traditional chemist.

Continue the process with measured actions. Do not rush. There can be no hurry, as the Ormus product will be affected - even if the effect is subtle. Halt the business of the world around you and enter the process with appreciation. (Actively appreciate everything you can think of.)

Additional detailed explanations regarding the mindset of an alchemist are found in *Sorcerer's Stone: A Beginner's Guide to Alchemy* by Dennis William Hauck: *www.DWHauck.com*

NOTES:

Alchemists consider consciousness a force of nature that can be harnessed and purified through prayer and meditation and then added to the process just like a chemical ingredient.  Thomas Norton, a fifteenth century English alchemist, summed this up in instructions to his students:  "The mind must be in perfect harmony with the work."  *The Ordinal of Alchemy*

# ✸ SECTION NINE

**Appendices and Glossary**

List of Ormus Resources and Supplies
Ormus Pins
Barry Carter
Local Ormus Groups
Mysterious History of Ormus
General Ormus Inormation
Basic Explanations of the Ormus Process
Sources for the Ormus Process
Book Selections/Web Searches
Moon Chart
Experiment Documentation
Common Measurement Conversions
Chemicals of the Process
Best Practices Labware Choices
pH (Meter)
Toning/Smudging/Background
How to Manifest
Imprinting/Charging
Aloe Vera
Seawater Collection with Pump and Filter
Ormus Use (theoretical), Directions
Bioavailability and PRECAUTIONS
Chemistry of the Ormus Process
Glossary
Author and Listed Contributors

# APPENDIX I
## List of Ormus Resources and Supplies

The list is referenced regularly.  You may move forward quickly towards performing Ormus collection when aware of locations to buy supplies.

(Note: These supply sources are suggestions and searching the Internet will locate many others.)  Telephone numbers and web sites listed are accurate at the time of publication, but they are subject to frequent change.

**Ormus Information and Internet Forums**
Subtle Energies
*www.subtleenergies.com*
Contact Barry Carter at *bcarter@igc.org*

**Agricultural**
Sea-Crop
*www.sea-crop.com*
pH: 360-942-5698

**Alchemy Website**
The Alchemy Website
*www.alchemywebsite.com*

**Aloe Vera**
E-book
*www.aloe-vera-advice.com*

**Colloidal Gold Information**
Metospheric Plasma Products
*www.metosphericplasmaproducts.com*
*www.colloidalgoldmachines-central.com*

## Colloidal Silver Information
### Internet Source
*www.silvermedicine.org*

### Book Source
*"The Micro Silver Bullet"* by Farber

## Essential Oils
Star Babies
*www.giftsfromthestars.com*
Ph: 702-293-4283

Young Living Essential Oils
*www.youngliving.us*
Ph: 1-800-371-2928

White Lotus Aromatics
*www.whitelotusaromatics.com*
Fax: 360-457-9235

## Essiac Tea
First Opinion-Health Discovery Center
*www.magnetitewater.com*
Ph: 801-226-7589

## Food Grade Lye
Boyer Corporation
(Lye in a 2 lb can)
*www.boyercorporation.com*
Ph: 708-352-2553

Snowdrift Farm
*www.snowdriftfarm.com*
Ph: 520-882-7080

The Chemistry Store
*www.chemistrystore.com*
Ph: 1-800-224-1430

## Food Grade Lye, continued

Essential Depot
*www.essentialdepot.com*
Ph: 1-866-840-2495


## Milk Glass Bottles

Stanpac Company
(1/2 gallon size sample milk bottle pack with 6 bottles and 12 caps)
*www.stanpacnet.com*
Ph: 905-957-3326 ext. 222


## Have a Source or Precipitate Analyzed

ACME Analytical Labs
*www.acmelab.com*
Ph: 604-253-3158
Ph: 1-800-990-2263

Midwest Laboratories
*www.midwestlabs.com*
Ph: 402-334-7770


## HDPE (high-density polyethylene) Plastic Bottles

Specialty Bottle
*www.specialtybottle.com*
Ph: 206-382-1100

E-Bottles
*www.ebottles.com*
Ph: 1-888-215-0023

Medi-Dose Group
*www.medidose.com*
Ph: 1-800-523-8966


## 35% Hydrogen Peroxide (HP)

Lighthouse
*www.Lighth2o2use.com*
Ph: 1-800-683-0867

**Labware (Supplies and Borosilicate glass)**
Macnan Biologicals
*www.onlinesciencemall.com*
Ph: 205-853-2711

Cynmar Laboratories
*www.cynmar.com*
Ph: 1-800-223-3517

American Supplies Surplus
*www.sciplus.com*
Ph: 1-888-724-7587

Another suggestion is to search E-Bay at *www.e-bay.com*

**Laminar Crystals**
Star Babies
*www.giftsfromthestars.com*
Ph: 702-293-4283

**Mayan Galactic Signature (Decode a birth date)**
13 Moon
*www.13moon.com*
Ph: 1-800-596-0835

**Magnetite Effect Ormus Water**
(MEOW) Information
*www.ormuslike.info/index.html*

Also web search: "MEOW Kettle"

**Magnetite Source**
Octahedral Sales
E-Mail: *aufrom0@hotmail.com*
Ph: 505-452-7144

**Magnetite Source, continued**

First Opinion-Health Discovery Center
*www.magnetitewater.com*
Ph: 801-226-7589

## Mineral Source

Azomite Mineral Powder (volcanic ash source)
*www.azomite.com*
Ph: 877-296-6483

Pureganic Mineral Powder (volcanic ash source)
*www.Pureganic.com*
Ph: 877-587-6189

Humic Shale (plant source minerals)
*www.richearth.net*
Ph: 757-625-3886

## Moon Chart

Celestial Products, Inc.
Moon Dazzle Moon Chart and Moon Dance Moon Calendar
*www.mooncalendar.com*
Ph: 1-800-235-3783

## Music to Collect Ormus

Healing Sounds
*www.healingsounds.com*
Ph: 1-800-246-9764

## Ocean Plasma Information

Ocean Health
*www.oceanplasma.org*
*www.truthquest2.com*

## Ormus Lapel Pin
Ormus Book
*www.ormusbook.com*
Ph: 305-942-9555

## pH Indicator Sticks
GFS Chemicals
(pH range 7-14 Stock# 88952 Item# 2660)
*www.gfschemicals.com*
Ph: 1-800-858-9682

## pH Meter
Omega Engineering
(#PHH-5012 (pH meter kit that includes Buffer Solution)
*www.omega.com*
Ph: 1-800-622-2378 or Ph: 203-359-1660

Hanna Instruments
(Model H18Hanna membrane meter H18314 or Checker pH meter by Hanna)
*www.annainst.com*
Ph: 1-800-426-6287

## Precious Metal Source
CC Silver and Gold Inc.
(A source for gold, silver and platinum wire, bars, etc.)
*www.ccsilver.com*
Ph: 602-242-6310

Camino Coins, LLC
*www.caminocompany.com*
Ph: 650-348-3000 or Ph: 1-800-348-8001

## Purchase Ormus
Ocean Alchemy
*www.oceanalchemy.com*
Ph: 727-546-9659

Search the Internet for others and one site that contains a listing is www.subtleenergies.com

## Pyramids

Pyradyne

*www.pyradyne.com*

Ph: (949)499-2603

## Safety Equipment

McMaster-Carr Supply Co.

(Equipment such as PVC apron, rubber gloves and safety goggles with face shield)

*www.mcmaster.com*

Ph: 562-692-5911

## Salt Crystal Lamp

Pacific Spirit

*www.pacificspiritcatalogs.com*

Ph: 1-800-634-9057

Search the Internet for Salt Crystal Lamp sources.

## Sea Salt

Salt Works

("Botek" is Dead Sea salt [coarse])

("Sel Gris De Guerande" is Celtic Sea salt [coarse])

("Sonoma" is Pacific Ocean salt [coarse])

*www.saltworks.us*

Ph: 1-800-353-7258

## Sea Salt with Sea Solids

Seaagri Inc.

www.seaagri.com

Ph: 770-361-7003

## Seawater

Catalina Water Company, LLC

(5 Gallon pack)

*www.catalinawater.com*

Ph: 562-901-1400

**Stainless Steel Pots (18/10 stainless)**
World Kitchen
(This company owns Revere stainless steel pots. Revere "copper advantage" is currently without welding.)
www.shopworldkitchen.com
Ph: 1-800-999-3436

**Vortex Water Trap**
*www.cherokeegold.net*

A blueprint for a vortex water trap is at *bcarter@igc.org* and you can also contact Barry to find out who may be currently building and selling "vortex" or "magnet vortex" water traps.

**Water and Sea Salt Information**
Water Cure
E-Mail: *rbutts@watercure2.org*
*www.watercure2.org*

**White Sage**
Incense Warehouse
*www.incensewarehouse.com*
Ph: 1-888-288-2977

# APPENDIX II
## Ormus Pins

### Definition

The Ormus community constructed this pin to define and symbolize Ormus. The Ormus pin therefore represents the "global Ormus community." This community embraces, supports and is available to share the knowledge of Ormus.

The Ormus pin has been created in response to any who may attempt to patent Ormus for themselves and thereby make this substance less available to the world at large.

## APPENDIX III
### Barry Carter

### Definition
Barry Carter's mission is to be a conduit that allows the material called "Ormus" to be known to the people of the world. (NASA and governments are already aware of Ormus.) Barry is considered by many as the organizing figure of the modern day Ormus community. His website has an amazing amount of Ormus facts, research and up to date theory.
*www.subtleenergies.com*

### Information
Some say a picture is "worth a thousand words." This picture of Barry is included so you can "meet" him. Barry is available for lectures and explains that Ormus is a substance that is freely available in nature and can be extracted and used to improve the human condition. He has been researching the Ormus materials since 1989 and has started dozens of local and international discussion forums on this subject.

Barry is the central go-to person and is available for questions through his Internet Ormus outreach, e-mail and phone. He is familiar with and has most of the Ormus data. Contact Barry Carter (*bcarter@igc.org*) to join an Ormus forum or to schedule a lecture or workshop on Ormus.

### Final Thought
If it were not for Barry's work, the information in this book would not be possible and we would not be spending time together.

(Join a local Ormus group.)

# APPENDIX IV
## *Local Ormus Groups*

Many areas of the world have "local" Ormus forums.

One of the personal advantages to having a vibrant local Ormus community is establishing a rapport with other Ormus seekers and enthusiasts in your area. By definition, a rapport is talking to, seeing or communicating a minimum of twice a year.

After rapport is established, a next natural evolution is to have an occasional meeting. Ormus processes can be demonstrated first hand or performed as a group and Ormus supplies that have been purchased in bulk can be divided. Many personal transformational advancements occur during an Ormus community "get together" and your personal Ormus knowledge curve is raised through communicating with others in the Ormus community. There is also a spiritual growth from sharing knowledge with others who may be starting their own Ormus discovery path.

To begin this journey, contact Barry Carter.

# APPENDIX V
## *Mysterious History of Ormus*

*Courtesy Barry Carter*

When we look back at the histories and legends of ancient times we find many mysteries and puzzles still waiting to be solved. Many of these ancient puzzles involved a mysterious material, which had magical properties. The ancient alchemists of China, Israel, India, Egypt and Persia spoke of such substances. They called them Soma, the Elixir of Life, Chi, Manna, Prana, the Philosopher's Stone, Shewbread, White Powder of Gold, King Solomon's Gold and Gold of the Gods.

These substances have been associated with other ancient mysteries like the Fountain of Youth, the Ark of the Covenant and the Great Pyramid. They were also often associated with miraculous healing properties and mystical abilities.

Ancient Jewish commentaries describe how the Ark of the Covenant would levitate when it was brought out on holy days. According to the Zohar, the ancient Jewish priests would tie a rope around the ankle of any priest who was going into the presence of the Ark of the Covenant so they could safely pull him away from the Ark if it zapped him. The Ark of the Covenant was used to store (and perhaps charge) the pot of manna saved by Moses. It was also used to store the Ten Commandments and other sacred items.

Wei Po-yang the father of Chinese alchemy.

Moses took the golden calf the Israelites made for worship "and burnt it in the fire, and ground it to powder, and strewed it upon the water, and made the children of Israel drink of it," presumably in order to improve their spiritual connection.

The ancient Chinese alchemist Wei Po-yang wrote of the "Pill of Immortality" which is made of Huan Tan (Returned Medicine) an edible powder from gold. After one ingests Huan Tan "the complexion becomes rejuvenated, hoary hair regains its blackness and new teeth grow where fallen ones used to be. If an old man, he will once more become a youth; if an old woman, she will regain her maidenhood."

The ancient Egyptians had the "shem-an-na" which the Book of the Dead refers to as, "What is it." The shem-an-na was called both bread and gold and given in a cone shaped loaf as an offering to the gods.

Below we see on the left the king, 'Son of Re Amenhotep, ruler of Weset,' offering a conical loaf on a cup to 'Sopdu, the great god of the east.' This is also called the "gold of reward."

These ancient puzzles and mysteries have intrigued scholars of history for thousands of years. In the middle ages an alchemist named Artephius claimed he had solved some of these ancient puzzles. He finally got around to writing a book about his experience with the materials he obtained, after working with them *for the space of a thousand years, or thereabouts, which has now passed over my head, since the time I was born to this day, through the alone goodness of God Almighty, by the use of this wonderful quintessence."*

Modern science has generally dismissed the stories of these amazing substances as being fantasies and fictions of ancient superstitions and religions. Perhaps scientists have been too hasty in dismissing these ancient and mysterious substances. Let's look at some of the properties that have been claimed for these things.

The manna of the Bible (which appears to be similar to the shem-an-na of ancient Egypt) is described as like "coriander seed, and the colour thereof as the colour of bdellium." The Israelites "ground it in mills, or beat it in a mortar, and baked it in pans, and made cakes of it, and the taste of it was as the taste of fresh oil." It arrived in the morning with the dew.

Chi and prana are described as energetic substances that can be accumulated in the body through certain breathing techniques. The Philosopher's Stone is said to be an evolved form of the precious metals gold and silver. Soma and the Fountain of Youth would be liquids which confer youth and vitality when one drinks them. Here is a list of some properties we might look for when searching for a scientific basis for these ancient puzzles:

• They are a form of gold, silver or other precious metal elements.
• They have an oil form.
• They can be dried to a white flour-like substance.
• They exist as a gas or vapor which can be extracted from the air.
• They can be energized or accumulated in structures like the Ark of the Covenant or the Great Pyramid.
• They should levitate under certain circumstances.
• They have remarkable healing and spiritual properties.
• They would have to be difficult to identify using modern scientific tools because they have not been identified this way before.

Numerous scientists and researchers around the world are finding and working with materials with the properties described above. We are calling these materials the ORMUS or M-state elements.

# APPENDIX VI
## General Ormus Information

### Definition

"Ormus, orme and M-state all are generic terms which apply to any element, normally metallic found in a spectroscopically "invisible" non-metallic form. These terms apply regardless of which method was used to obtain them or the relative effectiveness of the element."

*also*

"The term Ormus has been used for many centuries. Currently, we use the word to identify transition elements in micro cluster or monatomic size. Most prominent of these are gold, silver, copper and the platinum group."

*also*

A group of essential minerals that were previously unknown to science.

### Information

There is much yet to learn about Ormus and the information presented contains the best postulations available at this time. The study of the "Ormus" material is in its infancy and as science evolves, these paradigms may change.

It is exciting to think that if only a small percentage, maybe 10%, of what has been postulated or observed about Ormus proves out, this material may well be one of the greatest discoveries in human history!

A starting point regarding "General Ormus Information" begins in the "Introduction: Part 2" (page 8) and "Getting Started" (Section Two).

The Ormus material is a naturally found substance on the earth and is in us, water and other living substances including the foods we eat. (Transcripts: David Hudson lectures)

Ormus has also been found in the air we breathe and a belief is that, in the modern days, these sources may not be as enriched with these materials as in earlier times and we may benefit by Ormus supplementation. The goal of Ormus researchers and empowered Ormus collectors is to use an extraction process to concentrate and collect Ormus from its hiding places in nature.

We are finding that Ormus is very common in plants, animals, air, soil and water. Ormus is found everywhere. It is under our feet in the soil, in the water that has been used to wash our clothes, in the air and in clays. Some say there is a lot of Ormus found where the first water meets with land (in the sand) and it is abundant in the sea. It is also trapped in silica minerals, and to varying degrees in limestone minerals and mica. Some lava has Ormus - it has been said that sulfate-containing lava would contain Ormus but lava-containing sulfites would not. (At 420 degrees C, gold Ormus is thought to boil off—and for a volcano that is not very high heat: consequently, some volcanic deposits will have boiled off most of the gold Ormus into the atmosphere.) Ormus is in organic material (plant and animal) and therefore it is in everything that is alive or has been alive. Ormus has been found in materials that fall to the earth termed "cosmic dust" or "star dust." (20 Billion tons of cosmic dust falls on the Earth annually with the bulk of it emanating from our own Sun. The gravitational pull of our Sun also brings tons of cosmic dust into our Solar System from other stars.) To sum up, Ormus has been collected from rock, food, water and air with one estimate being that the Ormus elements may make up to as much as 10% of the earths mass. Ormus can be found everywhere.

Ormus elements are thought to hide out in "tight spaces." Because the Ormus material has a "Meissner effect" there is speculation that they retreat from magnetic fields. This may cause these elements to "hide out" inside molecules of other elements, which might provide some shielding from these fields. Therefore, one theory holds that we may find Ormus inside the icosahedral shaped water molecule, which provides some protection from magnetic fields, or inside a salt molecule, which further increases the shielding ability from magnetic fields. Ormus can hide in air and rock source materials also. The Ormus material then becomes "camouflaged," so to speak, and therefore, not assayable by common spectrographic techniques. This may explain why David Hudson said the material assayed only as iron, silica or aluminum until the removal of all traces of these materials, whereupon the material assayed as pure nothing. It may be that iron, silica and aluminum are three such materials where Ormus can "hide out," (be camouflaged) and act as "stealth atoms" (hidden). During David Hudson's search for answers, he learned of a Russian emission spectroscopy procedure called "fractional vaporization." This procedure burns the source material for 300 seconds (5 minutes), which is a tremendously long burn time at high heat. (Common spectrographic techniques burn the source material for 15 seconds.) As the material vaporized, it emitted a light spectrum that was analyzed using light spectra analysis. Because the burn time was 5 minutes, the Ormus state of the element was analyzable.

In addition to the water molecule, the salt molecule, air, rock and organic source materials, some have said that Ormus also utilizes sugar to form a "shielding" crystalline structure that protects it from the "magnetic field" of the earth. Ormus is thought to like "tight" places that are away from magnetic fields and the crystalline structure of both salt and sugar provide such a place. In his lectures, David Hudson said that Ormus has a higher affinity for sugar than for salt. Therefore, a theory is that the body competes with sugar for Ormus. Note: There is no consensus regarding the use of a "sweet" versus a "non-sweet" as Ormus source material. (I have used coconut water as source material and it produced a precipitate when performing the "Wet Process.")

There are five elements associated with the physical earth: "Earth," "Air," "Fire," "Water" and "Spirit" and it is these five represented in the five sided pentagram shape. The first four elements are self-evident and the last, "spirit" represents the consciousness that having "life" experiences. However, there appears to be something more: a sixth element - and this element may be considered "of the earth" as well as more universally an element "of the heaven." It is "quintessence" and it is thought to equal Ormus. Quintessence has also been termed "Yuan" or "Origin" and it is the "first cause" or "point of beginning." Quintessence is like "The Source" and is found everywhere in heaven and earth and in every time: from the beginning to the end. The "Single" Yuan or Origin is the "Great" beginning. To recap: Quintessence is considered the "life force" itself and is in a completely separate category from the other five elements associated with our physical earth.

Ormus has been said to facilitate positive mental effects as this material appears to assist communication between cells in the body and between the body and the spirit. This defines the terms "biological" and "quantum" coherence. Other reported effects of Ormus include: stimulation of the body's toxin elimination process, enhanced energy flow within the body, clarity of thought, increased intuition and feelings of contentment.

Ormus supplementation also appears to cause feelings of peace and contentment in many. Many have said that everything is alive including minerals. They explain that the role of Ormus is to synchronize the life in minerals with the life in plants and animals. Once this happens, an awareness results, at some level, of the "life force" that is everywhere - including in us. Therefore, little can occur which causes a "distress." There can be no distress when realizing the "connectedness" and feeling the "total unity of oneness" with the "all" (all living things, all animals, all humans, all life). A change occurs in "how we be" in daily life circumstances as our selves and our purposes are seen fully as part of the universe and from this perspective we might come to understand the meaning of human existence.

Ormus appears to benefit life and is thought to cause vibrancy in the physical body. Some have said the body has experienced increased stamina and/or achieved "good health" while the mind has strengthened (advanced), causing a sense of thinking with greater clarity. Because "thoughts" in the mind are not the same, different realizations can enter the minds awareness and these thought can allow for a new way of "looking at things."

It seems the ancients may have known about this form of food and this knowledge was lost. (*Lost Secrets of the Sacred Ark* by Laurence Gardner) The bible also speaks of the Ormus material (detailed in Laurence Gardner's book). Because the knowledge of Ormus was lost, we haven't been heartily feeding the light body, we haven't known what to feed it and we have been without access to collecting this natural form of nourishment for centuries. (We still need to take care of our physical body - our low energy physical body of molecules. We need to be sure to supplement with proper diet and minerals.)

One theory holds that Ormus in the form of a "wet" precipitate or one that is dissolvable on the tongue is more bioavailable to the body than a "dry" form of Ormus. (Note that if a "dry" form of Ormus dissolves in the mouth it has become "wet.") Some have said do not bother taking a dry Ormus product unless the product dissolves in the saliva. There is not a clear consensus regarding "wet" versus "dry" Ormus products and alchemists make both forms. Ormus collectors have reported that dried Ormus worked well and a researcher has annealed (heated) the precipitate from the "Wet Process" and reported it was exceptional. There is much yet to learn about Ormus and its collection. This is a reminder that we are on the learning curve right now.

When taking Ormus supplementation, "shifts in consciousness" have been reported and a different "speed of consciousness" may be experienced. Because of this different speed of consciousness, the perception of time passing may be "marked" differently. (Note that when your perception is aligned with higher consciousness, time is actually elastic and not marked by a clock.) In addition, some say these shifts in consciousness may have a physical manifestation and if this occurs, the manifestation is temporary and sometimes just instantaneous. For example, if living in a "stiff-necked" manner - a "crick in the neck" may develop or it could be the eyes will see more clearly and everything in the field of vision looks sharper and more defined.

When working with Ormus (manna), thoughts, insights, and realizations may be experienced and so it seems to teach. The ancients called it "Teacher of Righteousness" (it teaches you) and the Ormus collected during an Ormus collection process is considered such a teacher.

Each person comes to his/her own understanding, realization(s) and/or conclusions about "life" and I believe Ormus in some manner helps with the unfolding of this process. Whatever we believe (about life) ties to our sense of reality and therefore our reality is actually a self-"created" one. This created and personal "reality" relates to that which we "pay attention to" in life and consequently it is what forms the basis of life experiences. There is truth in the old sayings: "As you believe so shall it believe," "we are what we can digest mentally as well as physically" and "when the student is ready the teacher will appear."

Some have suggested that questions are asked of "self" before going to sleep. Write dreams and answers to questions on a pad next to the bed upon awakening. Reality is what you pay attention to and so when attention is focused on such areas as the "energy of the body" and the esoterically known "field of universal energy" (the implicate order), results that may benefit life can be observed as reality. These may include a heightened insightfulness as well as a type of "sparkle" being brought into the physical life walk.

Attention is often given to potential health benefits that are thought to be associated with Ormus and health improvements have occurred when taking it. The real purpose, however, of using Ormus has been said by David Hudson and others is to raise the level of "consciousness" (towards enlightenment) and not physical healing. Enlightenment causes feelings of being connected to a higher state of awareness and is a state of consciousness that intuits or feels insights or wisdoms that cause life to be more workable. For more information, see "Use, Directions, Bioavailability and Precautions-Humans." (Appendix XXI.)

Ormus is surmised to differentiate into whatever is needed in the body. In this way, some researchers have likened it to "stem cell" research. (This research involves fetal cells that differentiate into whatever type of cell needed.)

When taking Ormus supplementation for the first time, many have commented how sleepiness is experienced (this has happened to me) and dizziness, spacing out, headaches or energy spurts may be felt. If one becomes very sleepy, some have said that DNA shifts may be occurring that cause sensory stimulation in the body. Combining this with potential sensory stimulation caused by "shifts in the level of consciousness" that may be occurring can deepen the feeling of sleepiness. Since the body heals best when at rest, feeling tired may be the body's way of taking a "time out" to heal itself and it is possible that the degree of weariness experienced correlates to the degree of health initially found in the body.

Some have said that with time you may not feel any effects of the Ormus. This does not mean it's not working for you; rather, that you have tuned to it. Some say that Ormus may respond differently from one person to another because we are all diverse and our bodies each operate on *different* frequencies. This variation in frequency is thought to be the basis of what makes us each unique and postulated to be the reason some respond differently to one Ormus source material versus another.

Many feel that Ormus works to perfect the body, mind and spirit and that it is how our cells communicate with each other, interact with DNA and the way the "energy body" is "fed" (energized). This feeding of the light body seems to enable it to grow and become what it is meant to become. (I have experienced Ormus as a link between physicality and consciousness because I perceive that it nourishes the essence of what is "me." I call this my soul, although not in a strictly religious sense, and Ormus seems to act as a type of "soul food" that enables me to pull together and maintain a wider outreach in my life.)

Some note that Ormus seems to cause a person's behavior to be more along the way of how they are "naturally." For example, if there is a tendency to be a worrywart, the condition may become intensified. Now, a time may come when personal traits bothersome to life step forward into conscious awareness. If this occurs, it is time to do some serious thinking and figure out the "why" and "how" to overcome that trait and in this manner Ormus may be considered as bringing us to our personal "revealing" place. This may explain why some say that more "stop" Ormus supplementation than those who stay with it for years. When we understand how "evolving" in a life doesn't automatically equate to occurrences that happen according to our personal beliefs or wishes, we can grasp how any occurrence can lead to progress. Therefore, it has been observed by some that no matter what the "reasons" anyone has for beginning Ormus supplementation, what comes from it is never predictable.

(Personally, I have experienced Ormus supplementation to act subtly as a sort of "clarifier" in my life. I understand events occurring in my personal sphere of life more clearly so I rarely become upset. This somehow allows me to distinctly feel what I should be doing about matters in my personal sphere and, in addition, enhances my feeling of being incredibly grounded. For more information, see "Introduction: Part 1.")

Is Ormus alive? Many have said that everything is alive and that Ormus resonates with the electro-magnetic zero point within us. This point is within all life and is what life is. It's what makes up life. It's what makes up matter. It's the energy where it all began - where all matter that we know in this universe came from and is the underlying vibration that contains immense amounts of energy. It is everywhere in the universe, timeless, "all," every nucleus runs on it, every electron runs on it. It's where particles are born out of the vacuum energy every day. It's the creative force and where "it all" came from. Therefore, everything is alive. Additionally, others have said that Ormus is alive because an energy field surrounds it. Many also feel that when an image is formed of the reality desired, Ormus can both understand it and take instruction from it.

A belief is that when collecting Ormus a lot of energy is attracted and by adding "Love and intent" the work area becomes a powerful spot. This spot may draw energies to it such that when a bowl of Ormus (manna) is left out, the manna "disappears." This is explained as "the angels are eating our manna" and a suggestion made to leave some finished Ormus (manna) out when collecting Ormus to "feed the angels." (*Don Nance*)

Many of the Ormus collected are "transition" metal group elements in a different state. These elements are listed on the "periodic table of elements." (Ormus has also been said to originate from the "rare earth" minerals.) Transition group elements have more of a neutral nature (in relation to their positive or negative electro-charge) and they are also less reactive to chemical reactions. Because of these unique properties, it is felt by some that transition group elements are able to remain stable in a single atom state (monoatomic). Some say they may also be diatomic (two atoms per molecule). When an element is in this stable different state, it is felt by many that it has formed Ormus. This stable state is found to exist naturally: even at room temperature and when in this state they are considered non-metallic and postulated to interact in two dimensions. (Note: Two or more atom size clusters from the transition group elements make a metal-metal bond that exists in three dimensions. When the clusters reach 33 atoms they become a fully metallic state, having electrical conductivity and the appearance of true metallic properties.)

In the two-dimensional state the single atoms arrange themselves separated and in a long chain. For example, iridium atoms arrange 6.3 angstroms apart and the conclusion drawn is that a "Coulomb Wave" has been produced by single atoms causing atoms to be attracted to each other, but only to the point that repulsion occurs from the Coulomb wave of the first atom. The second atom then nestles itself in the wave of the first (instead of attaching to it) and perpetuates the Coulomb wave with its own wave. Atom by atom separated by distinct spacing, the wave is perpetuated and results in a resonance coupled system of quantum oscillators resonating in two dimensions. The atoms have arranged with perfect spacing, having the appearance of a long chain and are in two dimensions not three dimensions. Now in a metal, the atoms bind much closer to each other by sharing electrons and combine into clusters that are three dimensional having length, width and depth. (*from David Hudson transcripts*)

The "transition group elements" contain two categories called the "precious" elements and the "non-precious" elements. While there are 38 elements in the transition group, only a few are (currently) being investigated in relation to their Ormus state. "Precious elements" have two sub groups called the "light platinum" group and the "heavy platinum" group. The "light" platinum group contains ruthenium, rhodium, palladium and silver. The "heavy" platinum group contains osmium, iridium, platinum and gold. The "non-precious" elements include copper, cobalt and nickel. Some have also said that the rare earth elements are a good source of Ormus.

The focus when collecting Ormus material revolves around the light and the heavy platinum group elements as well as the copper element. To the Ormus collector the most sought after elements are gold, silver, copper and the platinum group. Because David Hudson cited iridium and rhodium (in this different state) as being relatively abundant in the human being, and therefore important to humans, source materials containing these two elements are valued.

Cobalt and Nickel (from the non-precious category) form the natural, stable state of Ormus, but we do not hear much about them. This may be because David Hudson found they made the Ormus state after he filed his patents and therefore did not extensively study them.

Ancient alchemists felt there was an association between planetary planets (visible planets) and corresponding metals. (They considered the Sun and the Moon planets.) Their belief included the feeling that a single spirit (force, energy) was contained in both the planetary planet and the metal on earth. It is interesting that the terrestrial metals associated with the planetary planets all have an Ormus form. For the sun (Sol in Latin) it is gold, the moon (Luna) it is silver, for mercury (Mercuriu) it is mercury (called Quicksilver), venus (called Venus in Latin) it is copper, mars (called Mars in Latin) it is iron (the pure form, not the mixtures we are accustomed to seeing), jupiter (Iuppiter) it is elemental tin (stannum) and for saturn (Saturnus) it is lead.

While one theory states that transition elements that have entered into a "different state", have become "Ormus", it does seem very clear that Ormus is a "non-metallic" (or "non-mineral" in the case of rare earths) form of the (metallic) elements. The theory holds that material collected when performing an Ormus collection process (usually in the form of a precipitate) contains the Ormus and this is the name most often referred to when describing the materials collected. However other interchangeable terms have been used to describe Ormus collected in the form of a precipitate and these include: "Ormus," "manna," "doves" or "the drop,"

An alchemist of our modern days who goes by the name, "Essene" has called all these materials "M-state," thus designating them as the "meta-physical form" or "manna-form" of the elements. Therefore, an abbreviation for the Ormus form of the elements, in nature and in the collected Ormus is to place the letter "M-" in front of the name of the element. For example: The rhodium element in the Ormus form in nature may be termed M-rhodium. When Ormus is collected from a "single" element, the product has the designation "M-1" in front of the name of the source. A single source Ormus product collected from rhodium is termed "M-1 rhodium and a single source Ormus product collected from copper is termed "M-1 copper." In the case of gold, the single source product is termed "M-1 gold" and, because gold Ormus is held dear, is abbreviated "M-1." M-1 (Ormus made from gold) has been said by some to be good for heart ailments, glands and chakras. Some feel that, as an analogy, M-gold is the one that opens the doors to the "pathways" and "shines the light" so M-rhodium and M-iridium "know" where to go.

"M-3" is a mixture of M-gold, M-iridium and M-rhodium. It is made from a specific rock mineral source and contains approximately 70% M-rhodium, 15% M-iridium and 15% M-gold. M-3 has been said by some to give clarity in thinking. Some have said that M-3 is best taken in a "wet" form because this form is absorbed in the stomach and intestines while the "dry" form is absorbed only in the fat layer of the small intestines. A "wet" form is a liquid "suspension" and is the most common form of Ormus collected. (The liquid suspension is a mixture consisting of small liquid droplets dispersed in a liquid and if allowed to stand the particles separate out.)

"White Dove" Ormus is collected from the same mineral source (Essene's Black Sand) with some gold metal added to it. Therefore it contains the same ingredients as M-3, but in differing ratios. "White Dove" contains more M-gold and slightly less M-rhodium and M-iridium.

Ormus made from copper is called "M-1 copper." Many consider copper Ormus rejuvenating and displaying anti-aging properties. Some have said it may be helpful for Lupus. There are those who have said that grey hairs restored to color and that copper Ormus may rejuvenate the telomeres of the DNA strand leading to rejuvenation of the body. The telomeres are at the ends of the chromosomes and protect our genetic data. (Telomeres make it possible for cells to divide and protect chromosomes from fraying and sticking to each other. If fraying and sticking occurs, a theory holds that genetic information "scrambles." Each time a cell divides the telomeres become shorter and, when they become too short, the cell can no longer divide.) Therefore, short telomeres are thought to be associated with aging of the body and a higher risk of death.

"Doves of Luna" or "Diane" is the name for Ormus made from silver. Some have said that silver Ormus acts like colloidal silver against pathogens just more powerfully. **For cautions regarding silver**, see "Sources for the Ormus Processes-Metal." (Appendix VIII.)

Iridium is the heaviest (and one of the least abundant) element on the planet. In the Ormus state it has been said to be the lightest.

Not much is known about ruthenium, palladium, osmium and platinum therefore, we don't hear much about them.

Some believe we don't need much cobalt and nickel Ormus and that they may accumulate (like their elemental counterparts) in the body. This is possibly why we don't hear much about them.

Mercury goes into the Ormus form. However, Ormus made from mercury is a "No-No;" we have nothing to do with mercury. In the Ormus form it is called the "Semen of Shiva" and is not poisonous, but mercury in the elemental form (metallic) is toxic. Ancient Ayurvedic medicine in India has recipes that include mercury in a non-toxic state. However, many of the medicine men have died of mercury poisoning so they all apparently don't know how to do this today.

"C-11" is Ormus collected from seawater. C-11 is said to contain 10 M-state elements plus magnesium. Since it comes from the sea, the letter C is included in its designation. Because there are 11 main ingredients in the Ormus (manna), the number 11 comes after the C. Now, different locations in the ocean have differing balances of the M-state elements. For more information, see "Sources for the Processes." (Appendix VIII.)

(In my own experience, I do not feel Ormus collected from a "single" element is usually necessary for the average collector. This would be substances like M-1 made from gold and M-1 copper. A better choice may be Ormus collected from source materials that contain a mixture of Ormus thus giving a naturally balanced mix in the collected Ormus (manna) similar in concept to taking a multiple vitamin supplement. Common Ormus source materials include dissolved natural sea salt or "drawn" seawater, fresh drinking water and good oil. The "best" oil has been said by some to be grape seed oil.)

No matter what type of Ormus (M-state) one is working with during an Ormus collection process, some feel that the finer lighter Ormus material escapes and floats away. This is thought to occur more so when using an Ormus collection process that includes the addition of external heat, especially when the heat is used to cause a boil.

When collecting Ormus (manna) you may observe "sparkling flashes of light" in the solution. I have observed "sparkly flashes" in the "drawn" seawater while performing a "Wet Process." Some believe the "sparkles" are Ormus that appears shiny until they change form and become more of a solid. Explanations suggest that Ormus picks up hydrogen (from the sodium hydroxide or the hydrochloric acid) on its way to becoming more of a solid. (One theory holds that on-going transition from light to physicality are thought to occur in the universe beginning with the fissionable actions on the surface of the sun. The result is the "throwing out of light" (sunlight) that becomes hydrogen ions on its way to the earth. In this manner light is transforming into physical particles. Stated another way with important implications is that light is changing from spirit into matter.)

David Hudson is acknowledged as the person who discovered (or re-discovered) the substance generally called Ormus. He spoke about these materials in lectures presented during the 1990s. The content of many of these lectures can be found on the Internet. One such site is *www.subtleenergies.com* and the next set of Ormus information is from transcripts of his lectures.

Iridium and rhodium (in this different sate) are both relatively abundant in the human being and are important to humans. (Note: This is the reason that within the Ormus community, source materials containing these two elements are valued for Ormus collection processes.)

Gold (in this different state) is associated with the pineal gland. Both iridium and gold were said to speed body metabolism about 40% - and they do not seem to go into the bloodstream or through the kidneys. They seem to be taken into the acupuncture system of the body and be associated with the spinal cord and the thymus and this relates to the consciousness and the metabolic rate of the body.

Iridium (in this different state), by speeding up the metabolism, causes the cells to divide faster and in doing so they can repair faster. (Transcripts state that "rhodium" (in this different state) may kill cancer and that any cancer should be gone before taking "iridium" [in this different state] or the cancer cells may also divide faster.)

(Note: Rhodium and iridium in the metallic periodic table form, not the Ormus form, are also used for healing by traditional medicine. Platinum is used for testicular and ovarian cancer and gold has long been used for healing by the medical community.)

Copper (in this different state) has been said to help the thyroid gland, is needed by the Pineal gland and a lack of it can lead to Parkinson's disease.

(Author note: Others have said that copper may bring on Parkinsonism if it runs in the family or if a person has a tendency to Parkinsonism and that velvet bean extract may help with Parkinsonism. For more information visit *www.rain-tree.com*.)

Some say that rhodium and iridium (in this different state) do not react well with nitric oxide - and that we create nitrous oxide as we breathe. This postulate was set forth to explain how we have been losing these elements (in this different state) associated with the human being from our first breath. Now that we understand that this may be true we are learning proactive ways to get the material back into our system. Gold (in this different state) is theorized to be unaffected by nitric oxide as much, so the gold effects in the body are felt to be more permanent.

There are four substances that David Hudson said can change the state of the Ormus material to one not effective in the body-even bringing a portion back to the metal element (this conversion is a slow process). It may be said in analogy they "kill the light" (a mechanism of action attributed to Ormus is postulated to be that of a "super light.") These four substances are sulfites ($SO_3$), carbon or carbon monoxide, nitric oxide and short wavelength radiation. (A suggestion made was to wait until after radiation treatments for cancer were finished to begin taking Ormus.) This ends the references to David Hudson lectures.

(Note: Short wavelength radiation may include cell phones and microwave ovens. You may wish to ponder this while deciding how close in proximity to be with these items.)


## Storage

Store (Ormus) manna precipitate in HDPE plastic. This plastic ware has a triangle with the number 2 on the bottom. Plastic of this type is the most chemically inert and also chosen because some have said that Ormus can tunnel into glass (to get away from cold, scalar fields, EMF fields or light) - which may cause the glass to break. It is generally thought that time, light and sun cause the finer (lighter) particles of Ormus to be lost.

Wrap the container of Ormus (manna) in aluminum foil.

Ormus doesn't travel particularly well and it has some specific storage requirements. "Big" business creates product that is stored (often not at room temperature), transported, stored again and trundled from the manufacturer through wholesalers to merchants as it makes its way to the consumer. This type of storage and travel is considered unfavorable for an Ormus product as Ormus does not seem to fair well around scalar fields, EMF waves, high heat or light. In addition, many of the Ormus processes collect Ormus that has a shelf life generally considered to be one year. Because of these characteristics of Ormus, the material does not lend itself to mass production and therefore it may be expected that big business will not own a market share in "Ormus."

Alchemists on the other hand, collect Ormus from small custom-made batches. These are fresh supplies properly packaged and sent speedily through the mail. "Proper" packaging begins with the cap of the properly chosen container having tape placed securely around it. (This retards leakage and avoids the possibility of a mess.) This container is wrapped in aluminum foil to retard scalar fields and provide some shielding from radio frequency waves then placed in a plastic protective layer (perhaps some crumpled plastic bags, followed by the inclusion of shock absorbing stuffing. All of this is housed in a sealed cardboard box and mailed out directly. The combination of aluminum, plastic and cardboard may also create an "Orgone accumulator" to energize the Ormus.

Ormus collectors can collect their own Ormus products. The packaging of the finished Ormus is, at minimum, in an aluminum foil wrapped and properly chosen container. (Each of the Ormus collection processes has recommendations for containers as well as any additional storage requirements.) The best storage location is said to be in the dark, housed in a steel container and six feet or more away from refrigerators, stoves, TVs etc. For more information, see "Labware Choices-Aluminum Foil." (Appendix XIV.)

It is important to learn of a belief that Ormus flows through us and back to the earth all the time. Nothing can stop Ormus from flowing through anything when it is in its "free" state, and Ormus can never be forced to "stay put." However, methods may be utilized that Ormus "likes" so it doesn't "wander off." This includes the aluminum foil wrap placed on the container of Ormus. The aluminum acts as some sort of shield that protects the state of the Ormus, encouraging" it to "stay put." Other methods include the suggestion to house the foil wrapped container in a steel container. For more information, see "Labware Choices-Aluminum." (Appendix XIV.)

## Final Thought

If used orally, it *may* be best to take Ormus in the morning on an empty stomach when the body's pH level is most balanced and then wait 15-20 minutes before eating. If this is the first time taking an Ormus supplement, consider taking while at home in the event you wish to lie down. For more information, see "Usage and Directions." (Appendix XXI.)

It is a belief that the Ormus collected from a "Magnet Vortex Water Trap" (or "Vortex Water Trap") and a "Wet Process" each has about the same vibrational resonance because heat was not added to the process. Adding heat creates a higher spin and some Ormus floats away. For more information, see "Labware Choices-Heat." (Appendix XIV.)

A suggestion is to learn to employ Ormus collection processes for the good of your own "Matrix of Consciousness." In doing this work-taking the effort to explore this trail-you are on your way to becoming an alchemist. The book "The Doctrine of Transcendental Magic" by Eliphas Levi (1855) says: "Hereinafter follow the powers and privileges of him who hold in his right hand the clavicles of Solomon" (the keys Solomon). The book goes on to define an alchemist as: "He beholds God's face without dying," "converses familiarly with the seven genie who are in command of the entire celestial army" (converses with angels and a suggestion is to ask Ormus to help do this before going to sleep), "He is above all grief's and fears," "He rules his own health and life and can influence equally those of others," "He can neither be surprised by misfortune nor overwhelmed by disasters ...," "He knows the reason of the past, present and future," "He possesses the secret of the resurrection of the dead and the Key of Immortality," "To possess the universal medicine ..." Once you learn these recipes and invite Ormus to be part of your life, I have little doubt you will experience simpatico with this definition.

Collecting vibrant Ormus products is believed to include a "spiritual" part in addition to the traditional chemical reaction part. The Ormus collector brings himself to the work as an active part of the process and this adds a spiritual level to the work. Alchemy believes "spirit" is *in* all things and an active part of the process. Actually the addition of this "spiritual" level in the work is the difference between "alchemy" and mainstream (modern) "chemistry."

Some believe that all Ormus prefer human warmth. Therefore it is felt that Ormus will come to the person(s) who are collecting it. In this respect a person collecting Ormus receives it (Ormus) two fold and this is an additional benefit of learning to collect your own. For this reason, some have said, "The Ormus you collect yourself is better than anything you can purchase."

Understand how the possible benefits attributed to Ormus cause it to be an "agent of change." Many consider this a fact. By definition, we humans design structure to resist change. (We also do this in our personal life.) Governments are all about this and only the most progressive of businesses work constantly to be receptive and accept and even embrace change.

Awareness of the Ormus material covers the globe and awareness is the first step in learning. After awareness an individual can choose to enter into what is termed a "learning" process. A "learning" process is a personal upward progression that has the specific "stages" of "examination," "reflection," "knowledge," "understanding," "wisdom" and "truth." Enjoy your journey!

NOTES:

# APPENDIX VII
## Basic Explanation of Each Process

## Information

Note: Few processes are absolute and rigid regarding the choice of Ormus source material and many processes can utilize the same Ormus source material. As the energetics (heat) in the processes increase, tightly aggregated sources (such as metals and minerals) disaggregate to a greater degree.

### "Live Oil Process"

This process infuses Ormus from sea salt or Ormus precipitate (manna) or "drawn" seawater (from the ocean) into oil. The infused oil is termed "Live Oil." Depending on the oil chosen, the "Live Oil" may be ingested, applied topically or both. (The "Live Oil Process" is most often performed on sea salt.)

### "Wet Process"

Because the Ormus source material is wet, this collection method is termed the "Wet Process."

The object of the "Wet Process" is to have a precipitate form and then fall out of "reconstituted" sea or "drawn" seawater (from the ocean) by adding lye solution until the pH rises to a maximum of 10.78. This is an actual target point maximum pH and it should not be exceeded. This precipitate includes the "Ormus." Other terms used include: "manna" or the "wet precipitate."

It may be said we are "harvesting" or "concentrating" the Ormus that is in the "reconstituted" sea or "drawn" seawater.

### "Dry Process" ("Cold Fire Process")

Because the Ormus source material is dry, this collection method is termed the "Dry Process."

The "Dry Process (Cold Fire Process)" as well as any of the other *dry* processes allows the extraction of Ormus from dry or dried-out material.

The heat for this process comes from the lye solution (the "secret fire"). The secret fire is explained in "Lye Solution Preparation-Final Thought."

Source material for this process includes organic (biological) material such as carrot pulp, material from the mineral kingdom (such as ancient sea beds or dry land minerals like black sand) and other non-metallic materials.

### Dry "Lye Boil Process"

This process mirrors the "Dry Process (Cold Fire Process)." The only difference is the addition of a "boil" with external heat applied to the one-gallon lye solution containing roughly one cup (dry) Ormus source material.

Because of the "boil" added to this process, it is a more energetically active one than the "Dry Process" and can physically disaggregate (disintegrate or disassociate) to a greater degree, the molecules of Ormus source used in the "Dry Process."

Source material for this process includes land-based minerals, sands and less dense metal such as finely shaved copper. (Note: This is not the most efficient process to make Ormus (manna) from gold.)

### Dry "Lye Burn Process"

This is a less dangerous version of the "*dry* Sodium Burn Process."

First place the *dry* Ormus source material in a crucible (container) filled with dry lye crystals and then "burn" with high heat. Place the burned "cake" that results into lye solution (the "secret fire") in the same manner described in the "Dry Process (Cold Fire Process)." To be specific, allow the lye solution to sit covered, for weeks, while being stirred regularly. The secret fire has been explained in "Lye Solution Preparation-Final Thought."

Because of the addition of a "burn" to this process, it is a more energetically active process than the *dry* "Lye Boil Process."

Source material for this process includes gold and copper filings as well as land based minerals like black sand. (Note: This is not the most efficient process to make Ormus (manna) from gold.)

### Dry "Lye Burn and Boil Process"

This process mirrors the dry "Lye Burn Process" as a "burn" is first performed on the Ormus source material and then it is placed in lye solution. The difference is the addition of external heat to the lye solution to cause a "boil." This boiling prepares the "living menstruum" (Ormus-containing lye solution) in four hours versus several weeks in the *dry* "Lye Burn Process." The additional heat from the boil further disaggregates (disintegrate or disassociate) the source material. ("Living Menstruum" has been explained in *dry* "Lye Boil Process-Information.")

Because of a "boil" added to this process, it is a more energetically active one than the *dry* "Lye Burn Process" and can physically disaggregate (disintegrate or disassociate) to a greater degree the molecules in Ormus source used in the *dry* "Lye Burn Process."

Source material for this process includes gold and copper filings as well as land based minerals etc... (Note: This is not the most efficient process to make Ormus (manna) from gold.)

### Dry "Sodium Burn Process"

(A very dangerous process.)

The metallic bonds of the gold source material are broken using very high heat. Pure sodium metal is used to reach this very high heat and causes a "burn." The disaggregated (disintegrated) molecules of the gold source material are then wetted with lye solution (a step in every one of the *dry*

Ormus collection processes). With time or external heat (added to perform a "boil") and less time, one theory holds that Ormus moves out of the burned source material and into the lye solution. A precipitate is dropped from the solution using hydrochloric acid (as explained in all the *dry* Ormus collection processes).

Because of a "burn" caused by sodium metal, this process is more energetically active than the *dry* "Lye Burn Process."

Source material for this process includes tightly bound ones such as pure metals and ores of metals such as gold ores, silver ores and copper ores. (Ores are not usually used.)

This is a faster and more energetic way of extracting Ormus from metals. This process is dangerous and beyond the scope of both the average Ormus collector and this manual.


### *Dry* "Hydrogen Peroxide (Gold) Process"

The most direct way to the white powder of gold is to perform the very dangerous "*dry* Sodium Burn Process" as previously described. However, this $HCl/H_2O_2$ Process is a much less violent way to disaggregate the bonds between the metallic clusters of gold.

This is a process to disaggregate gold bonds by using, among other chemicals, 35% hydrogen peroxide. The core reaction revolves around thin leaves of 99.9 pure gold disaggregated using salt, hydrochloric acid and then 35% hydrogen peroxide, precipitated with lye solution, and re-dissolved with hydrochloric acid solution. (The wide pH swings break the metallic bonds of the gold metal.) There are further steps in the process.

So long as you have a way to capture chlorine gas fumes created and observe the precautions while working with acids and caustics described in this book, it is a "relatively" safe process although probably beyond the scope of most average Ormus collectors.


### "Hot Rock Process"

The "Hot Rock Process" is performed and then a "Wet Process" is done. The "Hot Rock Process" uses iodine. Iodine does work chemically and disaggregates gold. This process is beyond the scope of most Ormus collectors and this manual.


### "Heap Leach Process"

This process uses lye and potassium cyanide solution to dissolve precious metals for later deposition on carbon or charcoal and then collection from the carbon or charcoal is performed. This process is very dangerous and used commercially on large volumes of tailings from gold mines. This process is beyond the scope of Ormus collectors and this manual.


### Final Thought

Superconductivity of Ormus (manna) can be shown in two ways and demonstrate its presence. First, dry the wet precipitate as explained in "Dried-Out Precipitate" (Section Six) then grind it into powder. Place 1/4 to 1/2 teaspoon of ground-up air-dried Ormus (manna) onto a sheet of black paper. Next, place this black paper on a piece of glass or a thin layer of wood or an aluminum (not steel) baking pan and put a magnet underneath this layer. If the dried precipitate jumps away from the magnet, you are observing superconductivity (if the dried precipitate is not jumping away, turn the magnet around and try using the other side of the magnet).

The second way to show superconductivity of Ormus is at the time of rinsing of the Ormus (manna) during the "Wet Process." Use a glass container to see this. There may be particles next to the glass walls of the container. Bump the walls of the glass container and the particles will be discharged. Watch these particles. They may go up or they may go down. Some may oscillate and look like they are breathing. (Sometimes this occurs slowly and the particles are observed for a long period. Ormus researchers have videotaped the container and then reviewed the tape on high speed.) This is a sign of superconductivity (they are defying gravity). Please do not be disappointed if this does not happen as not all precipitates have the same properties and you may see only a few particles doing this, due to the fact that most of the manna is surmised to be locked up within its little "box." Note: The concept of being "locked in the box" is explained in the chapter titled "Wet Process." (Section Three.)

Another method that some say displays M-state in Ormus (manna) is to air-dry and then attempt to re-dissolve it. While hydrochloric acid re-dissolves wet Ormus (manna), it does *not* re-dissolve dried-out Ormus (manna).

In the end, after Ormus collection processes are read and mentally digested, you will probably agree that the "Live Oil Process," the "Wet Process" and (once you feel comfortable with that process) the "Dry Process" are the best processes for the average collector. The "Wet Process," the "Dry Process" and all the *dry* processes listed in this manual revolve around salty solutions. In the "Wet Process" the salty solution is the "reconstituted" sea or "drawn" "seawater." In the "Dry Process" and all the *dry* processes the "salty" solution is achieved by the mixing of an acid and a base. (The acid is the hydrochloric acid and the base is the sodium hydroxide.) While the resultant solution in the "Dry Process" and all the *dry* processes becomes "salty" tasting, not all salty solutions created from the mixing of an acid and a base taste "salty."

Caustic and acidic chemicals are used in Ormus collection processes. Do not work with these chemicals in "fear" as the emotions surrounding "fear" cause a mind to "close off;" this results in making the steps of a procedure very difficult to absorb. Approach these chemicals with respect and handle accordingly. In addition, some have said that feeling fear at the time of the "work" causes an "imprint" of "fear" onto the Ormus (manna).

An important tip while collecting Ormus (manna) is to have a useful way to add and measure the amount of lye solution or hydrochloric acid added to the Ormus-containing liquid. Using an HDPE bottle with an elongated spout top or using the barrel of an oral baby syringe or marinating syringe offers dispensing and measuring tools that are easy to work with. For more information, see "Labware Choices." (Appendix XIV.)

# APPENDIX VIII
## Sources for the Ormus Processes

### Information

Ormus sources vary in their content of platinum metal group or rare earths. One material source may contain more of the rosy red rhodium and less iridium or vise versa. The platinum metal groups are thought to be a large source for the Ormus material. To the Ormus collector: gold, rhodium and iridium are three elements given much consideration when choosing a source material.

If you are using a material that makes a precipitate and it is not known if you can eat the source, research must be done to determine what is in the source or in the precipitate. At the very least, send the precipitate off for an assay and always check the toxic levels of any element. For more information, see "Resources and Supplies." (Appendix I) For example: If the source has silver in the starting material, silver chloride is formed when you lower the pH during a *dry* process with hydrochloric acid and this is discussed later in this Appendix. **The silver chloride makes a white precipitate, but it is toxic.** (Note: The amount of silver chloride made is directly proportional to the amount of silver in the source material.)

When analyzing the content of a source material there are three common laboratory tests available. The first and the one most often performed is called a "Quantitative ICAP Screen." This test analyzes the presence of elements in the sample to amounts greater than 5-10PPM and shows the presence of assorted metals and minerals. The metals are aluminum, barium, boron, calcium, chromium, cobalt, copper, iron and the heavy metals arsenic, cadmium and lead. (Note: Heavy metal mercury is not detected in this assay.) The minerals are magnesium, manganese, molybdenum, nickel, phosphorus, potassium, selenium, silver, sodium, sulfur and zinc. This test runs about $150.00.

Enhanced sensitivity for the heavy metals is obtained by the test called "ICP-MS." This test analyzes levels of arsenic, cadmium and lead to amounts present in the sample up to 10PPM. (Note: The heavy metal mercury is not detected in this assay.) This test runs about $20 dollars per metal with a one-time preparation charge added on.

The level of mercury is analyzed in a separate test and it shows the amount present in the sample up to 10PPM. This test runs about $40.00, with a one-time preparation charge.

For more information see "Resources and Supplies-Have a Source Analyzed." (Appendix I)

If you choose to assay the Ormus source material before performing an Ormus collection process, two things can be determined. First, it is known if the source material contains ingredients safe to ingest. If the ingredients in the Ormus source material are safe to ingest, the Ormus (manna) is safe. Secondly, there is a baseline listing showing the presence of Ormus producing ingredients.

The most common sample that an Ormus collector may wish to assay is probably the Ormus (manna) precipitate. Such an assay determines that the manna contains elements that are safe to ingest. Determining safe levels of heavy metals is difficult as heavy metals present in amounts over 5-10PPM may be considered high in drinking water and not high in a spice for example because of the amount of drinking water ingested versus the amount of spice used. This explains why there can be found no specific value tied to acceptable PPM levels when discussing heavy metals.

If there is great curiosity and cost is not a consideration, assay the Ormus source material, the Ormus (manna) and the liquid over the Ormus (manna). If the Ormus source material and the Ormus (manna) precipitate had both been assayed, it may be determined if any toxic elements became more concentrated after the drop. It may also show how much Ormus producing ingredients are still present (in the elemental form) in the Ormus (manna). If assaying the liquid over the manna the amount of Ormus producing ingredients still present (in the elemental form) may be determined. A percentage calculation of Ormus producing ingredients in the liquid over the Ormus (manna) versus in the Ormus (manna) precipitate may show a missing amount of the Ormus producing ingredients. It may be a possibility the missing amount is in the Ormus (manna) in a spectroscopically invisible state. **Be aware of the need for testing if you are going to use Ormus source material with unknown contents.**

There is a website that may be useful which lists the metals content of plants and trees: *www.levity.com*. Another website that may be helpful is toxnet (select database HSDB).

New natural sources of Ormus source material are needed and this is an area we can all be actively on the lookout for. The list of Ormus source materials in this chapter helps identify currently known potential sources and may spark thoughts of possible new ones. The Ormus source materials are divided into four broad sections: "Organic, Mineral, Metal and Water."

**(Note: The author lists materials that some have said may be a source for Ormus and assumes no liability in any form relating to the contents of this list  The reader is directed to analyze the contents of any source chosen for its suitableness.)**

## Organic Sources

The dried-out form of these sources is good when performing the "Dry Process (Cold Fire Process)" because the source material is not highly aggregated. Carrots are a classic example of an organic Ormus source material. Dry the juiced carrot (organic carrot preferred) pulp in a gas oven set as 120 degrees F to create the dry source material. For more information, see "Labware Choices-Heat." (Appendix XIV.)

It has been said that Ormus elements are in every living thing and anything that has been alive. They are found in any dry material that contains the remains of living matter. Tests showed that 5% dry weight of brain and nervous system of the pig is rhodium and iridium (David Hudson transcripts). Bone marrow is said to have a lot of Ormus. (The three transitional metals especially sought out in Ormus source material are iridium, rhodium and gold.) For more information, see "General Ormus Information." (Appendix VI.)

If an edible source is used, there is never a problem-like the pulp of carrot-unless something grows in it such as mold.

Some have said that foods of deep red and purple color, such as purple or red grapes and beets, are naturally high in Ormus. As a side note, you can eat raw beets by peeling and then adding salt. Carrots and beets are said to be high in rhodium.

Elements that make Ormus have been said to be abundant in Aloe Vera, watercress, grape seeds, grape seed oil and olive oil. (I would expect that kosher grape seed oil would be outstanding because of the minimal amount of processing the kosher process does to the source material.)

David Hudson has said that Aloe Vera has the highest amount of rhodium and iridium from a natural source. This makes Aloe Vera a good choice to use as Ormus source material.

Carrots are high in rhodium and this is why they are also considered a good Ormus source material choice. When carrots are grown organically and in volcanic ash or rock, the values have been said to be the highest. Azomite® is ground up volcanic ash and it is added to the soil of plants at root level. A theory holds that high heat from an active volcano affects the elements in the rock in such a way to make them more prone to enter into the Ormus state.

(It is interesting that the "Food Detective" on the Food Network explained how carrot grown in mineral rich soils contained a lot of (elemental) metals in them. To demonstrate they cooked a raw carrot in a microwave oven. Sparking was seen, similar to when placing a metal spoon in the microwave, then the carrot caught on fire.)

It is felt by some that long-lived trees such as oak may live longer because Ormus is present in them. Therefore, the ash from their wood-or even the ash made from drying and then burning plants has been suggested (and some say used) as an Ormus source material. The ash from burning the organic material needs to be white. There can be no black carbon (charred) from the organic material remaining. Sometimes the ash must be double burned to remove any black charred pieces.

Plantains have been said to have a lot of the elements. It is also said to have good quantities of rhodium, iridium and gold.

Chlorophyll contains copper which has been said to make a rejuvenating Ormus (manna).

This has been said of the following: Essiac tea, sheep sorrel and slippery elm bark are high in rhodium and iridium • • Kampuchea (the Chinese mushroom) has some rhodium and iridium • • blue green algae contains rhodium and iridium • • watercress has a lot of rhodium and iridium • • flax oil, almond seed, apricot seed and grape juice and grape seed has rhodium and iridium in them. (The best grapes have been said to be Concord grapes.) (*David Hudson transcripts*)

David Hudson has lectured: "... we are learning that it really is in the herbs ...." Therefore, a study of herbs for Ormus-producing elemental ingredients is in order.


## Mineral Sources

Because these sources are often denser (more aggregated), higher energy in the form of a higher heat is needed to properly disaggregate them. Therefore, a theory holds that it is best to choose *dry* Ormus collection processes that include the addition of external heat when a mineral source is used. Exceptions include mineral sources in a *less* dense form such as those in a fine or granular particle size (some may be as fine as talc powder). In these cases, the "Dry Process (Cold Fire Process)" will work and bear in mind when preparing the source material: The finer the particle size the better the process works.

Now, it has been said that a mineral source is not to have appreciable amounts of sulfur in it or contain sulfites as these ingredients are thought to decrease the amount of Ormus collected.

Therefore, have assays of untried Ormus source materials done first and **recall that assays also ensure the source material is "nontoxic."**

## Black Sand

Some consider black sand a good Ormus source material and it comes in different grades. These grades include: extra fine, fine, medium and coarse. This is a heavy, glossy, partly magnetic mix of unusually fine sand. Black sand often contains additional valuable ingredients other than the precious elements. (They may contain rare earth elements.)

Gold also has black sand associated with it. When panning for gold, black sand is often present and there may be gold flecks in it to the amount of two to four oz of gold ore per ton of black sand. When looking for Ormus source material, it would make sense to find placer mines -mines which have been panned out - and look for black sand in the tailings.

## Dolomite

Some have said that pure dolomite may be a good source. (aka limestone)

## Essene's Black Sand

The one called "Essene" has supplied this black sand. This sand is running low and we are in need of another source. *Essene's black sand is gold ore and not common grade magnetite. It assays to contain about 4oz gold per ton.* To put the black sand concept together, take a moment and read the "magnetite" source information below. Black sand is close to surface sources of magnetite.

A theory holds that the best black sand for Ormus processes may be associated with water: on a beach or in a stream.

## Humic Shale

This is a plant derived mineral. Although it is shale rock, this source may fall more under organic sources. The definition of shale is layered compacted deposit of plant life which never composted (due to lack of rainfall) fossilized or petrified. Humic shale is a rock mineral that first had been broken down and digested by prehistoric plants. It was then locked for ages in the stratum of humic shale. Some say this source contains no toxic metals.

## Magnetite: aka Lodestone

In the Unites States, magnetite is mostly found in Pennsylvania and California's Mojave Desert. There are a few things to understand about magnetite. First, it can be mined and in this regard it is a natural magnetic stone. It is a mineral that contains, among other things, black colored iron oxide and it is also a natural magnet.

Some have said that iron contributes to making Ormus (M-state) while Iron oxide does not. You know the iron "oxide" form is present when it rusts after being wetted then allowed to dry. Therefore, if magnetite is taken from above the ground in a dry area (an area not near water, or the beach or a stream) add water, allow it to dry and check for rust. If rust forms iron oxide is present and using this as source material should not give very much Ormus (manna). (An experiment can be performed to see if a precipitate forms.)

Therefore, some say that the best natural magnetite is located near or in the water, on the beach or in a stream (this is the source of what has been called "The Essene's black sand"). This magnetite, although iron oxide, does not rust when wetted. Ormus surrounds the wet magnetite molecules and felt to protect it from rusting.

This magnetite is found on the surface and in wet places among sand. If the whole mass is shoveled out - including the sand - some have said that this is a very good source for collecting Ormus. (This is because the mixture contains both the form of magnetite that does not rust and the sand particles that may contain transition elements, as well as rare earth elements that form Ormus.) Magnetite seems to be located among sand rich in these elements.

If you buy magnetite it may be helpful to ask where the product was retrieved as some have said that the magnetite and co-occurring sand found near a wet area or in a wet area is better than that from a dry location. (This would be an area such as a beach, lake or stream.) Some believe that this may be because a good source of Ormus is where the first water meets the land (the sand) and this belief may just be so when considering how wet source magnetite has some sort of protection from rusting hypothesized to include the presence of Ormus.

There are different grades of magnetite and each grade has its use. There is a choice of purchasing magnetite that includes the sand found around it, purchasing only the sand or purchasing only the magnetite granules.

**"Ormus-like minerals magnetite"** is the grade that includes the co-occurring sand found mixed in with the magnetite.

It has been said to use this grade in Ormus processes and if it is from a wet source it is especially valued by some. This grade is also used as an ingredient in a "MEOW Kettle" (it is mixed with "wild harvest magnetite.") For more information, see "Magnetite Effect on Ormus Water aka (MEOW Kettle)." (Section Seven.)

**"High-Ormus non-magnetite"** is the grade that contains only the co-occurring sand co-mingled with the magnetite. The magnetite granules have been removed with a magnet. It has been said to use this grade in Ormus processes and if it is from a wet source it is especially valued by some.

**"Wild harvest magnetite"** is the grade that contains only the co-occurring magnetite granules that are co-mingled with the sand. This grade is used as an ingredient in a "MEOW kettle" (it is mixed with "Ormus-like minerals magnetite.") For more information, see "Magnetite Effect on Ormus Water aka (MEOW Kettle)." (Section Seven.)

To retrieve what some say is the best form of "wild harvest magnetite," bring a magnet to the beach, and if there is magnetite in the sand, it sticks to the ends of the magnet. (It is helpful to cover the magnet with a plastic bag so the magnetite is easier to remove from the magnet.)

## Synthetic Magnetite

Synthetic magnetite (not from a natural source) is produced by the "glass ceramic method" which provides a simple means of preparing nearly uniformly sized almost chemically pure and relatively unstressed magnetite crystals. This is not considered a good Ormus source material. Buy natural magnetite as explained above for the Ormus processes.

## Paramagnetic Sand

"Paramagnetic" sand repels a magnet. Paramagnetism is a low-level energy. Paramagnetism is a physical force that has been shown to have beneficial effects on all forms of life. A theory holds that there is a correlation between the paramagnetic properties of a soil or rock source and its Ormus (M-state) content.

High temperatures cause paramagnetism. Crushed toilet tanks are paramagnetic, red clay pipe after baking is paramagnetic. Burned soil is paramagnetic. Volcanoes create high temperatures and paramagnetic rock. All volcanic soil and rock are paramagnetic with readings in the range of 200-2,000.

The paramagnetism level can be measured with a "Phil Callahan Soil meter" (PCSM). The PCSM measures CGS (centimeters/gram/seconds). A good rock dust should read a minimum of 1,500 CGS. (*www.nutri-tech.com.au*)

It has been noted that the paramagnetic measurements for Ormus source materials are to be high (above 500 or so) and if used for Ormus collection, the assay provided by the rock dust supplier is not to include significant amounts of lead, arsenic, nickel or other toxic metals.

Paramagnetic sand chosen as an Ormus source material has been said to be acceptable; and magnetite, as explained above, from a natural source is thought a better choice for the Ormus processes.

## Pureganic® Minerals

Many consider pureganic® Minerals a good Ormus source material because it contains Ormus from platinum group elements. The product is a talc-like fine dust with particles that are small and therefore disaggregate easily in the "Dry Process." The minerals contain lots of silica. This is favorable because some think that silica actually holds Ormus to the ground. According to the supplier of Pureganic® Minerals, no paramagnetic value is known for this product.

## Azomite®

This is pulverized ash of an ancient volcano on the bottom of an ancient seabed. Movement of the land caused a pushing up of the ancient ash to the surface in the form of hills. One theory holds that the high heat from an active volcano affects the elements in the rock in such a way to make them more prone to enter into the Ormus state. Azomite® Minerals can be taken internally for animal supplementation. It has not been approved for human use. The paramagnetic value is good, but not great. Some say that Azomite® is equivalent to Pureganic® Minerals. I have seen assays of each and read them as identical.

## Stone Sources

It has been suggested that silica-based stones may be a good Ormus source material as silica has been said to hold the Ormus to the ground. Examples of silica-based stones are Opals, Agates and Moldevite.

## Exotic Sources

Some say Ormus material has been found in the remnants of meteors, comets and materials that fall to the earth termed "cosmic dust" or "star dust." Each year 20 billion tons of cosmic dust falls to Earth - the bulk of this cosmic dust emanates from our own Sun. The gravitational pull of our Sun also brings tons of cosmic dust into our Solar System from other stars.

# Metal Sources

Note: The metal chosen for an Ormus collection process must be 99.999 percent pure and it must be thoroughly cleaned.

## Copper

The copper used is to be pure drawn "Oxygen Free" Copper. Pure drawn copper won't have oxides on it (the copper used in the Ormus process is to have no oxides on it). This means it is not to be tarnished. Tarnishing occurs when copper develops an outer layer of copper oxide. (The copper is to be thoroughly cleaned.)

To purchase pure copper see "Resources and Supplies." (Appendix I)

A source of copper may be Monster Cable® speaker wire as it is said that this wire is pure drawn "Oxygen Free" Copper. (Check to be sure that this speaker wire still is pure copper.) Strip the plastic coating covering the wire immediately before shaving (filing) the wire to prepare it for the Ormus process.

The copper used must be pure and contain no other alloy. For example: Pre-1974 pennies are 90% copper. This is not pure copper and therefore it cannot be used as an Ormus source material. (Note: If the penny attracts a magnet, it is magnetic and can't be pure copper.) Copper bracelets are also not pure copper and cannot be used as an Ormus source.

Most copper ores are associated with sulfur or sulfite and some have said that these are not to be in copper ore used for an Ormus process. Sulfate in an ore is said to be acceptable. (*David Hudson transcripts*)

## Gold

A gold coin may be used as an Ormus source material as long as it is 99.9 percent pure and it must be thoroughly cleaned. (This would include gold coins not gold coins with alloys mixed in. Note: The formula used to make gold coins can change. Therefore confirm the ingredients in a gold coin with a coin broker before using.)

Pure gold can also be purchased. For more information, see "Resources and Supplies." (Appendix I)

• 1/10 oz Canadian Maple Leaf is currently 99.9 percent pure (the metal industry calls this .9999 fine).

• 1oz gold bars are 24 karats, 99.9 percent pure, readily available and the premium charged for them is the most modest.

• 1/10 American Gold Eagle is currently gold *and* an alloy: The alloy part is mostly copper, but does have some silver. Because the alloy contains silver we would not use this coin as an Ormus source material. For more information regarding silver in a source see the next metal listed.

Most gold ores are associated with sulfur or sulfite and some have said that these are not to be in gold ore used for an Ormus process. Sulfate in an ore is said to be acceptable. (*David Hudson transcripts*)

Note: Don Nance has said that gold wants to be a metal in the summer. Gold fights transmuting in the summer and behaves differently in the winter. Therefore an aware alchemist doesn't collect gold Ormus during summer months.

## Silver

An important fact regarding collecting silver Ormus in Ormus collection processes that utilize hydrochloric acid: **hydrochloric acid can never be used to precipitate the silver Ormus (manna) or silver chloride will be made. Silver chloride makes a white precipitate but it is toxic.** (Note: The amount of silver chloride made is directly proportional to the amount of silver in the source material.) Now, to get around using hydrochloric acid, 20% citric acid is used to drop the precipitate. The precipitate that forms will be silver "citrate" instead of silver "chloride." This is the preferred way to make silver Ormus. **Never ingest silver Ormus made with hydrochloric acid.** Now you must know the stability of a precipitate collected by using "citric acid" is not as long and therefore the shelf life is shortened. This is because an organic (citrate) salt has been made instead of an inorganic (chloride) salt. (Authors note: This manual provides chemical *information* regarding precipitating silver Ormus however I do not recommend this be performed as products that have caused the rare condition of argyria include *silver citrate*, silver nitrate, and *silver chloride*. Argyria causes the skin to turn a grayish color.)

- The silver used must be 99.9 percent pure and contain no other alloy. The silver must be thoroughly cleaned.
- Pre 1964 quarters and dimes are 90% silver. (This is not pure silver and cannot be used as an Ormus source material.)
- Pure silver in bar, wire and coin shape can be purchased. To purchase pure silver see "Resources and Supplies." (Appendix I)
- Most silver ores are associated with sulfur or sulfite and some have said that these are not to be in the silver ore used for an Ormus process. Sulfate in an ore is said to be acceptable.

(*David Hudson transcripts*)

## Iridium

Iridium and rhodium are thought to be two elements important to humans in the Ormus form. (*David Hudson transcripts*)

Iridium is one of the least abundant elements in the earth.

The "KT Boundary" is a meteor site and iridium can be found there. It is located in Arizona and the Geology department of a local University there can point to it on a map.

## Copper ore, gold ore or silver ore

Precious metal elements in an "*altered*" state (the Ormus state) are postulated to be in the ore because they are in a transitory form. Ores are said to be a good source in the appropriate processes if there are no sulfur or sulfites present. If using an ore, have the source material sent in for analysis first. However, most Ores are associated with sulfur or sulfite. Sulfate in an ore is said to be acceptable. (*David Hudson transcripts*)

# Water Sources

## Fresh Water

For Ormus to be in fresh water, many believe the water must have gone through the sand and limestone layers of the earth. When percolating through these layers the water picks up the transition elements in soluble form and these create Ormus. However, others have shown that Ormus remains with the water even through the distillation process and therefore Ormus is also in the distilled water.

These are two differing mindsets regarding Ormus in fresh water - and the question addressed may be more a matter of the quantity of Ormus in fresh water that has percolated through the ground versus distilled water.

## Ocean Water/Seawater

Ocean water and dehydrated sea salts are so commonplace they do not carry the level of respect due. When comparing Ormus source materials it is important to realize that land-based mineral salts originate in rock. However, no rock powder contains the full spectrum of elements found in seawater. In addition, dehydrated seawater (sea salt) is water-soluble and as a result, all nutrients available in mineral rich seawater are immediately bio available.

There is a generally held belief regarding seawater that it naturally contains more Ormus to begin with than other sources. In addition the form of Ormus in seawater is easier to collect than the form of Ormus in land-based (dry) source materials. The collection of Ormus from seawater is more akin to "harvesting" the Ormus that is in the seawater by "concentrating" it in a precipitate.

One theory is that Ormus is associated with the sodium molecule. The salts (dissolved chemicals such as sodium chloride, magnesium, and calcium) in the waters of most oceans and seas is approximately 97% sodium chloride. Sodium chloride is common salt. Others feel Ormus is associated with the magnesium molecule.

For more information about sea salt, a book titled *"Sea Salt's Hidden Powers"* is available from ACRES USA. (*www.acresusa.com*)

## "Drawn" Seawater

A good depth from which to pull seawater is 50 to 100 feet down, and no closer than 32 feet from the bottom. For more information, see "Seawater Collection." (Appendix XX)

Since sunlight is thought to disturb the state of the Ormus and pollution stays pretty much in the top 25 feet of the water do not collect seawater from the top waters of the sea or from the shoreline because pollution can contaminate the Ormus (manna).

(Note: It has been said by some that if seawater is distilled, Ormus associated with the water part of the seawater crosses over in the distillation process. Ormus tied to the salt of the seawater does not cross over unless extremely high heat is used. The extremely high heat is a burning heat and destroys the salt bonds. (The Ormus become freed from the salt and available to cross over in the distillation process.)

*Catalina Water Company* sells Real Ocean™ seawater that is collected off the coast of Southern California. Pure clean Pacific Ocean seawater is filtered extensively then treated with UV Sterilization & Ozone, buffered for pH, and tested prior to shipment.

Saltwater aquariums contain this seawater and it may provide the inland located Ormus collector an opportunity to have seawater for the "Wet Process." As an experiment, perform a "Wet Process" on Catalina seawater to determine if Ormus is present.

Real Ocean™ saltwater is available nationwide through PETCO® in 5-gallon packs.

(Note: It has been said that one ounce of Catalina water per gallon of drinking water can be used for the following purposes:  1) It tastes good and provides trace nutrients for the body  2) Plants grow better 3) Fish are healthier after changing  the water in fresh water aquariums with this mixture.)

## "Reconstituted" Sea: (made by dissolving sea salt)

**Do not use table salt and do not choose any salt that has anti-caking agents or coloring added.**

Every ocean has its own unique Ormus content values.  The amount of gold, rhodium and iridium found in the seas are a consideration when choosing a sea salt.

### Celtic Sea Salt

There is a full spectrum of minerals, trace elements and Ormus producing elements in Celtic Sea salt. Gold, rhodium and iridium are present in this sea and some have said that they occur in a more "balanced mix."  Because of this, the Celtic sea is a favored sea among many Ormus collectors when performing the "Wet Process."  This sea does not contain as high a level of magnesium as in the Dead Sea and may be another reason it is favored.  Information on magnesium in the Ormus precipitate is described in "Wet Process-Information."

### Dead Sea Salt

The Dead Sea contains a high salt concentration (calcium chloride, potassium chloride, magnesium chloride and sodium chloride) and it has been said that this sea contains a bit more gold Ormus.  This is why some value this sea.  This sea is 8.6 times as salty as the ocean.  The Dead Sea has a geographical feature of being a totally encapsulated body of water.  It has no egress point and this may explain the high salt (and magnesium) content attributed to this sea.

This sea also contains a lot of magnesium.  It has more magnesium than even "regular" seawater and therefore a portion of the Ormus (manna) collected also contains magnesium.  Information on magnesium in the Ormus precipitate is described in "Wet Process-Information."  The Dead Sea is said to have about 70% gold and 30% magnesium.  This sea is generally considered a good source for beginners because it routinely drops Ormus (manna) in high volumes.  Therefore, using "Dead Sea" salt also acts as a "confidence" builder.

### Great Salt Lake Salt

Some have said that The Great Salt Lake in Utah is a good Ormus source material.  Both the Great Salt Lake and the Dead Sea share the common feature of being bodies of water with no egress point. Both are totally encapsulated by the geography surrounding them and have no exit points for water to leave.  This may explain the high salt content (calcium chloride, potassium chloride, magnesium chloride and sodium chloride) that is in both the Dead Sea and the Great Salt Lake. The Great Salt Lake contains gold, rhodium and iridium.

The Great Salt Lake is said to have about 19% gold, 30% rhodium, 5% iridium and 46% magnesium.  (*www.subtleenergies.com*)

### Pacific Ocean Salt

I have heard that more Ormus may be collected from Pacific Ocean water off the coast of the United States because of its proximity to the underground "ring of fire."  Ring of fire is a term used to describe the many geo-thermal vents that occur along an undersea "fault line." More Ormus material may be present in this sea because the geo-thermal vents upload both it and rare earth elements to the Pacific Ocean. These materials are then distributed to other seas. Pacific Ocean water off the coast of Washington has, as well as other elements, about 8-14% gold, 30% rhodium and 6-9% iridium. (*www.subtleenergies.com*)

Pacific Ocean source materials include Sonoma Gourmet™ sea salt. This sea salt is collected off the California coastline and available at *www.saltworks.us*. Catalina Water's Real Ocean™ Saltwater is seawater from the Pacific Ocean and Sea-90™ is dehydrated seawater from the Sea of Cortez. (The Sea of Cortez is also called the Gulf of California and is very near the Pacific Ocean.)

*Sea-90*™ is natural crystals of sea mineral solids produced through solar dehydration of seawater contained in retention ponds. The "Sea of Cortez" is chosen as the sea because it is considered one of the most mineral-rich and pollution-free on earth, is in an arid(dry) environment where temperatures continually exceed 100 degrees F and the annual rainfall is less than one half inch. Very little rainfall causes less chance of beneficial minerals leaching from the sea salt and being lost to the drying process. The Sea of Cortez (the Gulf of California) is a body of water that separates the Baja California Peninsula from the Mexican mainland    Water in this location is said (by the manufacturer) to have three beneficial properties. First, the water is near geo-thermal vents along an undersea fault line. These vents are thought to bring "rare earth elements" into the water. (Rare earth elements are considered valuable Ormus source elements.) Next, the seawater is near the "delta" of the Colorado River. This is where the river feeds into the Gulf bringing with it beneficial soils and nutrients. Finally, this seawater is in the same proximity as the Pacific Ocean. The Pacific Ocean is considered by some to be an exceptional Ormus source. (This has been addressed above.)

Sea-90™ is harvested twice each year from fresh seawater that naturally floods the retention pond. The dehydrated seawater varies in color from pure white to various shades of beige, and at times contains small amounts of wind-carried sediment. Color variations occur based on the speed of currents and tides moving the water and wind conditions.

The Sea Agri Company sells Sea-90™.

## Ocean Trace™ Sea Minerals

Ocean Trace™ is the thin layer of moisture left under the dehydrated Sea-90™. Ocean Trace™ is another sea mineral product and other terms for it are the "bitterns" or "Mother Liquor." The bitterns (very bitter tasting) contain approximately 33% magnesium chloride and everything else from the sea minus the sodium chloride (the salt). Some call this "liquid magnesium oil." This liquid has been used for natural healing for centuries and is said to be a good skin tonic.

The Sea Agri Company sells Ocean Trace™.

## Himalayan Salt

Some Himalayan salts have been said to be a good source material.

## Miscellaneous

The "Great Salt Lake Flats" is another potential Ormus source material.

# APPENDIX IX
## Book Selections/Web Searches

Section A contains book selections, web search topics and some of the general information collated from lectures given by David Hudson. David Hudson funded the research on this material and lectured around the country during the 1990s. During the presentations he suggested many books and some he strongly suggested. An *** is placed before the title if it had been strongly suggested and for the reader who wishes to study the subject in more depth, web searches have been included. The content of many of the Hudson lectures are found on the Internet. One such site is www.subtleenergies.com.

(While David Hudson indicated during his lectures that there are health benefits attributed to these materials, it is noted that none have been approved by the FDA.)

Section B contains reading material suggested by Barry Carter, Don Nance and other Ormus collectors and researchers.

There is much yet to be learned about Ormus - and much research yet to be performed. The following information may raise questions and/or spark research that can ultimately help the Ormus community.

## Section A

Book Selections, Web Search Topics and some General Information from the David Hudson Lectures
• "Secrets of the Alchemist" Time-Life Series Book • "The Sign and the Seal" by Graham Hancock • "Secrets of the Golden Flower" By Richard Wilhelm • "Holy Blood, Holy Grail" By Baigent, Leigh and Lincoln • *** "The Quantum Self: Human Nature and Consciousness" By Danah Zohar • Web search "Dan Winter" for information about DNA and Frequencies • Google Search: Planck's Frequency • "The Doctrine of Transcendental Magic" By Eliphis Levi • "The Egyptian Book of the Dead and Papyrus of Ani" by Budge • "Stairway to Heaven" By Zecharia Sitchin • *** Book on Genesis is: "The Creation and the Patriarchs" by Emil Bach • *** "Genesis revisited" by Zachariah Sitchin • *** The Book of Knowledge: "Keys of Enoch" By J.J. Hurtak • *** "Sacred Science" by R.A.Schwaller De Lubicz. (D.Hudson commented that he understood it) • "Ages in Chaos" by Immanual Velikovsky. Written 1957  (you need to find an old copy.) • "Dead Sea Scrolls Uncovered" by Robert Eisenman and Michael Wise. (The first complete translation and Interpretation of key documents that have been withheld for over 35 years.) • "Lost Books of the Bible" By Solomon J. Schepps • "The Last Days: Types and Shadows from the Bible and Book of Mormon" by Avraham Gileadi • *** ""New Teachings for an Awakening Humanity: The

Alchemy of Ascension" by Virginia Essene • "Stalking the Wild Pendulum: On the Mechanics of Consciousness" by Itzhak Bentov • *** "New Radio activities" in the Scientific American March 1990 • ****"Possible Discontinuity in the Octupole Behavior in the Platinum through Mercury Region" in Physical Review C Vol 39 No 3 March 1989 • "Quantum Size Effects and Rapidly Rotating Nuclei" in Physical Review C Vol 41 No 4 April 1990 • "Inertias of Super-Deformed Bands" in Physical Review C Vol 41 No 4 April 1990 • "Super deformation in Palladium 104 and 105" in Physical Review C Vol 38 No 2 Aug 1988 • "Structure of Osmium Platinum Isotopes" in Physical Review C Vol 38 No2 Aug 1988 • "Collective and Single Particle Structure in Rhodium 103" in Physical Review C Vol 37 No 2 Feb 1988 • "Physics of High Temperature Superconductors" by J.C.Phillips • "Amorphous Solids and the Liquid State" by March,Street and Tosi • "High Temperature Superconductors and other Super fluids" by A.S. Alexandrov and Nevill Mott • "Introduction to Super conductivity" by Rose-Innes • "Introduction to Superconductivity: International Series" in Solid State Physics V6 by Alister Christopher Rose-Innes, E.H. Rhoderick • "The Analytical Chemistry of the Platinum Group Elements" by Ginsberg • "The Holographic Universe" by Michael Talbot • Web search: "Zero-point," "Gamma Emitters without Fission," and "Bosnic Field of the Nucleus" • Print out or buy a periodic table • Web search: Chemical properties of Sodium and Magnesium Hydroxide • Search definition of Fission • Web search: the speed of Light and the speed of Sound • Web search: Liquid light of Superconductivity • Search Definition of: "Nucleus," "Electrons," "Protons" and "Neutrons" • Search Definition of: "Two Dimensional coupling" and "Two Dimension" • Search Definition of: "Element" • Web search: the "Actinide Group" (found in the periodic table) • Web search: "Rare Earth elements" • Web search: "Nucleus Harmonic orbital versus Electron Harmonic Orbital." • Search Definition of: "Strong Force" • Search Definition of: "Voltage Potential," "Electron and Electron Pair" • Web search: "Bosonic Physics of light," "Fermion Physics," "Einstein Physics" • Search Definition of: "Electron Transitions on atoms" • Search Definition of: "Two dimensional Resonance", "Quantum Oscillator," "Coulomb Wave" and "Two Dimensional Oscillator" • Search Definition of: "Resonance Wave" • Search Definition of: "Gamma Radiation" (a very short wave of light) • Search Definition of: "Voltage potential" versus "amperage" • Web search: "The Order of Enoch" • Search Definition of: "SO3" (sulfite) • Search Definition of: "SO4 (sulfate) • Search Definition of: "Bone Ash Cupel" (Crude Calcium Phosphate) • Search Definition of: "What is a Platinum Metal Group?" • Search Definition of: "Allotropic" form • Search Definition of: "gnosis" • Search Definition of: "Coulomb force" • Search Definition of: "The Actinide group" and "The Lanthanide group" (in the Periodic table) • Search Definition of: "Cooper Pair" • Search Definition of: "Coulomb field" • Search definition of: "Josephson Effect" • Carrots raised in volcanic soil have Ormes. Rhodium is in carrots raised in volcanic soil • Blue-Green Alga has rhodium and iridium • Rhodium and iridium Ormes react with nitric oxide. (Nitric oxide is part of human breathing.)  Gold Ormes does not react with nitric oxide therefore the effects of gold are more permanent • 5% of brain is rhodium and iridium Orme element • Our body contains primarily rhodium and iridium • OR Gold means gold or the highest light • Ruthenium, Osmium, Iridium, Rhodium, Palladium, Platinum, Gold, Silver, Copper, Cobalt and Nickel are all elements that make Ormes • In Ancient Egypt Ormus was known as "Golden Tear from the Eye of Horus." It was the White Powder of gold mixed in water.  Also called the "spittle of God" (not the word of God), also known as the "Semen of the Father in Heaven" • The Bible says "Golden Tree of Life."  In Hebrew it is the "ORME" Tree. • The U.S. and World Wide Patent is "Orbitally Rearranged Monoatomic Elements" (ORME) • Blue- Green Algae, Maharishi Amrit Kalash, Watercress, Flax oil, Almond Seeds, Apricot Seeds, Grape Seed and juice have Rhodium/Iridium.  They are also in Essiac Tea, Sheep Sorrell, Slippery Elm Bark, Emprise Corporations "Manaloe" and Carrington Laboratory's "Acemannan" (inject in blood and is 90% Rhodium), they are also in DHEA • Rhodium Ormes is said to be good for cancers • The presence of sugars offsets the benefit of the monatomics in Seneca (Concord) Grape Juice.  Therefore, carrot juice is probably a better source for Ormus.  Seneca is no longer made - Welch's Concord grape juice is in the freezer section of the grocery store • It is said that 80% of rhodium Ormes passes thru the urine • Iridium Ormes doesn't dissolve in HCl - it forms a gelatinous polymer in HCl.  It doesn't dissolve • Iridium seems to relate to the spinal chord and pituitary gland.  It may be connected to the acupuncture meridians • Gold Orme is associated with the Pineal gland• Rhodium Orme is associated with the thymus.  After a month and a half, the Thymus grows by 40% • Gold Ormes becomes Iron when the high-spin variants come apart • Web search: S1 Elements in the periodic table are lithium, sodium, potassium, rubidium and cesium:  All are explosively reactive.  Gold has same structure as these alkaline metals but does not let go (5d106S1) • Web search:  Enoch (Hebrews = Thor (Egyptians) = Hermes Trismegistus (Greece).  Possibly all were the same person • Web search:  U.S. Naval Research proved cell communicate with each other via Superconductivity • Web search:  Orme = Nucleus deforms and goes to a high spin state called high spin nuclei which theoretically should be superconductors (pass energy atom to atom with no net loss of energy) • Web search:  Melchizedek Priests and the bread of the presence of God • Web search:  Qumran Community preoccupied with "The Teacher of Righteousness." The High Priest swallowed the Teacher of Righteousness (Holy Spirit, The light, the Zero Point Light that is not measurable, God Force.)  It shows us how to know all things, we just know • Revelations 2:17:  Paraphrased:  "The man who will overcome will be given the hidden Manna, the White Stone .... will be written a new name." You will not be the same person • Web search: Four things take the high spin atoms to the low spin state. 1) Sulfites (SO3), 2) Carbon and Carbon monoxide, 3) Nitric Oxide, 4) Short Wavelength radiation (deep ultraviolet or shorter) • Ormus is Manna.  It is a philosophical material and because church and state are separated is not regulated by the Government (FDA or AMA). We are administering a sacrament • Web search: The Vibhuti is pure iridium in high spin state • Web search: Actinide groups and lanthanide groups on the periodic chart experience deformed nucleus. They are transition elements. Dipole atoms have counter rotating electron so they have no vibration •

Snippets of General Information from the David Hudson Transcripts

• This material is an element not a metal. 5% of dry matter weight of animal brains is rhodium and iridium

• Sheep Sorrell, Slippery Elm Bark has high rhodium and iridium content while carrots have high rhodium content only.

• The product Acemannan has much Rhodium. Iridium and gold speed body metabolism about 40%, goes into acupuncture system of body and is associated with the spinal chord and thymus. (The spinal chord and thymus are the sites relating to consciousness and metabolic rate of the body.) It does not go into bloodstream or through the kidneys.

• Aloe Vera (contains Ormes)

• Flax oil, Almond seed, apricot seeds, grape juice and grape seeds, watercress: All have a lot of Rhodium and iridium.

## Section B
Other Suggested Reading Material

• "Lost Secrets of the Sacred Ark" by Lawrence Gardner • "DNA: Pirates of the Sacred Spiral" by Horowitz • "Alchemy Key" by Stuart Nettelson • "Pillar of Celestial Fire" by Robert Cox • "The Secret Book" by Artephius • "Le Mystere des Cathedrales" by Fulcanelli • "Explicate Order and Implicate Order" by David Bohm • "Rainbow and the Worm" by Mae-Wan Ho (about quantum Coherence) • "Secrets of the Soil" by Peter Tompkins and Christopher Bird • "Secrets in the Bible" by Tony Busby • "Cosmic Serpent" by Jeremiah Narby (DNA Serpent Helix) • Great book: "Occult Chemistry" (investigation by clairvoyant magnification) by Leadbeater and Besant ("All matter is consciousness stepped back") • "Ancient Mysteries, Modern Visions" by Philip S. Callahan • Web search: The Keys of Enoch • "The Red Lion" by Maria Szepes investigation by clairvoyant magnification • "Bridging Science and Spirit - Common Elements in David Bohm's Physics, the Perennial Philosophy and Seth" by Norman Friedman • Web search: The Emerald Tablets • "Secrets of the Lost Mode of Prayer" by Gregg Braden • "The Universal One" by Walter Russell • "Saint Germain on Alchemy" by Prophet • "The Egyptian Book of the Dead (The Papyrus of Ani)" by E. A. Wallis Budge. Page 35: Manna correlates to tchefa food of the god's, begetter of million of years, Ra is in it, I pass over the way, speaks of a "what" and "who" by the god's names, "Raising the hair" is opening the third eye • "Egyptian Book of the Dead Coming Forth by Day" is a newer version by Muata Ashby. • "Alchemy the Ancient Science" by Time-Life Series books • Read books written by Roberto Mondi • "Paramagnetism - Rediscovering Nature's Secret Force of Growth" by Philip S. Callahan • Get this book: "Collectanea Chemica" by Philalethes Eirenaeus (Kessinger Publishings) • "Chemistry for changing times" is a good book but doesn't include the newer paradigms • "Extra-Sensory Perception of Quarks" by Stephen M. Phillips • "The Jewish Alchemist" by Raphael Patal is the best kept secret book of all Alchemists. It contains 900 recipes and treatises • Books by Col. James Churchward. These include the famous Mu series: "The sacred symbols of Mu," "Children of Mu," "The lost continent of Mu", "The books of the Golden Age" • "A monument to the end of time" by Jay Weidner and Vincent Bridges • "The Bible Fraud" and "The secret in the bible" by Tony Bushby • Web search: Dr Dan Burisch's books • Web search: Kryon.com Kryon writes books about Hawthorn's • "Resonance in Residence" by Harezi • "The Field" by Lynne McTaggart • "Sorcerers Stone: A Beginners Guide to Alchemy" by Dennis William Hauck • "The Land of Osiris" by Stephen Smehler • "Genesis of the Grail Kings" by Laurence Gardner • "Hidden Messages in Water" by Masaru Emoto •

# APPENDIX X
## Moon Chart

### Definition
A "Moon Chart" (or moon calendar) shows the daily phases of the moon throughout the year.

    The chart shows the date and time of the "new" and "full" moons calculated to Universal Time. ("Greenwich Mean Time.")

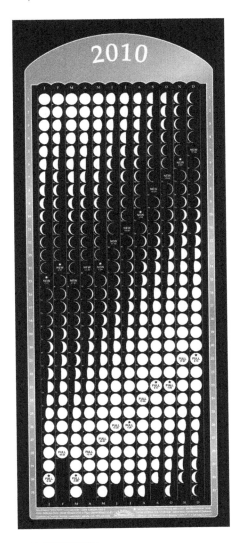

## Information

> "Ormus (manna) can be collected at any time or on any day of the year"
> "Ormus (manna) can be collected at any time or on any day of the year"
> "Ormus (manna) can be collected at any time or on any day of the year"

The following explains "moon periods" and "equinox periods" and has been included for any who seek to perform an Ormus collection process following alchemically suggested time frames.

Ormus can be collected any time on any day of the year and alchemically ideal times are said to exist when performing a collection process. The time frames chosen are based on the "energetically active" ones. Energetically active times cause observable "rising" tides on the waters of the world and they affect the earth's magnetic field causing it to decrease.

"Energetically active" times include "Full Moon Periods" and "Equinox Periods" and the term period is discussed later. (Note: The "New Moon Period" is also energetically active however it is not included in the list of the ancient alchemically ideal time frames.)

Now, during a "Full" moon, a belief is that the pull of the moon draws Ormus up off the land at the same time the Earth is receiving a particular and special light. This light is a polarized light resulting from reflections of the sun off the moon. The light frequency vibration of the moon reflecting the sun rays to the earth versus the sun rays shining directly on the earth are different and Ormus (manna) has been said to benefit from the reflected rays of the sun off the "Full" moon. This explains a reason why the Ormus (manna) may be placed in the moonlight of the full moon to charge (energize) it and make energized Ormus.

"Light cast by the moon is 500,000 times less bright than the sun. This light, reflected from the sun, presents a distinctive spectrum composed of more reds and yellows, and possesses a different frequency than sunlight. This specific light spectrum has never been artificially duplicated." (www.starlightuses.com)

Since antiquity, the moon has been associated with water and this link is observed in the rising and falling of the tide. It may be noteworthy that the "wet" and dry Ormus collection processes explained in this manual are both "water" based and said to benefit by the presence of a "Full" moon.

While the "Full" moon displays an "energetically active" trait of causing "rising" tides both the "Full" moon and the Equinox cause a dip in the Earths magnetic field (the magnetic field holds the atmosphere to the earth).

The occurrence of a "Full" moon seems to cause Ormus to be pulled up from the earth and, therefore, it has been said that more of it is collected in an Ormus process during these times. (This is the underlying thought when directed to perform the "Dew Collection Process" during the night of a "Full" moon.)

The occurrence of an "Equinox" has been said to affect the Ormus in a positive manner and this may be due to the dip in the Earths magnetic field combined with the trait of "superconductivity" found in Ormus and/or it may be that a reduced magnetic field enables different "dimensions" to interact to a greater degree.

"Equinoxes are a scientifically-provable doorway or opening of the magnetic field of the Earth. The Earth's magnetic field is affected by the Sun's alignment with the equator and this produces a reduction in its magnetic field, providing easier access to other dimensions. It is as if the thick veils between Earth and dimensions beyond the physical become their thinnest, creating a threshold that is charged and pulsing with energy, which in turn, encourages the walls of density to collapse." (Carol Ann Ciocco: *www.threemoonocean.com*)

"It would appear probable the Celtic State worship was what is called "solar." All its chief festivals related to points in the Sun's progress, the equinoxes having been considered more important than the solstices." (*Celtic Myth and Legend* by C. Squire)

The "equinox" signifies the "great balance" and it occurs at a moment in time when the center of the sun can be observed directly above the Earth's equator causing light and darkness to be approximately equal on the planet. The two equinoxes during the year are said to "open the windows" to powerful energies both before and after the equinox and an equinox is a "cosmic" event because of the proportion of its effect. (This has been explained earlier.) An equinox is a moment in time that occurs two days in the year when astrologically everything goes into alignment because a "cosmic balance" has occurred. The moment of the cosmic balance is said by some to result in such observable things as the ability to place an egg on its end and have it remain there, standing on its own, for a short period of time.

There are 12 "Full Moon Periods" and two "Equinox Periods" during each calendar year. There is an "Autumnal" Equinox around September 23 and a "Spring" Equinox ("Vernal" equinox) around March 21. The "equinox" has the most powerful energies of any of the fourteen ideal periods and their energetics cause effects for about fifteen days before and after the day the equinox occurs. The most energetically active equinox between the two is the "Spring" equinox as springtime is when the earth's magnetic field is affected the most and Ormus has been said by some to be influenced by the earth's magnetic field in some manner that makes it exceptional.

The "Spring" equinox occurs during late March-May and because of its effects, "Full" moons and "eclipses that occur during the March-May time period are even more energetically active than those occurring other times of the year. Between a "Full" moon and an "eclipse" occurring during a spring equinox, the eclipse is considered the more energetically active event.

The second window during the year when energies are most powerful is the "Autumnal" equinox and it occurs during late Sept-Nov. Because of its effects "Full" moons and "eclipses that occur during the September-November time period are more energetically active than those occurring other times of the year. Between a "Full" moon and an "eclipse" that occurs during an autumnal equinox, the eclipse is considered more energetically active.

Therefore, according to the ancient alchemists, the "most" ideal time frame to perform an Ormus collection process is the "Spring" Equinox "period" and the next ideal time frame is the "Autumnal" Equinox "period" followed by any of the "Full" moon "periods" that occur during the year.

(Other good time frames to perform an Ormus collection process within these alchemical parameters include the springtime "eclipse" period, springtime "Full" moon period, autumnal "eclipse" period and autumnal "Full" moon period. This is because they occur during the time frame affected by the two equinoxes during the year.) Remember, though, that "Ormus (manna) can be collected at any time or on any day of the year."

All "periods" of the moon are seven days long and the full period encompasses **three days prior to the event, the day of the event and three days after the event.** (The "New" moon period follows the same seven-day guidelines.)

Therefore, when following alchemical principles: the ideal time to **begin precipitation** of Ormus (manna) in any "wet" or *dry* Ormus process is three days before the day of the event. The three days prior to the event are "energetically" active times and are part of the full seven-day period. Ormus (manna) collected during these three days is thought to be exceptional in quantity and performance. The same belief is true when collecting Ormus from the "Magnet Vortex Water Trap" (or "Vortex Water Trap") and the "Live Oil Process."

(Mark your calendars and do not miss out during these times of the year. By performing an Ormus collection process during one, or maybe two of these time periods, you can, with a large enough volume of Ormus source material, procure enough for use during the entire year.)

**When following alchemically ideal time frames during an Ormus collection process:**
**Gather and have prepared Ormus source materials and Supplies three days prior to the chosen event.** In this way you may be best assured an Ormus collection is performed within the three days prior to the event.

**Perform a "wet" or a dry Ormus collection process on the prepared Ormus source material.** This is also considered a good time to perform a "Live Oil Process" or collect trap water from the "Magnet Vortex Water Trap" (or "Vortex Water Trap)."

**Allow the Ormus (manna) that has precipitated to settle through the day and night prior to the day of the event.**

**The Ormus (manna) is allowed to sit during the day of the event.** (If the chosen event is a "Full" moon and "energized" Ormus is desired, the container is placed in the moonlight and no sunlight is allowed to touch the container.)

**Purify (rinse) the Ormus (manna) beginning anytime after the day of the event.** If the Ormus (manna) is forgotten about and mold develops on it, throw it out or use on plants. For more information, see "Usage on Plants." (Appendix XXI.)

## Perform the Process

To follow alchemically ideal time frames when choosing to begin an Ormus collection process, it is helpful to know the date as well as the *time* of a *"Full" moon* or an *equinox.*

A "Moon Chart" (or the moon calendar) lists the date and time of all the phases of the moon. (It also records the date and time of an equinox and the date of an eclipse.) Locating the date of the event is easy with a "Moon Chart." However, knowing the time of the occurrence can be helpful. By knowing the time of the "Full" moon, we can more precisely plan when to begin an Ormus collection process.

(A "cheap and cheerful" alternative idea that avoids having to calculate precise time from a moon chart is to start the Ormus collection process on the fourth day prior to the event. In this manner, the Ormus collection process is definitely occurring during the three days prior to the event.)

Following is an example of how to calculate the precise time of a "Full" moon. There are four main time zones in the United States: Eastern Time, Central Time, Mountain Time and Pacific Time. Eastern Time is chosen for this example.

**In this example the month is June 2008:**

**Find the column labeled J for June on the "Moon Chart" and scroll down the column to note the day and time of a "Full" moon.**  The column shows a "Full" moon occurring at 17:30 on the 18th of June 2008.

**The "Moon Chart" records the hour in military time.**  Therefore 17:30 translates to 5:30 pm.

**Time is recorded in "universal time" on a "Moon Chart."**  This is more commonly called "Greenwich Mean Time."

**"Eastern Time" is 5 hours less than Greenwich Mean Time.**  Therefore, June 18 at 5:30 pm minus five hours is June 18 at 12:30 pm Eastern Time. (Central Time is six hours behind Greenwich Mean Time, Mountain Time is seven hours behind and Pacific Time is eight hours behind.)

**If the date falls after the second Sunday in March, the local clock (of most areas in the United States) has been artificially moved forward one hour.**  This time is "Daylight Saving Time." June 18 falls after March in an area of the United States where time is artificially moved forward so one hour is added to account for this. Therefore, June 18 at 12:30 pm plus one hour is June 18 at 1:30 pm.

**Gather the prepared Ormus source material and supplies three days prior to the "Full" moon and perform the Ormus collection Process.**  June 18 at 1:30 pm is the time of the event minus three days equals June 15 at 1:30 pm as the time to perform the Ormus collection process.

## Final Thought

A yearly periodical called the "Farmers Almanac" also shows dates and times of different phases of the moon and equinoxes. Some common calendars also display them and 12-month "moon" calendars show the phases of the moon during the month.

# APPENDIX XI
## Experiment Documentation

### Definition

An experiment documentation sheet records observed events during the Ormus collection processes.

### Information

The first and most important reason to have experiment documentation sheets on all of your work is: You can't trust memory!   There is also a possibility that helpful insights result from the effort.

These insights may be noticed by reviewing past documentation sheets. (For example, I observed even better results during a "new" moon.  It may be possible that a resonance is occurring between "my" frequency and the moon's.)

Other insights may also percolate into awareness.  For example: "Warm Mineral Springs" water from Northport, Florida dropped only a small amount of precipitate. After mulling over the experiment sheet, a thought occurred that more precipitate might occur by adding more "sodium" (adding sea salt) to the spring water's naturally occurring sodium content.  One theory holds that Ormus processes are "sodium" driven.  Therefore the reasoning was that perhaps the "Wet Process" performed on Warm Mineral Springs water could benefit from additional sodium.

Know that you are a type of researcher and the study of Ormus is in infancy.

### Perform the Process

To be the most helpful, the information on the documentation sheet is in a uniform layout and only pertinent data collected.

Be specific when recording information so the documentation sheet is as useful as possible. To help with specificity, use containers that measure ml or ounces.

# Experiment Documentation Sheet

## Suggested Experiment Documentation Sheet Questions

- The phase of the moon
- The date and time of the process
- The source of the Ormus material
- List anything special done to the source or the process
- Volume of source material used
- Strength of the lye solution
- Strength of the hydrochloric acid
- Ml of lye required (or ml. of hydrochloric acid required)
- Final pH attained
- Appearance of the Ormus (manna)
- Any unusual occurrence during the process
- Precipitate volume after 8 hours
- Percentage of precipitate after 8 hours
- Precipitate volume after 12 hours
- Percentage of precipitate after 12 hours

| Date/Time | Procedure | Observation |
|-----------|-----------|-------------|
|           |           |             |

# APPENDIX XII
## Common Measurement Conversions

Note: Conversions from *"common household"* measures to the *metric* measurements are approximate, as given here, and do work in the Ormus processes.

### Definition
"Measuring" occurs during the Ormus collection processes. The units of measurement often utilized are "common household" measures of ounce, cup, quart and/or gallon. (The "metric" measurement of milliliter is also used.) A measurement comparison chart makes conversions between the two systems quick, easy and more stress free.

### Information
In the "metric" system, "milliliter" is a measurement of volume (liquid). The abbreviation for Milliliter is *ml*.

In the "metric" system, "gram" is a measurement of weight (solid). Gram is abbreviated as *Gm* or *gm* and milligram abbreviated as *mg* or *mgm*.

*** Although not an exact measurement, unless density of the liquid equals 1, 1 milliliter (liquid) is generally considered to equal 1 gram (solid) ***
In many circumstances this equivalency gives a measure acceptable for the Ormus processes. Therefore, if one tablespoon [15 mgm] of lye is required it may be measured in a one-tablespoon measuring container (providing the lye is not in the "flake" form).
Note: The "flake" form of lye is measured differently because this equivalency does not hold true when a solid material is very dense or very light (flakes are very light). In those cases you cannot use a simple tablespoon-measuring container - instead, you need a weight scale to weigh out the actual grams of "solid" material needed. In the Ormus manual there is one time that this may occur. This is when lye in a "flake" form is used. When the solid lye is in a "flake" form it is very light and fluffy and therefore must be measured on a weigh scale. Therefore if one tablespoon (15gm) of lye is required, the flakes are measured on a weigh scale and not poured into a one tablespoon (15gm) measuring container. (If lye pellets or granules are used these may be poured into a one tablespoon (15gm) measuring container.) For simplicity sake, purchase lye in the form of pellets or granules.

## Common Measurements

### Household Measure                    Metric in [Milliliters]

(1 milliliter liquid is generally considered equal to 1 gram solid)
20 drops= =======================================1 ml
1 teaspoon=====================================5 ml
1 tablespoon ============================= =======15 ml
1 ounce - 2 tablespoon - 1/8 of a cup=================30 ml
2 ounce - 1/4 cup= ==============================60 ml
4 ounce - 1/2 cup= ============================120 ml
8 ounce - 1 cup= ============================240 ml
16 ounce - 2cup - 1 pint= ==========================480 ml
32 ounce - 4cup - 2 pint - 1 quart= ===================960 ml
64 ounce - 8cup - 4 pint - 2quart - 1/2 gallon= ========1,920 ml
128 ounce - 16cup - 8 pint - 4 quart - 1 gallon=========3,840 ml

Now, in the *metric* system, one kilogram is a measurement of *weight* (solid). (Kilogram is abbreviated *Kg* or *kg*.)

One kilogram is 1,000 gm and in household measure this equals about 2.2 pounds (Note: This conversion is useful in calculating amounts of ormus to use based on the weight of animals and humans.)

In the *metric* system, one liter is a measurement of *volume* (liquid). (Liter is abbreviated L.) One liter is 1,000 milliliters and in household measure this equals about 32 ounce/about two pint/about one quart.

# APPENDIX XIII
## Chemicals for the Processes

### Definition

*Chemical:* As relating to chemistry; material produced by or used in a reaction involving changes in atoms or molecules.

*Chemical Reaction:* A process in which one or more substances are changed into others.

*Reagent:* Any substance used in a chemical reaction for the purpose of producing other substances.

### Information

*Lye is a "chemical" used in the "Wet Process Ormus collection and a "reagent" in all the dry Ormus collection processes.*

*Hydrochloric acid and lye are "reagents" in all the dry Ormus collection processes.*

In the "Wet process", lye is a chemical added to break the equilibrium in seawater and to raise the pH level by dissolving into (Na+) and OH-. One theory holds that the presence of sodium (Na+) causes a place for Ormus to go. As an analogy it is like "little houses" with Ormus inside that are observed as particles. These "particles" coalesce into flakes, fall to the bottom of the container and are collected.

In the *dry* Ormus collection processes, hydrochloric acid is added to lye solution (the living menstruum) and this allows the formation of a precipitate. Explained in "Chemistry of the Ormus Processes." (Appendix XXII.) Both hydrochloric acid and lye act as reagents in *dry* Ormus processes because two *new* compounds form. These are salt and water. This is the reason that the solution at the end of any of the *dry* processes changes from lye solution to a salty non-toxic liquid.

# Lye (a.k.a. caustic soda and soda lye)

The chemical name for "lye" is sodium hydroxide (NaOH) and it is a "caustic" that goes by the common household name "lye." (It is also a caustic chemical that carries precautions regarding its use.) Until recently, lye was a commonly used household chemical. Lye unclogged drains and also is a required ingredient when making soap for use in the home.

Some may recall their grandmother working with lye for this soap making purpose. Mixing lye with fat is how soap formed. The lye material was handled with care in this work and precautions were taken. However there was no fear of the material. (Visit soap making websites to purchase lye and make your own homemade soap.) Because hand-made soap has utilized a better source of fat, homemade soap is more healthy than soap sold in stores. "Snowdrift Farms" is one such hand-made soap-making site.

Today, lye (sodium hydroxide) is a common ingredient mixed into many household cleaning products. (In the Ormus collection processes the lye used must be in its pure form.) Therefore, while lye is very caustic and care is to be exercised in its presence, it is not an "exotic" seldom seen chemical.

Lye is absolutely vital in the Ormus collection processes. Note that at the end of the "Wet Process the lye is rinsed off and its presence gone and at the end of all the *dry* processes the lye has changed to harmless salt and water. Please keep the facts about lye in proper perspective and do not work with lye in "fear." Work with lye in "respect" not "fear." The emotions surrounding "fear" cause a mind to "close off;" this results in making the steps of a procedure very difficult to absorb.

## Precautions:

Lye is caustic and the following are precautions associated with its use. If lye comes in contact with eyes, it can damage them by rendering the cornea opaque, a form of eye damage that is irreparable. If lye gets into eyes **flush the eyeball with water immediately** and seek medical attention if the burning persists.

If lye contacts skin it hurts and damages it. If lye contacts clothes it damages them. If lye gets onto your clothes or body, immediately **flush the area with lots of water** and seek medical attention if necessary.

It is very helpful to work near a sink, faucet or other source of wash water.

The area must be well ventilated as breathing fumes from lye is harmful and can damage air passages and the lungs. Lye solution creates caustic fumes. Do not breathe in these fumes. Handle lye with adequate ventilation such as a laboratory range hood vented outside or conduct the work outside. It is advisable to keep a spray bottle of distilled white vinegar handy to use against spills.

When working with lye, or any chemical, avoid touching your face or rubbing your eyes. Do not handle around food. Do not dump waste water on the ground. Lye is generally safe to put down the drain, but first run water in the sink while slowly pouring the lye directly into the drain. Don't mix it with any acid that may be in the drain as it can react explosively.

When working with lye, please wear goggles or a full-face visor (an industrial face protector), neoprene gloves and a PVC lab apron as well as protective clothing such as long sleeves and long pants.

Keep children and pets away from the work area and do not leave it unattended. Even if no one is around, any unsuspecting person could venture by and be at risk.

Glass can shatter with hot liquids. Allow lye solution that has been prepared time to cool prior to pouring it into another glass container.

Without a proper perspective, it can be easy to feel fearful about the use of lye and consider its presence a "nuisance" which must be endured. Rather, I would have you understand how special lye is and feel respect for the lye substance. (I appreciate the fact that we have such a unique chemical at our disposal for use in the Ormus collection processes.)

Lye is central to the Ormus processes because lye interacts with all the kingdoms of the earth: the animal, the vegetable and the mineral. This makes lye extremely useful as it can be used in all of its pure forms, to interact with every Ormus source. The **pure** forms of lye include "granular," "pellet" and "flake" (flake form not preferred). **Do not use lye mixtures** as might be found in some toilet bowl cleaners, many drain cleaners and openers, many oven cleaners, some gel laundry stain removers, some bathroom disinfectant cleaners, some grill cleaners, some laundry detergents, some all purpose cleaners, some cleaner and degreasers, some degreasers, some dishwashing liquids, etc. For more information, see "Resources and Supplies-Food Grade Lye." (Appendix I.)  Note: Food grade simply means it is pure lye with nothing else mixed in.

Because the Ormus collection processes require the presence of lye, there is a need for choices of labware able to withstand contact with this chemical. For more information, see "Labware Choices." (Appendix XIV.)

Label the bottle of lye solution made "Lye (NaOH) - Poison" and store in an HDPE plastic bottle placed in a non-metallic catch basin (in the event the bottle leaks). The HDPE bottle that has a plastic triangle on the bottom and the number 2 inside the triangle is the type to use. Do not store in glass because lye eats away at it and, with time, weakens the glass. (Note: The lye solution may be placed in glass containers while performing an Ormus process.)

Note: Potassium hydroxide (KOH, potash lye) can be used in place of sodium hydroxide (NaOH) however sodium hydroxide is considered the better choice. We favor sodium hydroxide because it is less costly *and* stronger than potassium hydroxide. (Less sodium hydroxide is used in an Ormus collection process because 56 parts of potassium hydroxide are required to perform what 40 parts of sodium hydroxide performs.)

# Hydrochloric Acid (a.k.a. muriatic acid, hydrogen chloride)

The chemical abbreviation for hydrochloric acid is HCl. Hydrochloric acid is an acid and, like lye (mentioned above), must be handled with care. Hydrochloric acid carries the same precautions as lye.

### Precautions:

If hydrochloric acid comes in contact with eyes, it can damage them by rendering the cornea opaque, a form of eye damage that is irreparable. If hydrochloric acid gets into eyes **flush the eyeball with water immediately** and seek medical attention if the burning persists.

If hydrochloric acid contacts the skin it hurts and damages it. Hydrochloric acid reacts with skin tissue and can cause permanent damage and scarring if severe. Even minor reactions can be very painful. If hydrochloric acid contacts clothes it damages them. If hydrochloric acid gets onto your clothes or body, immediately **flush the area with lots of water** and seek medical attention if necessary.

It is very helpful to work near a sink, faucet or other source of wash water.

The area must be well ventilated as breathing fumes from hydrochloric acid can damage air passages and lungs. Handle hydrochloric acid with adequate ventilation such as a laboratory range hood vented outside or conduct the work outside. An open stock bottle of hydrochloric acid creates corrosive fumes and when added to water a pungent corrosive "fog" forms. Do not breathe fumes or fog. It is advisable to keep a bottle of baking soda solution handy to use against spills and baking soda powder can be sprinkled on if the spill is large.

When working with hydrochloric acid, or any chemical, avoid touching your face or rubbing your eyes. Do not handle around food. Do not dump wastewater on the ground. *Hydrochloric acid* is generally safe to put down the drain, but first run water in the sink while slowly pouring the hydrochloric acid directly into the drain and don't mix it with any *"pH basic"* material that may be in the drain as it can react explosively.

When working with hydrochloric acid, please wear goggles or a full-face visor (an industrial face protector), neoprene gloves and a PVC lab apron as well as protective clothing such as long sleeves and long pants.

Keep children and pets away from the work area and do not leave it unattended. Even if no one is around, any unsuspecting person could venture by and be at risk.

Just like lye, hydrochloric Acid is not an "exotic" seldom seen material. **Do not use hydrochloric acid mixtures** as might be found as a common ingredient mixed into grout cleaners, tile cleaners, some lime away products, some toilet cleaners, humidifier cleaners and some spa cleansers, etc.

We use hydrochloric acid in its pure form in the Ormus collection processes. The pure form is a clear liquid. A common use of pure hydrochloric acid is in the maintenance of the pH in swimming pools. This is a source for procuring hydrochloric acid. Actually, hydrochloric acid and sulfuric acid are stocked for this purpose and it is important to visually confirm the container is hydrochloric acid and not the sulfuric acid.

Do not work with hydrochloric acid in "fear." Work with hydrochloric acid in "respect" not "fear." The emotions surrounding "fear" cause a mind to "close off;" this results in making steps of a procedure very difficult to absorb.

Label the bottle of diluted hydrochloric acid "Hydrochloric Acid (HCl) –Poison" and store in glass container placed in a non-metallic catch basin (in the event the bottle breaks). Borosilicate glass is the best type to use although regular glass also works. For more information, see "Labware Choices-Borosilicate Glass." (Appendix XIV.)

Note: A household type item that can be useful for storage is the glass container of a 40oz beer bottle covered with a plastic lid. A metal lid is not used because fumes from hydrochloric acid corrodes metal and Saran™ Wrap cannot be placed as a dividing material between metal and glass as it also corrodes. (I have seen plastic caps sold in the grocery store.)

While performing an Ormus Collection Process, the diluted hydrochloric acid may be placed in HDPE bottles.

NOTES:

Ways in which the alchemist can draw spirit into the
work area include ritual, prayer and meditation,
contemplation, and focusing techniques.

# APPENDIX XIV
## Best Practices Labware Choices

### Aluminum Foil
### (Also information on shielding from electric and magnetic fields)

Ormus cannot be "forced" to do anything. The more we protect the state of the Ormus (manna) from external forces, the easier it is to have the Ormus "stay in place." Two such forces are considered to be "Electric fields" and especially "electromagnetic fields" (EMF fields).

*"Electric fields"* can be blocked by the use of "electrostatic shields." This is also called "static shielding." Nature produces electric fields when local build up of electric charges in the atmosphere occur during thunderstorms. Electric fields are found in our created environment as well and there is controversy regarding their affect on our health. The strongest electric fields we may be exposed to are beneath high voltage transmission lines.

Aluminum (foil) is electrostatic and shields from an "electric field" (but *not* a "magnetic field"). The effectiveness of this shielding is dependant on the integrity of the aluminum shielding. For maximum effectiveness there is to be no tears or breaks (even the size of a pinhole) and the aluminum foil is to be overlapping around the container of Ormus (manna) to ensure the shielding is continuous. Another factor in how well aluminum foil shields from an "electric field" is the thickness of the aluminum foil. You may choose to wrap the container with the shiny or the dull side of the foil facing out. It works just as well either way because aluminum foil is practically all metal.

The brand of aluminum foil most often purchased is Reynolds Wrap® and this is 98.5% aluminum (the rest is silicon and Iron). Reynolds Wrap® produces three thickness grades of aluminum foil: "regular" (.01625mm), "heavy strength" (.02362mm) and "super strength" (.03479mm). The "heavy strength" is commonly found on the grocer's shelf and the "super strength" may require a special order. Thicker aluminum foil sheeting tears less and shields more. Therefore, it is suggested that you purchase the thickest aluminum foil sheeting available. *(www.reynoldskitchens.com)*

Aluminum provides some shielding from "radio frequency waves." Radio frequency waves are a particular combination of an "electric field" and a "magnetic field." Aluminum provides shielding from the "electric field" component only.

Because aluminum acts like a shield protecting the state of the Ormus (manna) in some way, its presence is felt to "encourage" the Ormus to "stay put." Therefore, the bottle of finished Ormus product is always wrapped in aluminum foil for storage. The aluminum foil is also felt by some to shield the Ormus from scalar (spin) fields in some way.

*"Magnetic fields"* generally penetrate *all* objects. Nature produces a "magnet field" called "The earth's magnetic field." It is this field that causes a compass to point in the N-S direction and guides animals and birds that migrate. Magnetic fields are in our created environment as well and these are called an "electromagnetic field" or "EMF." There is controversy regarding their affect

on health. The strongest magnetic fields we may be exposed to are close to running motors, in electrical appliances and other "running" electrical appliances (including imaging equipment in the medical profession). While magnetic fields pretty well cannot be shielded against, they are, to varying degrees, able to be "shunted" (reduced to some extent). Ferrous containing material (steel) mitigates (somewhat effectively) magnetic fields by magnetically "shunting" the field around it (not shielding from it). Because of the magnetically shunting action of steel, it has been said the best storage container for bottles of aluminum wrapped prepared Ormus product is steel cans or canisters (check for steel construction with a magnet). Some sources for metal cans are paint cans, holiday popcorn cans and those that held candy or liquor. I have seen garden seeds packed in metal cans. For the best protection possible, the steel container is to be "earth grounded" (on the floor) and to even further increase its shunting action, the steel can may be placed in a metal (steel) file cabinet.

(Note: To best ensure electromagnetic waves (commonly called magnetic fields) cause no interference on the stability of the Ormus in the source material or the finished Ormus product, it is prudent to keep the work and storage area six feet or more away from them.)

The home has both "electric fields" and "magnetic fields" (electromagnetic, EMF) in it. Examples include: "electric fields" from (plugged in) hair dryers, vacuum cleaners, fluorescent lights, microwave oven, portable radios, electric ovens, washing machines, irons, dishwashers, computers, refrigerators, color TVs, stereo receivers, mixers, toasters, coffee machines, light bulbs and "magnetic fields" that occur when these items are operating (turned on). According to the World Health Organization, the "human guidelines limit" on exposure to these fields is often met while being 12 inches away from these items when operating although we choose, during the Ormus collection processes, and storage of the prepared Ormus product to remain six feet or more away from both these fields and especially the electromagnetic fields.

(The difference between a "magnetic field" and "electric field" is the movement of current, or lack of movement. Electric charges that move produce a "magnetic field." Therefore a "plugged in" appliance has an "electric field" even when the appliance is "off" and has a "magnetic field" (electromagnetic field or EMF) when both plugged in and operating. While operating, electric charges, commonly called current, are flowing and the more current that is flowing the stronger the "magnetic field." This is why appliances with motors (such as refrigerators) generate a larger field (motors require more current). In both types of fields, the "field strength" decrease with more distance from the source.

Remember: We choose to remain six feet or more away from both these fields.

## Barrel Syringes

Barrel syringes (called oral baby syringes) administer liquid medicine to babies. Pharmacies stock these and often, when asked, will give you one. Oral baby syringes are also sold in the OTC section of the pharmacy. Barrel syringes are available in 1 ml., 5 ml. and 10 ml. size. Barrel syringes as large a 50 ml. are sold in grocery stores for injecting turkeys (remove the needle). These syringes can be a labware choice in the Ormus collection processes to control and measure the "lye solution" or "hydrochloric acid" as it is added to smaller batches of the prepared Ormus source material or when the pH is close to the "target" pH. The oral syringes are also useful when measuring the finished Ormus (manna) for use.

## Baster - Choose One That Is Plastic

A properly chosen baster has a squeeze bulb on the end. Do not choose the type with a brush on the end. A baster can be used during the "Wet Process and dry processes to bubble and mix the Ormus (manna) during purifying (washing) and to draw up the Ormus (manna) precipitate from the bottom of the container.

## Borosilicate Glass Containers

A trade name for this type of glass is Kimax® and Simax.®

Borosilicate glass is a strong, soda-lime glass containing 5% boric acid. It is best to use borosilicate glass containers (called beakers) when processes require glass because it is highly resistant to heat and shock. This glass also features a high resistance to chemicals and a very low "thermal expansion coefficient." The result is the glass doesn't crack as easily when heat is applied. This glass can withstand continuous temperatures of up to approximately 485 to 500 degrees Fahrenheit (230-240 degrees Centigrade) and a maximum temperature of approximately 1,000 degrees Fahrenheit (500 degrees Centigrade). *(www.aceglass.com)*

Abrasions, micro-cracks or star cracks weaken the glass (especially when subjecting it to high temperatures.) Therefore inspect the glass before use by holding it up to normal sunlight and looking for areas of stress. These would include cracks and abrasions.

Wash the glass with a soft bristle brush and a soft plastic or wood handle to reduce the amount of scratching that may occur. Take care not to bump the glass against the sides of the sink or other glass vessels.

In addition to the safety reasons for choosing this glass, some have proposed that there is an affinity of gold Ormus for "regular" glass and that it may hang onto the walls of the glass container.

I have ordered Borosilicate glass (called beakers) from labware companies as well as from e-bay. For more information, see "Resources and Supplies-Labware." (Appendix I.)

(Note: Pyrex® *used* to be made of borosilicate glass. After the company was sold in 1998 the Pyrex® products *sold in the United States* stopped being made out of the glass it is named for (borosilicate glass). Anchor® Hocking, another common brand name is also *not* made out of borosilicate glass. Use a web search of "Borosilicate Glass Measuring Cups" to find household type items made out of borosilicate glass.)

## Buchner filter funnel (a.k.a. Flat Strainer)

The shape of this labware is a *cross* between a funnel and a strainer. The shape is of a flat strainer on the bottom with slanted sides. For more information, see "Resources and Supplies-Labware." (Appendix I.)

In place of purchasing these from labware companies, similarly shaped items can be found in the kitchenware department of Kmart,® Walmart,®, etc.

### Candy / Deep Fry Thermometer

The best type to buy has *no* metal in its construction because it is the easiest to use in the Ormus Collection processes. This type is hard to find; and a thermometer with metal in the construction of its housing can still be used in the Ormus processes (with consideration as to its placement).

### Enamel Pan with a Lid

This is an enamel covered steel pot with a lid. They are often blue enamel speckled with white. If you use this type of pot, there *must* be no cracks or chips in the enameling, which would allow contact of the solution with the metal below the enameling.

An enamel pan can be used to dissolve the sea salt or boil the seawater during the "Wet Process." Other Ormus collection processes are too energetically active for the enameling to hold up.

### Filters

The least expensive choice in filters, for home use, is the Mr. Coffee® type of pleated (unbleached) paper filters. Two or three of these filters are stacked together and wetted before filtering liquid through.

Buchner filter funnels (more expensive) are available through lab supply companies. For more information, see "Resources and Supplies." (Appendix I.)

### Flashlight

Choose one with a *focused* beam. This tool is useful when observing Ormus (manna) precipitate as it is forming in the solution. A Mini Maglite® flashlight is an example of a focused beam light.

### Flat Strainer

(See Buchner Filter Funnel)

### Funnel

The funnel that is used should have *ribs* sticking out along the outside of it. This way the funnel won't "vapor lock" as liquid runs through it into a container. Vapor locking can cause a mess because liquids may back up and flow out of the funnel.

## (Separatory Funnel)

One way to remove Ormus (manna) precipitate from the *bottom* of the container is to make a homemade "separatory" funnel. Cut the bottom off a washed sport drink bottle (that has a nippled sport lid) and tip the container over. Close the nippled sport lid and fill the container with the Ormus (manna) precipitate from the "Wet Process" or any of the *dry* processes as well as the liquid above the Ormus (manna). Once the Ormus (manna) has re-settled, open the nippled sport lid and allow the manna precipitate to flow through and into your catch container. Stop the flow when reaching the level of the liquid over the Ormus (manna.)

## High Density Polyethylene plastic:  Abbreviated HDPE

*HDPE is the plastic material of choice for storage bottles of Ormus (manna.) Containers made of this material can be chosen when "plastic" may be used during an Ormus collection process.*

**Choose plastic containers that have a triangle on the bottom with the #2 in the middle. This is a "recycling code" and a recycling code of #2 means this is HDPE material.** I have observed plastic vinegar containers, five gallon empty buckets (in the painting department at Home Depot), Easter cookies (packaged in a plastic bucket), one-quart containers of milk and containers of ground coffee displaying a #2 recycling code. (If a suitable container is "re-used," clean it thoroughly). For information on ordering HDPE bottles see "Resources and Supplies-HDPE Bottles." (Appendix I.)

HDPE material is compatible with a wide range of products including acids and caustics. HDPE resin is the most widely used for plastic bottles and containers. This material is economical, impact resistant and provides a good moisture barrier. It is FDA approved for food use. Plastic bottles made from HDPE are naturally translucent and flexible. The addition of color makes HDPE bottles opaque - not glossy. (Note: In Ormus work either "white" or "opaque" may be used, but not any other color.) HDPE plastic bottles are not suitable for use with essential oils.

A question often heard is if a recycling code other than #2 may be chosen. For example: Can the nutritional product Boost,® which has a #7 recycling code, be used? The short answer is no, and detailed information follows.

Recycling codes of #1, #2 or #5 are "phthalate-free" and because phthalate often is used to make polyvinyl chloride (PVC), these bottles are considered PVC-free. (A #3 recycling code indicates this plastic contains phthalate.) Phthalates, several of which are in a process to be banned in children's toys, and bisphenol A (BPA) is also being considered for banning. These are hormone-like chemicals found in plastics and studies have suggested they affect the reproductive system. Plastic with a #7 recycling code is a category that includes bisphenol A and therefore recycling code #7 is avoided in Ormus work. Recycling code #6 contains polystyrene (styrofoam) and evidence suggests this substance can leach potential toxins into foods (especiallly when heated) (USA TODAY, August 5, 2008 and MIAMI HERALD, December 14, 2008).

Recycling code #1 is not used in Ormus work because it does not have the inertness (resistant to chemicals) as #2 recycling code does and recycling code #5 is not used in Ormus work because the container is not as dense (thick) and is available in jar shapes and specialty baby bottles not standard bottle shape.

(Note: Not all products contain a recycling code. If one is not present, a suggestion has been made to keep it out of your life.)

Remember: Choose plastic containers that have a triangle on the bottom with the #2 in the middle.

## ("Spout Capped" HDPE Container)

The cap shape of "spout caps" creates a steady liquid stream with the squeeze of the hand. The "lye solution" or "hydrochloric acid" easily and safely streams into the liquids used in the Ormus collection processes.

## (Nalgene)

Oil won't adhere to this plastic. (Some have said that Ormus is an oil in pure form.) Nalgene provides more of a barrier against oil than HDPE plastic. Nalgene containers are more expensive than HDPE containers. For the Ormus collection processes we are content to use HDPE plastic.

## Heat Source

Some have said that a benefit of adding an outside source of heat during an Ormus process is the Ormus collected is "annealed." The Ormus (manna) collected is said to be in a slightly higher energy state (higher spin on the Ormus material) and be more energetically active (potent) by having a higher "quantum resonance frequency."

It has also been proposed by some that there is a possibility the Ormus collector standing near the heated pot may receive some of the lighter Ormus as they float away.

However, it is generally thought adding external heat during an Ormus process affects the Ormus (manna). A theory holds that any Ormus process which uses external heat, *especially when heat is applied to cause a "boil,"* places a slightly higher energy state (higher spin on the Ormus material) and there is more precipitate when a process is performed that does not cause a boil. When boiling, some of the lighter Ormus boils off and are lost to the collection. *(Note: The "Dry Process (Cold Fire Process)" does not add heat from an external source (external heat), and for this reason is considered a valuable Ormus collection process. The "Dry Process (Cold Fire Process)" is also a process the average Ormus collector is able to perform.)*

A *gas* flame is *preferred* for Ormus processes that require heat. Alchemists only use a gas flame and caution to never use electric heat when working with Ormus. They say that if you have an electric range/stove-top, buy a propane turkey ring burner as your heat source. A propane turkey ring burner with a *double* ring of flame generates enough heat for the requirements of Ormus collection processes that include a "burn." (Note: The *dry* "Lye Boil Process" does not need the heat of a double ring of flame on the propane turkey ring burner.) If you need to buy a propane turkey ring burner, consider buying one that has a "double ring" of propane flame.

This way you have the level of heat needed for any Ormus collection process. Builders Square® sells Bayou Classic® which is a "double ring" burner.

The preference for a gas flame stems from the "pulsed" electromagnetic field generated by an electric stove when it is turned on. This pulsed electromagnetic field is thought by many to drive (some or all) Ormus away. The explanation regarding a "pulsed electromagnetic field" begins with the term "alternating current" (AC). AC is the type of power received from wall plugs (versus batteries). AC current reverses its direction at regular intervals. In North America, electricity has a frequency of 60 cycles per second or 60 Hertz. When the current's direction is changed, the electromagnetic field changes its orientation 60 times every second. The field is therefore "pulsed."

Some have said that more than the "driving away" of Ormus is occurring and that the EMF waves from electric stoves place a pressure on Ormus to drop out of the state it is in (this is a slow process) and return to metal with the resultant release of harmful radiation. (This may be a good reason to own a gas stove for daily cooking and warrants further research.) However, there are others who do not subscribe to this and their line of reasoning is that the pulsed electromagnetic field of an electric stove may potentially reduce the amount of Ormus collected however not drive Ormus to metal. They cite the fact that we are exposed to pulsed magnetic fields every day (consider the common light bulb when it is lit) and are suffering no ill health. This dialogue is outside the scope of this manual and has been included to help you in making an educated decision regarding both the source of heat and its use.

Three areas that all agree on: First, it may be beneficial to stand near the heated pot to allow the Ormus that does leave to possibly come to you and personally align with you. Secondly, the use of external heat is as low a temperature as practical (to reduce the amount of Ormus that boils off) and thirdly, the heat applied is for no longer than necessary to ensure the minimal amount of the lighter Ormus floats off.

## Measuring Container

Choose one-cup to four-cup measuring containers. (The most common measurements found in the Ormus collection processes are 1/2 cup and one cup of solid material and the *dry* processes most commonly utilize 65ml. and 35ml of liquid material.)

Measuring containers made of plastic material may be chosen when measuring out the Ormus source materials however when lye crystals are dissolved and when hydrochloric acid is measured, the material chosen is to be glass. Borosilicate glass is preferred and especially when heat is involved (dissolving the lye crystals or adding the hydrochloric acid) because of its resistance to breakage in the presence of changes in temperature (heat).

A "graduated" cylinder (purchased from lab supply companies) measures liquid accurately to the level of ml. Graduated cylinders offer more accurate measuring than standard measuring containers although it is not a necessity to have one. (Again, the most common liquid measurements found in the Ormus collection processes are 65ml. and 35ml.)

Chose assorted size *non-metallic* measuring spoons. (The most common measurements found in the Ormus collection processes are 1/2 tablespoon and 1tablespoon of solid material.)

## Paper Towels
These are always helpful to have.

## Non-Metallic Catch Basin
As a safety measure, always place containers used in the processes into a larger non-metallic "catch basin" (in case of leakage or breakage). For example: a (new) cat litter box or the bottom of an under-the-bed storage container. As a safety measure, place the stock bottles of "lye" solution and "hydrochloric acid" in a catch basin while storing.

## Safety equipment
Safety eyeglasses, full-face visor (industrial face protector), long sleeves/long pants, neoprene (or rubber) gloves, a lab apron and the catch basin under the containers of liquid can all be considered safety equipment.

## Stainless Steel Container
This is to be 18/10 stainless steel. Stainless steel needs a special awareness and notes of warning. *Now it must be known that if there is a screw or bolt in the pots manufacturing process that is attracted to a magnet, it is* **NOT** *made of stainless steel material and must be replaced with a stainless steel screw or bolt.*

It is important to look closely at the construction of the stainless steel pot. The handles are to be welded on or bolted on - there are to be no rivets. Rivets have aluminum (which is attacked by lye) and are toxic. There appears to be more and more evidence that aluminum can cause Alzheimer's. THIS IS VERY IMPORTANT. If the stainless steel pot has ANY rivets, there is some aluminum alloy and the rivets HAVE to be drilled out and replaced with stainless steel bolts. (Also if the pot is used for a "burn", the handles must be removed.)

Some of the Ormus processes require lids be on the pots. Check the knob on the lid to be sure no aluminum is there (check this with a magnet). If there is aluminum, the knob must be removed and replaced with a stainless steel bolt.

It is important to continuously check all areas of the pot to be sure the stainless steel is intact, not discolored, and has not been breached. Do not use the pot if there are visible rust spots, any pitting, any chipping or discoloration that can't be polished away with stainless steel cleansers.

It is important that the heated "lye solution" (used in a collection process that includes boiling) or "lye granules" (used in a collection process that includes a "burn") is in contact with the stainless steel pot for as short a time as possible. **THIS IS VERY IMPORTANT.** Remove the heated "lye solution" from the stainless steel pot as soon as it has cooled down when performing the dry "Lye Boil" and *dry* "Lye Burn and Boil Process." Remove the burned lye crystals from the stainless steel pot as soon as it has cooled when performing the *dry* "Lye Burn Process" and *dry* "Lye Burn and Boil Process." (Remove the heated sodium as soon as it has cooled down in a *dry* "Sodium Burn Process.")

Stainless Steel pots have a very short useful life when "lye granules" are burned in them during the *dry* "Lye Burn Process" and *dry* "Lye Burn and Boil Process." These processes have caused permanent discoloration or breaching with pitting in as few as three "burns." (The *dry* "Sodium Burn Process" is more energetically active and therefore even more damaging to the stainless steel pot.)

When observing pitting in the stainless steel, this means that iron is showing. Iron is not desired in the Ormus collection process. For information on procuring stainless steel pots, see "Resources and Supplies-Stainless Steel Pots." (Appendix I.)

## Stirring Utensils

Choose plastic stirring choices. These may include spatulas, spoons, etc. If a stainless steel utensil is chosen it must be continuously checked in every area to ensure the stainless steel is intact and has not been breached. Do not use the stainless steel utensil if observing any rusty spots, flaking or chipping. This means that iron is showing and we do not want iron in the Ormus processes. For this reason, plastic stirring utensils are most common and are suggested.

Borosilicate glass stirrers may be chosen, however, due to a combination of their cost and breakage potential, the average Ormus collector seldom uses these. For more information, see "Resources and Supplies-Labware." (Appendix I.)

Labware Equipment

Don't forget the paper towels and a non-metallic catch basin to set the container in that you are working with. A new cat littler box works well as does an under-the-bed storage container.

Lye granules and muriatic acid
(hydrochloric acid)

## Following is a list of Labware chosen for Ormus collection processes

### Labware and Supplies to perform a "Live Oil Process"

"Grape seed" oil, sea salt *or* Ormus (manna) *or* "drawn" seawater (from the ocean), glass container (with non-metallic top), aluminum foil, paper towels, flat strainer or funnel and (unbleached) filters.

(If using Ormus (manna) precipitate or seawater as the Ormus source material, add a barrel syringe or turkey baster - the type with the bulb at the end, not the brush).

### Labware and Supplies to perform a "Wet Process"

Sea salt or "drawn" seawater, lye solution, distilled water, pH meter, aluminum foil, barrel syringe or baster, flat strainer or funnel, (unbleached) filters, enamel pan or stainless steel pan, focus beam flashlight, heat source, measuring cup, plastic catch basin, plastic or borosilicate glass stirrer (stainless steel *not* preferred), safety clothing/equipment, container made of HDPE plastic or borosilicate glass (regular glass may also be used). Do *not* use leaded glass (lead may contaminate the product). Therefore, if you have a leaded crystal punch bowl that seems to be a good size for the process, don't use it as lead or iron contamination is not desired. Store the finished Ormus (manna) in HDPE plastic. "Long-term" storage of lye solution is in HDPE plastic containers and during the Ormus collection process it can be placed in HDPE plastic or glass containers.

### Labware and Supplies to perform a "Dry Process" (Cold Fire Process)

Ormus source material, lye solution, hydrochloric acid, distilled water, pH meter, container made of HDPE plastic (to house the lye solution as it disaggregates the Ormus source material), borosilicate glass container (to perform the process in), measuring cup, aluminum foil, barrel syringe or baster, funnel or flat strainer, (unbleached) filters, focus beam flashlight, plastic catch basin, plastic stirrer (or *borosilicate glass*), safety clothing/equipment, HDPE container (to store finished manna). The hydrochloric acid used as the "reagent" in the process can be placed in an HDPE plastic bottle.

### Labware and Supplies to perform a *dry* "Lye Boil Process"

Ormus source material, lye solution, hydrochloric acid, distilled water, pH meter, stainless steel pot for the "boil" (follow the stainless steel precautions in Appendix XIV), 5 lb flat weight (weight-trainer type) or a brick, heat source: propane turkey ring burner, *borosilicate glass* container (to perform the process), measuring cup, aluminum foil, barrel syringe or baster, funnel or flat strainer, (unbleached) filters, focus beam flashlight, plastic catch basin, plastic or borosilicate glass stirrer, safety clothing and equipment. Hydrochloric acid used as the "reagent" in the process can be placed in an HDPE plastic bottle. Store the finished manna in HDPE plastic containers.

### Labware and Supplies to perform a *dry* "Lye Burn Process"

Ormus source material, lye crystals and lye solution, hydrochloric acid, distilled water, pH meter, lidded stainless steel saucepan (follow the stainless steel precautions in Appendix XIV), 5 lb flat weight (weight-trainer type) or a brick, metal sleeve (to condense the heat in the area around the saucepan), a heat source: propane turkey ring burner with a *double* ring of flame (for the higher heat required for the "burn"), container made of HDPE plastic (to house the lye solution as it disaggregates the burned Ormus source material), container of *borosilicate glass* (to collect the precipitate), measuring cup, aluminum foil, barrel syringe or baster, funnel or flat strainer, (unbleached) filters , focus beam flashlight, plastic catch basin, plastic or borosilicate glass stirrer, safety clothing and equipment. The hydrochloric acid used as the "reagent" in the process can be placed in an HDPE plastic bottle during the collection. Store the finished manna in HDPE plastic containers.

## Labware and Supplies to perform a *dry* "Lye Burn and Boil Process"

Ormus source material, lye crystals and lye solution, hydrochloric acid, distilled water, pH meter, stainless steel lidded saucepan for the "burn" (follow the stainless steel precautions in Appendix XIV), 5 lb flat weight (weight-trainer type) or a brick, metal sleeve (to condense the heat in the area around the saucepan), a heat source: propane turkey ring burner with a *double* ring of flame (for the higher heat required for the "burn"), stainless steel pot for the "boil" (follow the stainless steel precautions in Appendix XIV), container of *borosilicate glass* (to collect the precipitate), measuring cup, aluminum foil, barrel syringe or baster, funnel or flat strainer, (unbleached) filters, focus beam flashlight, plastic catch basin, plastic or borosilicate glass stirrer, safety clothing and equipment. The hydrochloric acid used as the "reagent" in the process can be placed in an HDPE plastic bottle during the collection. Store the finished manna in HDPE plastic containers.

## Labware and Supplies to perform a *dry* "Sodium Burn Process"

(The author suggests that you DO NOT perform this dangerous process. This list is provided for information, historical and posterity purposes only.)

Ormus source material (pure metal if using metal), pure sodium metal (explosive with even the smallest amount of moisture such as your breath vapor), face mask or respirator and a face shield, dry sodium carbonate, pH meter, flock lined rubber gloves, meat cleaver, olive oil, lidded titanium crucible preferred or a good stainless steel saucepan (for the "burn.") If using stainless follow the stainless steel precautions in Appendix XIV, stainless steel pot (if performing a "boil") or container of HDPE plastic (if not performing a boil), heat source: propane turkey ring burner with a *double* ring of flame (for the higher heat required for the "burn"), metal sleeve (to condense the heat in the area around the crucible), mister bottle, distilled water, Ziploc® freezer bags, chisel, lye solution, hydrochloric acid, distilled water, 5-lb flat weight (weight-trainer type) or a brick, container of *borosilicate glass* (to collect the precipitate), measuring cup, aluminum foil, barrel syringe or baster, funnel or flat strainer, (unbleached) filters, focus beam flashlight, plastic catch basin, plastic or borosilicate glass stirrer, aluminum foil, safety clothing and equipment. The hydrochloric acid used as the "reagent" in the process can be placed in an HDPE plastic bottle during the collection. Store the finished manna in HDPE plastic containers.

## Labware and Supplies to perform a *dry* "Hydrogen Peroxide (Gold) Process"

Pure gold, jewelers roller mill, hammer and anvil, 35% hydrogen peroxide, lye solution, lye crystals, hydrochloric acid, one-liter *borosilicate glass* filtering flask with tubulation attachment and solid stopper, polypropylene tubing, glass container with stopper, one-liter flask, distilled water,

Morton's canning/pickling salt, stirrer of plastic or borosilicate, Visions (trademark) glass/ceramic Dutch oven with lid, propane turkey ring burner, 5 lb flat weight (weight-trainer type) or a brick, non-metallic funnel or flat strainer, (unbleached) filters , container made of *borosilicate glass* not regular glass (to collect the precipitate), sand, thermometer, focus beam flashlight, plastic bucket, steel can, cardboard box, Saran™ Wrap, aluminum foil.

### Labware and Supplies to perform a "Magnet Vortex Water Trap" process

Good drinking water, "Magnet Vortex Water Trap" (or "Vortex Water Trap"), *glass* storage container away *from light* or electromagnetic wave (EMF) producing appliances, aluminum foil.

### Labware to perform a "Dew Collection Process"

#### •Labware and Supplies to perform "Dew Collection Process 1"

You will need ice, a large "regular glass" container and something plastic or glass to hold it up a bit, non-metallic catch basin and aluminum foil.  Store dew in a glass container.

#### •Labware and Supplies to perform "Dew Collection Process 2"

Plastic sheeting, container to catch the dew

#### •Labware and Supplies to perform "Dew Collection Process 3"

Natural sea salt, lidded glass bowl

# APPENDIX XV
## pH (Meter)

### Definition

Getting the correct pH is **CRITICAL** in the Ormus collection processes.

### Information

It is important to have a pH meter that *works*.

pH stands for "potential of hydrogen." The concentration of hydrogen *ions in a liquid determines* its pH value and is measured on a scale of 0 to 14, with lower numbers indicating higher acidity and higher numbers indicating alkalinity. Maximum acidity is pH 0 and maximum alkalinity is pH 14. An acid is a substance that releases hydrogen into a solution. An alkaline substance is one that removes hydrogen from a solution. Water, which is considered neutral (neither acidic nor alkaline), has a pH of 7.

Long electrodes with a thin tube of glass at the end are necessary components of pH meters and are rather fragile. Therefore, treat them gently and don't bang them around. The electrode is replaceable in most pH meters, but it usually costs as much as the meter. It is useful to own two pH meters (in case one breaks).

It is important when calibrating a pH meter to factor in any calibration differences. Calibration differences cause inaccuracies. For example, if a pH meter is calibrated with the pH 7 calibration buffer solution (usually sold with the pH meter) and the closest reading the meter reads is 7.1 -there is +0.1 actual difference between what the meter is reading and what is so. Therefore, if an Ormus process is to stop at pH 8.5, the process is instead stopped when this pH meter reads pH 8.6. (An even more accurate calibration requires the use of a second buffer. The second calibration buffer solution is pH 9 if you are titrating to a basic pH [as when using lye solution]. If titrating to an acidic pH [as when using hydrochloric acid], the second calibration buffer solution is pH 4. After checking both buffers, the meter can usually be adjusted so that no correction is necessary. Note: Two buffer solutions do not have to be used in the Ormus collection processes.)

The most accurate pH meter readings occur when hands are not touching the meter. The electrical energy generated from hands affects the pH meter so it is important to clip the pH meter to the side of or hang from above the container. Therefore, it is helpful to have a way to hold the pH meter to or above the source container. To make a pH meter holder using household materials glue two clothespins in the shape of an X with non-toxic glue. Another simple idea is to hang the pH meter over the container using a string attached to a solid object. Labware companies also sell pH holders and these generally include a ring stand with rod (also called a retort stand base with rod), a universal clamp (also known as a universal bosshead) and a 3-prong clamp (also termed a clamp with overlapping jaws).

If the pH meter is not clipped to the sides of the container or hung down over it, its measuring prong must be removed from the liquid when the actions of stirring and adding a chemical (lye solution, hydrochloric acid) are performed. Be sure to rinse off the prongs of the pH meter with distilled water when they are removed from the solution or place the pH meter in a small glass of distilled water. This helps decrease the build up of residual dried material from the solution onto the prongs. Residual build up on the prongs leads to false pH readings from the pH meter.

Re-calibrate the pH meter using pH 7 buffer solution before beginning another Ormus process, if the pH meter is dropped, has the batteries changed or if the accuracy of the pH meter is in question. It is a good idea to calibrate the pH meter each day it is used. The buffer solution is good until the expiration date stamped on the original container.

## Storage

After use, rinse the pH meter in cold tap water or distilled water and don't touch the glass tip at the end of the pH meter. Store the pH meter in its storage box. There is often a sponge piece inside that is to be kept moist because the electrode at the end of the pH meter lasts longer in a moist environment. Tap water or distilled water or the pH 7 buffer solution can be used to moisten this sponge and there is no need to buy special storage solutions. (I also remove the batteries from the pH meter when storing it.)

## Final Thought

If performing Ormus collection routinely, a commercial grade meter can be purchased from suppliers such as "Hanna Instruments." One such model is HI8314 membrane pH meter. For more information, see "Resources and Supplies-pH Meter." (Appendix I.)

# APPENDIX XVI
## Toning / Smudging and Background Sound

### Definition
These are areas of consideration regarding our "conscious" self *and* our environment as we prepare to perform an Ormus collection process.

### Toning
Toning prior to collecting Ormus (manna) has been said to cause disharmonious ("bad") energy to leave the body. This internal area in the body then fills with our own unique individual energy. (I have heard that we each embody a tone that resonates with our body.) Sound out by humming until you find this tone--then continue humming out in that pitch. A peaceful sensation may be felt. Because we each resonate on our own personal frequency, we each have different pitches of sound during toning. Some say this diversity of frequencies is the basis underlying our individuality and the cause of each of us being special and unique. These same different frequencies are surmised to cause different Ormus source materials to produce Ormus that may respond distinctively to each person.

### Smudging
Smudging is the ritual of purifying the location ... (sic:, collector, helpers and labware) ... by using the smoke obtained by burning sacred plants, such as sage, sweetgrass and cedar. It alters the state of consciousness and enhances sensitivity ... ( Jonas: Mosby's *Dictionary of Complementary and Alternative Medicine*. (c) 2005, Elsevier.)

Smudging may be most easily associated with the American Indians who used it to keep sacred objects safe from negative energies. Smudging is also used to establish and amplify the positive and in this manner it finds use in helping to restore balance in both us and our environment. Some feel this balance causes the work area to be prepared for collecting Ormus.

Do **not** smudge in dangerous areas, such as near combustible materials (aerosol cans, combustible fuel). Smudging involves a fire, which is a powerful force. Refrain from smudging if you, or those around you, have allergies to sage smoke, pneumonia or a chest cold. In addition, smoke of any kind often aggravates the condition of asthma as well as bronchitis.

Sage is used to smudge and many consider that "white" sage is the best choice. White sage is purchased in bundles (called smudge sticks or wands) or in loose form.

For sources of white sage refer to "Resources and Supplies-White Sage." (Appendix I.)

### Perform the Process
The process of smudging entails allowing smoke from sage to enter the area and there is no one right way to smudge. Open a window or door to the outside so fire alarms are not set off (or turn them off while smudging). Light the sage material and then blow out the flame. The sage

smolders and "smokes." (Have a non-flammable catch basin under the smoking sage to ensure no lit embers, sparks or cinders fly or fall onto flammable material in the room or house.)

Focus your intention as you begin by "smudging" yourself. Start by circling the smoking sage around the body. Begin at the floor and work up to and over your head. It is difficult to get at your own back. A suggestion is to have another smudge you and in this way the most common pose of arms slightly out can be attained.

Next, smudge the room or the house. Focus your intention (perhaps to "cleanse, clear and purify") and start with the corner farthest from the entrance to the room or the house. Perform smudging by rotating your forearm and thus causing the smoke from the extinguished sage to waft from the air current you have created. Begin near the floor and work up to the ceiling allowing the smoke to waft and generally fill the area. Continue to the next corner of the room or the house and work your way towards the entranceway. Following this pattern is thought to "drive" negative energies that may be present towards the entrance/exit. When reaching the entranceway circle the "smoking" sage from the ground up around the door jam to seal the negative energies from re-entering the room or the house.


## Background Sound

It is desirable to allow background music to fill the workspace with sound frequencies personally chosen to create a "space of purpose."

A suggestion for background sound while collecting Ormus (manna) is the music entitled *Holy Harmony* by Jonathan Goldman with Sarah Benson. This collection contains the tones of tuning forks cut to frequencies known as the "Healing codes." For more information, see "Resources and Supplies-Music." (Appendix I.)


## Final Thought

If energy is not expended to create the most suitable environment, the environment is a repository of unused potential.

Through entrainment, a space dedicated to *only* Ormus collection processes becomes a "conditioned space" and that area is thought to perform this one particular action very well. Exceptional "Magnet Vortex Water Trap" or "Vortex Water Trap" water, "Live Oil" and "Ormus (manna)" are said by some to be collected in such a space.

It is also possible that performing "rituals," such toning, smudging and choosing background sound, facilitates a "transcending of the mind." The mind stops thinking thoughts based on the body's senses as well as thoughts of past, present or future and instead goes through intellect into the "state of awareness." Awareness is linked to consciousness and falls in the realm of "spirit" since it is separate from "matter." Spirit comes from "the above" and when we connect with it, the "above" has been said by some to assist in manifesting energy into matter in "the below" (our earth). Consequently, in the Ormus Collection processes, entering into a state of *consciousness* through awareness may assist in the collection of the Ormus material.

# APPENDIX XVII
## How to Manifest

### Definition

Manifesting is the process of creating our desires through *"conscious"* thinking.

### Information

Incorporating the "manifesting process" into daily life can lead to sustained feelings of appreciation and gratefulness. Feelings of contentment or even happiness follow. Therefore, these feelings may come to you twice, both before the manifested desire occurs in your life and then again after.

### Perform the Process

The "Manifesting Process" is a three-step process. To begin, focus your character (your being) on a "list of wants" you have determined to *want*. (The focus is *never* to be on what you do not want as this creates more mental space for those very things to take root and thrive.)

Now choose an item from the "list of wants." (Sometimes the "list of wants" stems from an area of your life that doesn't feel good and you desire to be better.) Think about this want or desire. Usually thinking about this shoots off "rockets of desire" with resultant positive feelings (note the feelings).

Pause now and imagine the attainment of the want (desire.) Reflect on how you feel about this choice of desire and its attainment (include all ramifications you can think of from its fulfillment). Recall the feeling that occurred when this desire was still "on the list." If both feelings resonate and match, then this is what you truly desire.

(For example, I have on my "list of wants" the desire to own a new saddle - and that thought felt good. I imagine attaining the saddle, and my thoughts turn to the time required to maintain the saddle as it is stored in the open-air building at the stable. I feel stress. The two feelings do not resonate and match. Therefore, in a life being created by "conscious" thinking, it is known that a new saddle is not what I [the "me" that is the core of me: my "spirit"] truly desires.)

The second step begins when you "declare" the desire. Some have said that source is already delivering it to you. (God is one way of looking at source.) To phrase this in another way: As soon as the "rocket (of desire) is launched, the wheel is in motion for life to deliver what is desired."

The third step (an important step) involves "letting" this desire into your life because it helps to "let" things in. Be receptive. We are very capable of sabotaging our desires from entering into our life. Therefore actively visualizing the desire as occurring is helpful to the process.

Know well that attaining a desire causes change in your life, including those you don't expect. That is what life is truly about at its core:" having wants - choosing desires - achieving attainment - experiencing change." Our whole life "in every way" follows this pattern.

(Following is an example of the "manifesting process" I have experienced and the happenings surrounding it are explained in "Introduction: Part 1." (Section one.) First step: Barriers during the work day cause me to feel overwhelmed and frustrated. I push against these barriers and my energy becomes drained. Second step: I desire to feel peaceful at work. (An awareness of Ormus shows up in my sphere of life.) Third step: I let it into my life. The result: The pharmacy work is performed while being "in the moment" and a feeling of peace and contentment is experienced. Unexpected changes happen that manifested in the form of a company "award."

## Final Thought

Above all: Appreciate everything you can think of as the highest life walks are appreciative ones.

Other cultures have incorporated ways to experience contentment. The Mayans were one such culture. The core synthesis of the "Mayan codex" is: "All is one," "Life has purpose," "God is love." (Sean David Morton *www.delphiassociates.org* )

"All is one" reminds us how "we" are all connected. There truly is no "us" and "them."

"Life has purpose" causes a realization that "all events unfolding during life have guided towards a fulfillment of the reason(s) for my being here. There comes a knowledge of how "I am exactly where I am supposed" to be in this unfolding regardless the "current" circumstances.

"God is love" confirms that the outcome from any happening is the "right" outcome" and consequently, it is in my expectations that this is always so.

Following the Mayan Codex is another powerful addition to a personal "way of being" that moves your life forward.

"All is one," "Life has purpose," "God is love."

# APPENDIX XVIII
## Imprinting / Charging

## Definition

### Imprint

The concept of imprinting involves the *state* of the "cosmic universe" and the energy of the celestial bodies at the time Ormus is collected. Some have said that this occurs involuntarily during the collection of the Ormus material and is kind of like a zodiac sign for the Ormus. The concept ties into the energy of the celestial bodies relating to "full moon" and "equinox" periods described in Appendix X.

Imprinting is also thought to include the Ormus material picking up the physical and spiritual energy in its immediate surroundings. If this is a proper mindset, then ways to improve the imprinting taken by Ormus include meditating, clearing the energy in the environment with white sage or in us by "toning," placing pyramids in the area, playing music or any number of other things. For more information, see "Toning/Smudging/Background." (Appendix XVI.)

Included in the concept of imprinting are our own feelings at the time of the work. In this way, imprinting also occurs without a person even realizing it. For example, when watching the flakes of Ormus (manna) fall, we are often full of joyful feelings and those feelings could be imprinted on the flakes, as well as through the watery liquid. This joyful imprinting may help us keep that wondrous and joyful awe feeling as we use the Ormus (manna). This feeling of joyful awe is a good place to start anything concerning imprinting.

Dr. Emoto has shown that water takes on an imprint or holds memory. (*Hidden Messages in Water* by M. Emoto) Pictures posted on the Internet and in his books show water taken from random property and the effect an imprint has on it. There are differences clearly seen when comparing the picture with that of non-imprinted water from the same area. After this experiment, the water was re-imprinted by writing something on a piece of paper left under the glass of water - or just sending thought waves. The water did change. Now, we have no similar pictures of Ormus before and after imprinting. It may be that "as we believe it is so."

The question is this: Did the watery liquid take the imprint and then the Ormus in the watery liquid "back up" that imprinting - or even reinforce it? Some have said that Ormus may have at least backed up the imprinting that was taken by the water.

### Charge

With conscious thought we choose what we would have Ormus do and in this way charging may be called "conscious" imprinting.

## Information

The concept of charging involves the addition of intention as the Ormus is collected or when the collected Ormus is used. For example, some add aloe juice to the rinsed (purified) Ormus (manna) and charging can be done as you add this aloe juice. "Conscious" imprinting (charging) can be done at any time. For example, charging can be performed when collecting the Ormus, diluting the Ormus and using the Ormus. It wouldn't hurt to re-charge, or reinforce the imprint or initial charge at the time of using the Ormus. This action may also help make an imprint upon our self as well.

Charging is an individual decision. The individual decides what form is best for them: spoken word, thought, sound or written message.

Some have said there is an energy field around the Ormus (manna) and this is why they feel it is alive. Many feel that by forming an image of the reality desired, Ormus can both understand and that it likes instruction. This line of thought follows that Ormus does a job it is meant to do or wants to do and this would be as if Ormus knows what a body needs. When asked to do something specific, the feeling is that Ormus works out whatever is asked. Although not known exactly it is a belief that many have.

## Perform the Process

Charging the Ormus (manna), "Magnet Vortex Water Trap" (or "Vortex Water Trap") water or "Live Oil" does not have to be elaborate. At the time of collecting and/or using, place a hand on the container and simply ask for the "highest good to come from the Ormus."

Following are ideas for charging ("conscious" imprinting): "Love and Gratitude," "Give Health thru rejuvenation," "Give me as much clarity with wisdom, understanding and compassion as I can handle," "Teach what can be taught," "Show a workable way to live," "Heal the body," "Let me realize that all human (and animal) relationships are temporary and let grow in my heart grateful gratitude for the life I have known."

## Final Thought

Charging efforts keep us centered and focused on the process at hand. Charging does not only occur at the time of collecting the Ormus. Charging can occur when the Ormus is used.

# APPENDIX XIX
## Aloe Vera

### Definition

Aloe contains rhodium and iridium. Iridium and rhodium are valued in the Ormus processes because these two elements in the Ormus form are thought to be specifically associated with the human being. Therefore there is merit in bringing aloe into our Ormus process.

### Information

Aloe also has a number of beneficial effects on the physical body. It assists in the repair of damaged tissue and balances and normalizes the digestive system. It stimulates the immune system, is anti-inflammatory, promotes liver health, lowers cholesterol levels in the blood, improves liver and kidney function, reduces the rate of growth of urinary calcium crystals, is an anti-oxidant, and detoxifies the gastrointestinal system. Aloe also cleans mucus from the small intestines so they can better absorb nutrients, vitamins and minerals from our food. Our body benefits from the presence of aloe. (*www.HealingAloe.com*)

If aloe is grown, consider providing it Azomite® volcanic ash at root level. Some have said that this offers a good opportunity to have more rhodium and iridium elements in the plant (from the Azomite.) For more information, see "Sources for the Ormus Processes-Mineral." (Appendix VIII.)

### Preparing the Source

Cut off a thick arm of the aloe plant. Be appreciative and thank the plant. A golden colored liquid immediately drains from the cut plant arm. Drain the arm for a few seconds of this golden liquid. This liquid has laxative effects - if a laxative effect is desired, don't drain the arm of the golden liquid.

Take a paring knife and cut the thorns off the sides. Fillet the green skin from the aloe arm just as you would fillet a fish. What is left is a semi clear, stiff, jelly-like aloe "fillet." All the skin and thorns are gone. Place the jelly-like aloe fillet in a blender with or without a little bit of good water or distilled water. Blend on high for about one minute.

### Perform the process

The Ormus (manna) collected from the "Wet Process" and *dry* processes can be diluted with (good quality) aloe juice. Aloe enhances absorption. Since aloe is a source of rhodium and iridium it may also make sense to add some to the bottle of Ormus (manna) currently being used. It may be said that the presence of aloe assists both physically and "ormaceutically."

Adding aloe is not advised for long-term storage or when mailing the manna, because it is an organic material and spoils with time.

### Final thought

Following is a thought that finds a use for the leftover aloe skin rinds.  Blend the skin rinds with water and add to the soil of plants.  Use the thin liquid puree right away or let the blended aloe skins set for a few days before adding to the soil.

# APPENDIX XX
## Pump and Filter Seawater Collection

### Definition

A 12 Volt marine pump with a filter attached removes particulate matter from seawater as it is drawn from the ocean for use as source material in the "Wet Process."

### Information

It is *always* advised to filter particulate matter from seawater. Affix a standard "under the kitchen sink" water filter and a 12 Volt marine pump onto a carrying board. Connect the electric wires of the pump to a 12 Volt boat or car battery and attach long hosing to the pump and a short hose from the filter. A garden type hose draws up the seawater and sends it through the "under the kitchen sink" type of filter. The filtered seawater then flows out of the filter and into a storage container. Five-gallon blue water jugs are useful seawater storage containers.

Do not purchase or use a carbon type filter. Carbon has been said to hold onto Ormus thus preventing it from passing through. There are factors that affect the amount of Ormus held by the carbon. These factors include the speed of the waters flow through the carbon filter and how long the carbon filter has been in use. Because there are other filter choices we avoid carbon filters.

Review the "under the sink" type of water filters at the local hardware store for the range of particle size that is filtered out. Filtering ranges include 0.5 microns to 15 microns. Choosing a smaller sized micron filter removes more particles than a larger size. For example, a 5-micron filter removes more than a 10-micron filter. However the filter clogs up faster. Choose a filter with at least a 5-micron filtering capacity. This is a "particle reduction filter." A 2-micron filter is preferred. The 2-micron rated water filters are classified as a "micro filtration filter." However it is to be noted that a filter must filter one-micron or less to be effective at removing cryptosporidium or giardia cysts. This filtration range is outside the scope of the average Ormus collector. It is for this reason that seawater is always boiled prior to performing the "Wet Process."

Heat is added from an external source to cause a "boil." It is generally thought that adding external heat to "boil" causes some of the lighter Ormus to boil off and be lost to the collection. Consequently, when adding external heat to boil the seawater, "use heat as we must and only as much heat as needed to do the job." (These lighter Ormus materials that leave the heated container may come to you and personally align with you. Therefore, this is one more reason that some point to, for performing the Ormus collection processes for yourself.) For more information, see "Labware Choices-Heat." (Appendix XIV.)

A useful way to sterilize seawater without external heat is to add concentrated 35% food grade hydrogen peroxide. Add six to eight drops of 35% food grade hydrogen peroxide per gallon of seawater. Allow the seawater to stand overnight before performing the "Wet Process." Note: The hydrogen peroxide used is 35% "food grade" and not the 3% first aid grade hydrogen peroxide found in first aid supplies.

Another way to prepare the seawater that avoids sterilizing with heat prior to performing the "Wet Process" is to use two different water filters. First, "the under the sink" filter type is used when bringing the seawater into the boat and then when back on land a second filter with a filtration range of 0.05-microns is used. This is classified as an "ultra filtration" filter and is beyond the equipment limits of the average Ormus collector. Therefore, plan to kill the living things in seawater by sterilizing the filtered seawater prior to performing the "Wet Process."

When sterilizing by adding *external* heat, the seawater is covered and boiled gently 12-15 minutes in a stainless steel container (follow the stainless steel precautions listed in Appendix XIV) or enameled pan that has NO chips in the enameling. A gas flame is generally preferred. For more information, see "Labware Choices-Heat." (Appendix XIV.) The seawater is ready for the "Wet Process" after it has cooled a bit.

An advantage to boiling is that the heat created in the seawater *speeds up* the "Wet Process" reaction. Adding heat causes an increase in the movement of the atoms in the water making the reaction in the "Wet Process" occur more quickly. An additional benefit of adding an outside source of heat is the Ormus is being annealed. Some have said that annealing raises its energy and gives the Ormus (manna) a higher quantum resonance frequency. When this occurs, many feel the Ormus (manna) may be more potent.

*Choose any method of sterilization but always plan to sterilize the seawater. If the seawater was not filtered when it was taken from the sea it must be filtered before performing the "Wet Process."*

## Perform the Process

**Place a weight at the end of a long garden hose and lower the hose into the ocean.** It is best that the first 12 feet of hose that leads from the boat to the top of the water is a "suction" hose. A suction hose has reinforced walls that do not collapse as the pump draws seawater up and out of the sea.

Depending on the geographical area, a good depth to collect ocean water is between 50 to 100 feet. Seawater is not drawn from the top waters because pollution generally stays in the top 25 feet of the water and sunlight filtering through the top waters is thought to drive Ormus away. Therefore, do not collect seawater from the top waters of the sea and do not collect ocean water any closer than 32 feet from the bottom as organic pollutants are near the bottom.

Note: Do not collect seawater from the shoreline because pollution can contaminate that seawater. As a guideline, "Ocean Plasma" (Section 8) is drawn from a depth of 96 feet from the surface and 32 feet from the bottom.

**Draw the seawater out with the 12 Volt marine pump and filter.**

To recap: Draw seawater from at least 50 feet below the surface and no closer than 32 feet from the seabed floor.

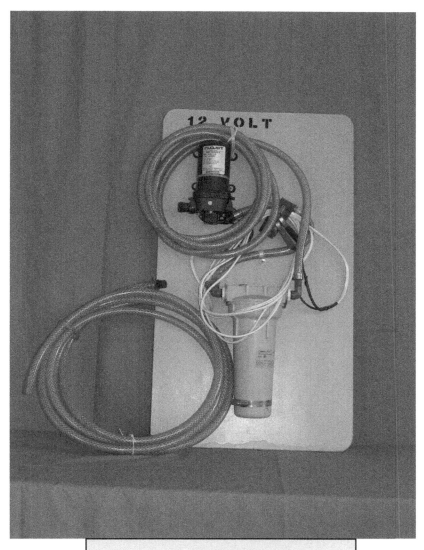

12 Volt marine pump and filter

# APPENDIX XXI

## Ormus (Theoretical) Use, Directions, Bioavailability and Precautions In Plants/Agriculture, Animals and Humans

These statements have not been evaluated by the Food and Drug Administration. These substances are not intended to diagnose, treat, cure, or prevent disease. (See: Disclaimer in the front of the book)

## Information

The Ormus material is a "naturally" found substance on the earth. It is in the foods we eat, water we drink and air we breathe. There is a belief that in modern days, these sources are not as plentiful with these materials. Therefore, we, in addition to plants and animals, may benefit from Ormus supplementation and this supplementation (like that of vitamin or mineral or protein) is the addition of a "natural" substance to our diet. While the Ormus supplement can be "Magnet Vortex Water Trap" water (or "Vortex Water Trap" water) or "Live Oil" it is often the extracted (concentrated) and collected Ormus (manna) precipitate that has formed during a "Wet" or any of the *dry* collection processes. For more information, see "General Ormus Information." (Appendix VI.)

Ormus (manna) is an energetically active (nutritive) medium and bacteria and fungi (mold is a fungi) can be expected to have a great breeding ground there. Therefore, keep the Ormus (manna) container free of these contaminants by drawing what is to be used into a separate container first. Because we do not want to introduce bacteria into the Ormus, do not place measuring tools inside the Ormus (manna) container or allow the stock container or any measuring droppers that it may contain to touch your mouth. (Do not drink directly from the stock bottle.)

Measuring tools or spoons are to be plastic or glass material and not metal. To measure out drops of Ormus (manna), glass bottles with an eye dropper inside are available and often seen in a pharmacy. There are also tools that increase the accuracy of measuring. First, there are "barrel syringes" commonly called oral baby syringes and are available in 1ml, 5ml and 10ml size. For more information, see "Labware Choices." (Appendix XIV). Agricultural use requires large measures such as cups and gallons.

To best ensure electromagnetic waves cause no interference on the stability of the Ormus material, it is prudent to keep the storage area six feet or more away from them. For more information, see "Labware Choices-Aluminum Foil." (Appendix XIV.)

Statements made regarding Ormus use, directions, bioavailability, and precautions in plants/agriculture, animals and humans contain some current postulations regarding the use of the Ormus material. As science evolves, these may change. When discussing Ormus use, directions, bioavailability and precautions in plants/agriculture, animals and humans we are reminded that Ormus experimentation is ongoing and evolving. Ormus used as supplements are for research and experimental purposes only and therefore there are no specific "dosages" to state. I can tell you what I/others use, or have heard of being used, on plants/agriculture, animals and ourselves. The opinions are believed to be accurate and the information sound based on the best judgment available.

The following statements have not been evaluated by the Food and Drug Administration nor are they intended to diagnose, treat, cure or prevent disease. Further, if there are choices made in determining how to use Ormus for plants/agriculture, animals and ourselves, make those decisions based on conservative thinking.

## Plants / Agriculture

### Definition

Seeds and plants given the Ormus material have shown more vigor, tolerance to transplanting and drought conditions as well as increased resistance to disease and insects. They demonstrate a shortened growing cycle and increased crop yield. They have also produced larger fruit with a longer shelf life, and some have said contain an increase in mineral and vitamin content. Similar benefits have occurred with plants grown for flowers.

### Information

The precipitate made from the "*Wet Process*" is non-toxic and can be used in agriculture. The Ormus source material in this process is reconstituted sea or drawn seawater. For more information, see "Resources and Supplies-Agriculture." (Appendix I.)

The Ormus (manna) collected during the "*Wet Process*" is used in plants and agriculture. The Ormus (manna) from the dry processes is not used because: 1) less volume of manna is produced from other Ormus collection processes and 2) the other processes cost more in terms of time, effort and price of materials.

Perform a "Wet Process." Remove the Ormus (manna) from the bottom of the liquid. A suggestion is to use a turkey baster or pour the top water off the Ormus (manna). Discard the liquid that was over the Ormus (manna) - do not use this liquid on soil or plants. This liquid is thought to contain Ormus and may be used *highly diluted* in your bathwater or as a foot soak. These rinse waters have a pH around pH 10.78 and must be highly diluted or may irritate or burn the skin. For more information, see "Wet Process-Purifying (washing)." (Section Three.)

When used for agriculture the Ormus (manna) does *not* need to be rinsed. Some do rinse it one time.

Dilute the Ormus (manna) prior to applying to the plant, soil or roots and you can OVERDO it when giving the Ormus material to the plant. The application of the Ormus (manna) is easy but if too much is used, it has been said the flowers grow on deformed stalks because the plant just grew too fast.

- For seeds, soak overnight in a 500/1 dilution of Ormus (manna) precipitate.
- For plants in a 6-inch pot, use one drop of Ormus (manna) precipitate diluted in about one ounce of water. This ratio is one teaspoonful (5ml) of Ormus (manna) in about 2 1/2 quarts of water although another suggested strength is 1/4 teaspoon/quart and to make a larger quantity, use one tablespoon (15ml) of Ormus (manna) in about two gallons of water.

If your garden is small, an added step of hoeing in the diluted Ormus (manna) precipitate has been suggested.

It may make sense to apply in the evening since sunlight is thought to disturb the state of the Ormus. I have not read or heard information regarding the effect of sunlight on the Ormus (manna) used for agricultural, and you may wish to consider the suggestion of applying in the evening or when the sun is low. It may also be beneficial to water the plants after dark vs. daylight hours when they are responding (growing) to the Ormus.

When the Ormus (manna) is used in agriculture, two to four gallons of Ormus (manna) precipitate (diluted with water) is applied per acre once a season. It is thought by some that no more than 10 gallons of Ormus (manna) per acre per season is to be applied.

I have heard that cucumbers grown from seeds that had been soaked in diluted Ormus (manna) prior to planting were very large and even better results observed when the second-generation seeds were soaked prior to planting. I have heard of and seen pictures of very large fruit and nuts based on four-year Ormus use. By the third year; some say the fruit may not fit in standard market boxes.

31.7 grams                    91.2 grams
Walnuts picked in October 2001
Picure taken June 11, 2008

The diluted Ormus (manna) may be used as a "foliar" spray (sprayed directly on the leaves of plants) as leaves do absorb it. It has been suggested by some to spray the leaves at least three times per season.

A color change in the leaves may be seen within 24 to 48 hours. They may darken to deep green and possibly flatten to maximize the sunlight.

> The smaller walnuts on the left all came from the same tree that was not fed Ormus (manna) and are of normal size. The walnuts on the right all came from the same tree that was given Ormus (manna) for four years. (Picture courtesy of Barry Carter)

For use on trees three to six feet high, 4oz of diluted Ormus (manna) per tree may be a proper amount to apply to the soil. For use on trees six to twelve feet high, 6oz of diluted Ormus (manna) may be a good amount to apply to the soil.

For use in transplanting: Dip the roots in diluted Ormus (manna) prior to repotting.

## Final Thought

The rinse water from the third washing of the "Wet Process" precipitate can be used on plants. (The rinse water from a fourth washing may also be used - many only wash three times.)

The rinse water from the first and second rinse water is not used on plants because we don't want the salt or the lye (even though it would be diluted) contained in those initial washes added to the soil.

## Animals

### Definition
Testing has shown that animals benefit from whole sea solids (Sea-Crop,®). More stamina may be observed and this may lead to decreased mortality, decreased infection and increased weight. (Note: It has been presumed that these benefits also apply to animals given "Wet Process" Ormus (manna) as this is collected from "Reconstituted" sea or "drawn" seawater). (*www.sea-crop.com*)

### Information
The precipitate made from the "Wet Process" is non-toxic and can be used in animals. The Ormus (manna) from the "Wet Process" is collected, *rinsed and diluted* for ingestion. The Ormus (manna) from other processes usually is not used because 1) Less volume of Ormus (manna) is produced from other Ormus processes and 2) The other processes cost more in terms of time, effort and price of materials.

Morning may be the best time to give animals Ormus. Gently shake the Ormus (manna) container and mix the Ormus (manna) with a little of their food. Ideally, the animal should not eat more food for 20 to 30 minutes after the Ormus. Giving Ormus (manna) on a consistent basis is suggested and this is always considered a truth in Ormus supplementation: More is not necessarily better and it is surmised to give only suggested amounts to animals.

Some have said that a suggested amount for animals ranges from a minute rate of 0.02ml./kg to a suggested rate of 0.04ml./kg of body weight per day

It is generally thought that the daily amount not exceed eight drops of Ormus (manna) for each five pounds of body weight. (www.liquid-chi.com)

Let's together determine the recommended rate for an 1,100 pound horse. There are 2.2 pounds in one kilogram. Therefore, the horse is 500 kilograms (1,100 divided by 2.2). A suggested rate for Ormus given to an animal is 0.04ml. per kilogram therefore the horse receives 20ml. of Ormus (manna) (500kgm x 0.04ml) once a day, in the morning, with a handful of grain. Feed "breakfast" 20-30 minutes later. For more information, see "Measurement Conversions." (Appendix XII.)

## Humans

The following observations have been reported after Ormus supplementation: rejuvenation, mental clarity, a sense of calmness, increased intuitive powers, insightfulness and a feeling of being connected to a higher state of awareness. Life appears enabled to reach a fuller measure of its biological potential.

A belief is the Ormus material is here to enlighten and raise the consciousness through the feeding of the "light" body so it may grow and become what it is meant to be. In this way, the nature of man changes and things that have "value" now are no longer important. It may be that this action could change the world more than anything in the last 2,000 years. Ormus seems to affect a person spiritually, mentally and physically. Ormus appears to be "transformational" elements because they seem to cause a deep and lasting change in an individual. Once you decide to supplement with Ormus, the raising of the consciousness has begun. A theory holds that your nature is changed and you will not be the same person you are now. If this is true it is not for everyone and is as big a step as you may take in your life. Consequently before proceeding, this deserves some serious thought and contemplation.

"The "bad" guys can't control you any more. They have nothing that you want. You don't need it and you don't want it. You know you are free. It is the ultimate "Emancipation Proclamation." It is science, it is here now, whether you believe it or not, it "ain't" going to change anything. It will not go away." (*David Hudson Transcripts*)

Ormus supplementation generally causes no need to feel driven to immediately change things in a life routine or way of thinking. In fact some have commented on how the guiding of a life through Ormus appears to be a patient and measured one.

Ormus seems to cause a person to be more of the way they "naturally" are and natural traits and tendencies can become more prominent. This occurs, in theory, because the "light body" (sprit, Ka, etc.) is nourished by the Ormus (manna). The light body and the physical body can not be separated from each other and need each other to function. The physical body does not affect the light body but the light body can affect the physical body. The light body is felt by many to keep the physical body corrected so it remains a living movable thing and doesn't become a "rock." It may be that Ormus (manna) causes more "vibrancy" in the "physical" body by providing some type of nourishment. Observe if "natural" traits are more prominent and, if this is occurring, be aware how you may be directed towards areas of "personal growth opportunities" that can lead to "spiritual" enlightenment. (It may be that those closest to you [perhaps a spouse] comment on natural traits being more prominent.)

Ingesting Ormus (manna) is a personal decision. The Ormus (manna) material has not been FDA approved. It is lawful to choose to ingest Ormus (manna) as this use falls under "research." It is lawful to perform "research" on yourself (and your animals) however you may *not* "practice medicine" on any other person. (Claims about medical benefits of any therapy may only be made for a product that is FDA-approved.) Therefore, any other person who wishes to have Ormus (manna) is doing his/her own "research" and a suggestion is to have that other person pour the Ormus (manna) themselves from your bottle. In this way, you clearly are not even "dispensing" as dispensing is also a part of the medical practice. (from: *Procedures for use of bio-active frequencies by Royal Rife Research Society*)


## Magnet Vortex Trap Water Ormus

### Definition

"Magnet Vortex Trap Water" (or "Vortex Trap Water") Ormus is collected from good drinking water.


### Information

Taking "Magnet Vortex Trap Water" (or "Vortex Trap Water") is different from the "wet (in liquid)" Ormus (manna) precipitate. When drinking trap water, drink it as you would regular drinking water. Use trap water for beverages as well as food preparation. If heating the trap water (for kitchen or beverage use), it is suggested to use heat for the shortest amount of time and a gas heat source is generally preferred. For more information, see "Labware Choices-Heat." (Appendix XIV.)

It is understood that consuming Ormus is *one* piece of the supplementation process. The other equally valuable part involves "focusing" techniques. When drinking the trap water, affirm what you would have it do. Focusing is part of "manifesting the life desired" through "conscious thought." For more information, see "How to Manifest." (Appendix XVII.) Also, "Imprinting/Charging." (Appendix XVIII.)

A method that calculates how many ounces of water per day, in the form of beverage, and food that should be ingested revolves around body weight. The formula is:

Body weight (in pounds) divided by 2 = daily water ingestion (in ounces).

## Ormus (manna)

A "Wet in Liquid"

"Wet in liquid" Ormus (manna) is the precipitate collected from the "Wet Process" and all the *dry* processes. After collection, the Ormus (manna) precipitate is rinsed and diluted as explained in the individual Ormus collection processes.

(Note: When the Ormus (manna) has been collected via the "Hydrogen Peroxide (Gold) Process" and the *dry* "Sodium Burn Process" the amount of Ormus (manna) to take may be less. Ask the alchemist who collected it to direct you. These two collection processes require laboratory expertise beyond that of most average Ormus collectors).

Now, *all* Ormus (manna) is taken as a "wet in liquid" form and the "Wet Process" and *dry* processes in this manual collect Ormus in this form (a "wet in liquid). An alchemist may term the Ormus (manna) precipitate a "wet in liquid" because it contains "wet" liquid droplets in liquid (versus solid particles such as earth particles held in a suspension of muddy water). If using a "dry" form of Ormus, it is expected that the product is composed of small water-soluble crystals that dissolve in the saliva. (Once the crystals dissolve in the saliva the Ormus has become a "wet in liquid.") Ask the alchemist who collected it to direct you as to how many of the dry crystals to take.

Ormus (manna) separates out if the suspension stands and gently shaking it re-suspends the "wet in liquid" prior to using.

When taking the Ormus (manna) it may be preferable to hold it under the tongue for 15 seconds before swallowing. The lingual vein is located under the tongue and a theory holds that this vein picks up the Ormus and carries it directly to the bloodstream. In this way the Ormus avoids the filtering action of the stomach and, especially of the liver. It makes sense to rinse your mouth before so there is minimal interference in absorption.

It is understood that the Ormus product is one piece of the supplementation process. The other involves "focusing" techniques. While holding the Ormus (manna) under the tongue utilize "conscious" intention (charging) and affirm what it is you would have Ormus do. Focusing is a part of "manifesting the life that is desired" through "conscious thought." For more information, see "How to Manifest." (Appendix XVII). Also, "Imprinting/Charging." (Appendix XVIII.)

The range of Ormus taken traditionally has been said to include amounts of 1/8 or 1/2 or one teaspoon once or twice a day. It may make sense to take this in the morning, perhaps 20 minutes before eating. Some have proposed a starting amount of 1/4 teaspoon per day with another 1/4 teaspoon later in the day, if the day is going to be long, full or stressful. If you have either a sensitive etheric or physical system a lower starting amount of 1/8 teaspoon/day may be a suggestion. There are Ormus collectors who record that 2 drops placed under the tongue was the proper amount to take for their system and there are Ormus collectors who have said they have tried up to one tablespoon per day and found that to be excessive. I have heard in conversation that many Ormus collectors take one to two teaspoons daily with a "general" overall range of one to three teaspoons daily. Sometime half of the amount is taken in the morning and maybe another half of the amount in mid-day if the day was being an active one (the whole amount can also be taken upon arising from sleep - for most people this is the morning). More is not necessarily better and every person is his or her own best judge of how much to take. Every person's starting point is an individual determination and the choice of how much Ormus (manna) to take is one of several decisions made regarding Ormus. Some have said that while there is wisdom in starting with a smaller amount that can later be added to, it is important to keep in mind that if you are doing well on a lower amount that is probably all you need. (Some information from www.subtleenergies.com)

A rate of 0.04 ml per Kilogram to 0.2 ml per Kilogram of body weight per day may be a suggested range. (www.sea-crop.com)

Let's determine such a rate for a 180 lb man. Since there are 2.2 pounds in kilogram this man weighs 82 kilograms (180 divided by 2.2). The range for Ormus in a person may begin at 0.04 ml per kilogram. Therefore this man receives 3.3 ml of Ormus (82 kg x 0.04 ml). The 3.3 ml is taken once a day, upon arising followed by breakfast 20-30 minutes later. (This may be divided in two and taken twice a day.) For information, see "Measurement Conversions." (Appendix XII.)

When first taking Ormus, you may become sleepy and personal testimonies of tiredness often include sleeping deeply for several hours. This happened to me and there may be logical reasons this it occurs. Some feel that DNA shifts in the body are occurring and this causes much sensory stimulation. In addition, the body heals best at rest and feeling tiredness may be the body's way of slowing down to facilitate healing itself. Therefore, the feeling of weariness may conversely correlate to the degree of health initially found in the body. If a headache should be felt or a desire to lie down, do so and take a nap. If you are a new Ormus collector it cannot be known how you will respond. Therefore, a suggestion made by some is to take Ormus (manna) in the afternoon or evening so that if tiredness is felt (or a headache) it is easy to pull back and have a nap. Some feel that a headache may occur from the integration of the right and left hemispheres of your brain. This is called a "hatband effect" and the sensation is thought to go away once the integration is achieved. If the hatband effect is too intense consider reducing the amount of Ormus taken..

The possibility also exists that alertness is felt and not being able to fall asleep occurs. Therefore, be aware that when an Ormus collector begins taking the manna no one can say with certainty what effect(s) in the physical may be observed or felt.

The balance that may occur between sleep and alert may be a good measuring tool to titrate the right amount for you.  A comment sometimes heard is that when you feel good about the amount you have selected, there is no need to keep increasing it.

The possibility also exists that the effects of Ormus (manna) can be subtle and takes time. Therefore, if this happens to you, keep an open mind.  (Note: One of the first reactions that may occur is the feeling of having greater "clarity" in thinking.)

Some suggest taking Ormus (manna) in the evening.  This way, it can be doing its work during the repair and healing that occurs during sleep while others suggest taking the Ormus (manna) first thing in the morning.  This way it can be in the physical body and doing something helpful for the body and spirit, during the time frame when we are creating a new day.  Others have suggested taking Ormus (manna) in the morning and in the evening.  Personal lifestyle can also have much to do with the time(s) of day chosen.  Most say that regularly taking Ormus is a big key to its usefulness.

Know that with the passage of time, the effects of the Ormus (manna) may stop being felt at the physical level and some have said that it is important to realize the Ormus is still working. What may have happened is you have tuned yourself to the frequency of the Ormus (manna) and more Ormus is NOT what is needed.  This is a point to be remembered.  Now, a decision may be made to take Ormus from another Ormus source material (as each Ormus source material may carry its own individual frequency) and if this choice is made, you are in a position to tune to the frequency of the new Ormus product.  Another decision may be to take a higher rate of the original Ormus but realize that a higher rate of Ormus is not necessarily better.  These scenarios highlight some of the personal decisions and choices made based on reasoning, intuitive thought and the method called "trial and error."

Be aware that a "healing crisis" may occur.  A healing crisis is part of physical detoxification and can be an uncomfortable physical experience as well as hard work for the body.  For a period this experience may entail a re-manifestation of unpleasant symptoms from past illnesses.  Other symptoms of a "detoxification" can include fatigue, allergies and headaches.  If experiencing a detoxification some have suggested decreasing the Ormus (manna) intake for the first few weeks of use and this offers another reason to follow conservative guidelines when taking Ormus (manna).  When experiencing effects of detoxification, some have said that it may be generally best to include liver cleansing protocols and nutritional support.

It may be important to consider how the detoxification experienced with Ormus (manna) is thought to possibly include a "spiritual" detoxification and an "emotional" detoxification in addition to a physical one.

Often the Ormus material is considered as being more of an alchemical supplement felt to work with "spirit" versus a nutritional supplement that works with the "physical" body.  Many feel that it works with the "spirit" for your higher good, and therefore, contains an "etheric" property. For example: After the Ormus, you experience a headache.  It is a possibility that this may be a physical manifestation caused by the feeding of your spirit with the etheric supplement called Ormus.  The "energized" (fed) spirit may have brought you to the place of the head because a personal trait and way of being is consistent deep analytical thinking.  The message you may be receiving is to stop thinking so deeply so often and place energy into other traits so a more "balanced" life may be experienced. Of course, the headache could be the hatband effect, a detoxification reaction or a number of physical reasons such as stress, constipation or triggers such as tobacco smoke, etc.

A general belief of many is that Ormus acts as the bridge between (our) spirit and the "Zero Point:" The "zero point" is considered the entryway of the "God" force energy into our world (and the universe). Consequently Ormus is referred to as "the matrix of consciousness." If this is so, be alert to even subtle changes in the physical as they may be resulting from a now "well fed" spirit or from communication with the "zero point" through a now "well fed" spirit. This is all part of living life through "conscious" thinking and many feel Ormus always seems to work for our higher good.

This example demonstrates an "intuitive" factor when taking Ormus. Sensing what is experienced all around, and even inside you causes a great opportunity for "spiritual" growth. Attaining spiritual growth often manifests in the physical as restfulness, clarity and peace.

Now, a question has been asked if Ormus (manna) is taken with or without food and there are opinions on either sides of the fence. Some choose to take Ormus on an "empty" stomach such that little or nothing is in the stomach before to 20 minutes after.

When taken on an empty stomach the "wet in liquid" Ormus (manna) encounters no interference with absorption and is available to our system directly. When combining the Ormus with *proper* foods, it has been said by some that the action of the Ormus can be slowed down and act a bit like a timed release product in our body and that in addition the Ormus may work on our food and make the food even better for our system. If this is so, the key word is "proper" foods and it is expected that evolving Ormus research will provide a list of foods and beverages known to mix exceptionally well with Ormus.

Some have said that foods of deep red and purple color - purple grapes or their juice (as well as Aloe Vera liquid) are all naturally high in Ormus and may be good to take with Ormus (manna). Others have said the crystalline sugar molecule (as is in grapes) has a high affinity for Ormus (even more so than the salt molecule) and the body competes with sugar for it. Therefore, it may make sense to drink purple grape juice however not take it with the Ormus (manna). In this way there can be no competition between the sugar molecule and our body for the Ormus.

Now, others feel it is best not to chance taking food with Ormus (because of Ormus's attraction to sugar and salt). Once Ormus leaves the Ormus product it is thought that it may drift to the sugar and salt in the food and therefore the body must compete for it. (I personally do not eat 30 minutes before or after the Ormus.)

One item often said to avoid is *sulfites* in the foods eaten as they tend to change the state of the Ormus material to one that is not effective in the body and this is not desirable. Sulfites are commonly found in foods (prepared salad dressings, for example) therefore read the ingredients on canned, bottled and dry goods.

There are four substances said by David Hudson to change the state of the Ormus material to one that is not effective in the body - even bringing a portion back to the metal element (this conversion is a slow process). We may say it "kills the light" and this is understood once you know that a mechanism of action attributed to Ormus is that of a "super light" (observed as the aura around the human body in Kirlian photography). These four substances are: sulfites (SO3) mentioned above, carbon and carbon monoxide (avoid burned food and smog such as in cities), nitric oxide (avoid smog such as in cities) and short wavelength radiation. David Hudson suggested waiting until after cancer treating radiation therapy before taking Ormus and it may make sense to wait until after x-rays, CAT scans and MRIs.

(Note: Short wavelength radiation include cell phones and microwave ovens and you may ponder on this when deciding how close in proximity you wish to be with these items.)

(Note: Some have said that garlic and other sulfur containing foods do not seem to cause this problem and that only the concentrated forms of sulfur like MSM or DMSO are to be avoided or spaced between the timing of the Ormus supplement.)

MSM is a common nutritional supplement that is thought best to well space between Ormus. Space the MSM and Ormus by one hour when the MSM is taken with little or no food and by two hours if the MSM is taken with a meal. (Note: MSM is usually part of a combination product taken for joint cartilage care and repair and it is suggested that MSM be taken on an empty stomach.)

If you are on prescription medicine, and choose to take Ormus, some have suggested that Ormus is taken one-hour before or one-hour after prescription medicine and if a meal had been eaten wait two-hours as it is preferred the stomach be empty of the medicine. There are two thoughts behind this reasoning: First, the prescription medicine could have sulfites in it and this is something you do not read on the prescription label. In addition Ormus may enhance the effects of prescription medicine. Ormus collectors have reported how they required less hormone replacement medicine and antidepressants. Therefore, if you are on prescription medication, it is an idea to monitor your medicine needs closely with a physician.

Finally, be open to awareness of how Ormus supplementation may be affecting your life in the physical, spiritual and emotional areas. Intuition can percolate answers such as how much to take, what to add or drop in your diet; and insights regarding personal routine and relationships. Insights can be valuable tools that move a life forward. There may also rise to conscious thought insights that direct us toward areas containing "personal growth opportunities." This may occur when personal traits rise up and become "bothersome" in the life. (Ormus seems to cause a person to "be" more of the way they "naturally" are and natural traits and tendencies can become more prominent.) This occurs, according to many when the "light body" (spirit, Ka, etc.) has been nourished by Ormus. These personal growth opportunities allow a chance to work through the process towards "emotional" and "spiritual" enlightenment. Enlightenment is a state of consciousness that intuits or feels insights or wisdoms that cause life to be more workable. Experiencing an emotional and/or spiritual enlightenment often culminates in positive feelings of "peace" and "contentment" and in this manner life has moved forward and for the better.

## Final Thought

If you are experimenting with Ormus from multiple alchemists, a suggestion made is to give each product a 2-3 week trial. It may be a good idea to not mix different product lines and only use one "product line" at a time.

There has been a comment that Ormus (manna) may be homeopathic and thus only a very small amount is needed. For example $^1/_{64}$ teaspoon diluted in one quart of good water and taken as two or three ounces once or twice a day. *(www.subtleenergies.com)* David Hudson has said in his lectures that the Ormus material is probably not conducive to homeopathy.

## Topical Use Ormus-containing Products

Several Ormus based products find use topically. These are collected by performing any of the following Ormus collection processes: "Live Oil Process," "Magnet Vortex Water Trap" (or "Vortex Water Trap") and the "Wet Process." In addition, the "first" *rinse* water from the "Wet Process" (highly diluted with much water and this is explained below) or rinse water from any of the dry Ormus collection process (diluted) can be used topically.

## "Live Oil" from a "Live Oil Process"

"Live Oil" can be used on food (when an edible oil, such as "grape seed" and "olive" oil has been used). For example, it can be added as "finishing" oil to salads and cooked vegetables.

"Live Oil" can be used topically for skin care such as softening the skin and during massages. (If used for the latter application, both the client and the massage therapist benefit.) When used on the soles of the feet, it penetrates through the skin quickly because of the large pores in that location. Some have felt that "Live Oil" was helpful for painful areas of the body such as arthritis, neuropathy and sunburn.

"Live Oil" can be *enhanced* with the addition of a good quality "essential oil," either alone or in combination. If the "Live Oil" is for food preparation, essential oils such as thyme, sage, rosemary, lemon, garlic, pepper, oregano, black cumin, carrot seed and marjoram are recommendations. If the "Live Oil" is for topical use essential oils such as lavender, frankincense or myrrh, grapefruit, helichrysum rose, cedar, geranium, hyssop and ylang ylang are popular. When choosing an essential oil, select a fragrance pleasing to you. This is as important as the oils listed beneficial qualities or its popularity. For essential oil sources see "Resources and Supplies." (Appendix I.)

## "Trap Water" from a "Magnet Vortex Water Trap" (or "Vortex Water Trap")

**Trap water is ready for external use directly from the "trap."** Use it on sores (in addition to proper first aid care) and to soften rough skin. The water can be used to soak the feet as Ormus enters the body easily through the large pores there and Ormus that enters the body through the soles of the feet bypass the filtering action of the liver. (Any substance ingested *orally* must go

through the filtering action of the liver.)  For more information, see "Magnet Vortex Water Trap."
(Section Five.)

## Spritz made with water from a "Magnet Vortex Water Trap" or "Vortex Water Trap"
### Supplies to make this topical product
Water from a "Magnet Vortex Water Trap" (or "Vortex Water Trap"), "grape seed" oil, glass
container, "spritz" bottle and aluminum foil.

**Place a *thin* layer of "grape seed" oil or "olive" oil on the bottom of a *glass* container.**

**Add "Magnet Vortex Water Trap" (or "Vortex Water Trap") water to the container.** If the
lid is metal, first place a layer of plastic wrap over the top of the glass container as metal is not to
come in contact with the product.

**Shake the container vigorously 21 times and then let the oil/water settle.**

**Repeat this shaking 9 times.** The reason the jar is shaken 21 times and repeated 9 times is
because these are "Fibonacci" series numbers - which have been explained in "Live Oil Process."
(Section Three.)

**Add the water/oil mix to a "spritz" bottle.** Spritz on small sores (in addition to proper first
aid care) and to soften rough skin.  It may be helpful when rubbed on painful areas of the body.

**Wrap the bottle in aluminum foil and gently shake before each use.** Use the spritz within
7-30 days. The shorter the time frame the better.

## Poultice made from Ormus (manna)
### Supplies to make this topical product
Washed Ormus (manna) or filtered Ormus (manna) from a "Live Oil Process" made from Ormus
(manna), oatmeal, a covering to put over the poultice

A poultice can be made with dry oatmeal mixed with either Ormus (manna) that has been
collected and washed (but not diluted) after performing a "Wet Process" or the filtered Ormus
(manna) after performing a ""Live Oil Process" made from Ormus (manna). The poultice may
find usefulness on pest bites, psoriasis and bruises. Ormus (manna) from the *dry* processes is not
used because less volume of Ormus (manna precipitate is collected from these processes and they
cost more (in terms of time, effort and price of materials).

Apply the poultice to the area, cover and let set. A large volume of Ormus (manna) is needed
if used topically versus orally.

### "First Rinse Water" from an Ormus Collection Process

Supplies to make this topical product: First rinse water from an Ormus collection process and the water to dilute it.

The first rinse water from washing Ormus (manna) collected from any of the Ormus processes contains Ormus in the water and can be added to bath water or diluted in foot soaks. Some have said Ormus is in that rinse water.  Foot soaks are nice when there is no time or accommodation for a bath.  The soles have large pores and Ormus is able to enter the body easily from that location.

**Important:**  The first rinse water from a "Wet Process" is to be diluted with much water. Dilute to around pH 7 as this is a strong "basic" solution of about pH 10.78 and is corrosive causing the skin to burn and scar. (Normal skin can generally tolerate pH ranges of pH 4.5 to pH 7.)  Even well diluted, the lye solution may act as an irritant to the skin therefore dilute the lye solution with a great deal of fresh water.  For more information, see "Wet Process-Perform the Process." (Section Three.)    (Note: If the first rinse water came from any of the *dry* Ormus collection processes, it is safe to touch being only a very salty solution.)  The "second rinse" rinse water from a "Wet Process" can also be added to bath water or diluted in foot soaks (diluted very well) as some have said Ormus is in second rinse water also.

### Manna Toothpaste using Ormus (manna)

Supplies to make this topical product: Washed Ormus (manna), toothbrush

Some have said that the washed (but not diluted) Ormus (manna) precipitate has been used to brush teeth and better mouth health may be possible.  If this is so there may be less inflammation around certain teeth or a decrease in bleeding gums or maybe a decrease in the amount of plaque around the teeth.  The Ormus (manna) from a "Wet Process" is usually used because Ormus (manna) from other processes cost more in terms of time, effort and price of materials.  Of course, there is no fluoride in Ormus (manna).

### Rectal Implant

Also called a rectal retention enema and it is designed as a retentive not evacutive enema.

(Note: I do not advise anyone proceed with rectal administration without first consulting with your physician.)

Now, you may wish to experiment with implanting Ormus (manna) in the rectum for a couple of reasons.  First, it takes merely seconds for implant material to reach the liver because it is absorbed through both the colon wall and large blood vessels surrounding the rectum (and often seen in hemorrhoids) called the hemorrhoidal vein.  This vein acts like a sponge providing absorption of the material and it connects with the hepatic vein which carries the material to the liver.  The second reason is that the liver is a vital organ with a wide range of functions and because it is the only internal human organ capable of natural regeneration of lost tissue, Ormus may assist in maintaining its vitality.

**Perform a water flush enema first or just add the implant.**

**Add the amount of Ormus (manna) taken to 3-4 oz of body temperature water (distilled water recommended).** The volume of this enema should be small enough that it can be retained until the next bowel movement or held in the rectum for as long as possible (or at least 5 minutes).

**Perform an enema with the Ormus (manna)/water mixture.** A bag or bulb enema may be used or specialized rectal implant equipment such as a rectal implant syringe. Visit *www.colonhealthinfo.com* for more information. If you need help slipping the enema tube in the rectum, coconut oil is one of the more slippery lubricants. Other lubricants include cold pressed oil (olive, sesame seed etc...), vitamin E oil, aloe vera gel and K-Y jelly. Do not use Vaseline or any other petroleum based or chemically manufactured substance.

**Clean the enema bag.** Cleaning and drying the enema bag before storage is important as the colon has fewer defenses from the invasion of microbes and parasites. First soak in and then wash the enema equipment with soap and water. Choose a soap that kills germs such as Betadine Surgical Scrub or Hibiclens. Rinse with plain tap water. It is helpful to follow this washing and rinsing step with a rinse using water that contains a little bit of Clorox. Perform a final rinse with water and then dry the equipment.

# APPENDIX XXII
## Basic Chemistry of the Ormus Processes

There exist many paradigms that can and have been used to explain the reactions of the M-state/Ormus elements. The reader is strongly urged to read the works of people such as C. Louis Kervran and Roberto Monti in order to obtain a broader view of the workings of Nature and of possibilities that you may be unaware of.

I am certain that the reactions that are occurring are significantly more complex than have been stated here however, the science of the M-state/Ormus elements is largely in its infancy and we expect that a more complete understanding will occur in the near future as more and more people become aware of the existence of these substances and more research is done and published.

That having been stated, I have decided to present this information in the most basic of forms and within the paradigm of conventional chemistry in order to give those readers who may be so inclined, something to wrap their head around. *Please be aware that many believe that there are low energy nuclear reactions occurring during these processes and in that light, the discipline of physics, especially quantum mechanics, would be necessary to explain them.* They are beyond the scope of this first edition.

### Wet Process:

The waters of our oceans and seas while seeming so common and simple are actually one of the most complex substances on our planet. They contain a multitude of ingredients including both elements and compounds. Some of these are completely soluble and some are not.

All seawaters and some sea salts contain the M-state elements along with such elements as calcium and magnesium. The presence of calcium and magnesium helps to explain why the average pH of our ocean waters is about pH 8.5 rather than being a more neutral pH of about 7. I mention the calcium and magnesium specifically because assays have shown that they account for as much as one half of the precipitates from clean ocean waters. Also be aware that there are trace amounts of numerous other cations and anions and that their concentrations, as assayed, are negligible.

You will also note that all ocean waters are not created equal, inasmuch as the quantity of the precipitates and their trace elements vary between the Pacific Ocean, the Atlantic Ocean, the Dead Sea and Great Salt Lake waters. Each of these sources will also tend to vary from one gallon to the next, being products of nature.

Since salt is already dissolved in the natural oceans and seas we will begin our discussion with reactions that probably occur when making our own seawater using sea salts that contain the M-state/Ormus elements.

When sea salt is added to pure distilled water the water molecules hydrate the salt's ion structure by action of the dipole water molecule. Otherwise said, when the salt is added to water, the dipole water molecule overcomes the ionic bonding of the salt molecule, causing it to dissociate and dissolve in the water. The salt has become "hydrated."

Figure 1

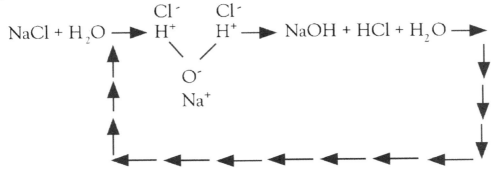

Since we know that water is never in a static state I have added the broken-arrow line to the equation above. Those elements are constantly moving about in the liquid. This illustrates yet another manifestation of Ouroboros. (The Ouroboros depicts the circle of alchemy where it has been said: What is now dry must soon become wet.)

In theory, the M-state element would relate in a similar way as the positive sodium ion (Na+) within this ionic system. These M-state elements are naturally in seawater and are believed to be in their elemental form. M-gold (MAu+) will be used as our example.

During the precipitation step, sodium hydroxide (NaOH) solution is added, drop-by-drop, to our seawater as it is being well stirred.

The expected reaction is that the sodium and hydroxide ions are hydrated by the dipole action of the water. The hydroxide ion forms a new complex with the M-state element almost instantaneously and it falls to the bottom of the beaker as a (normally) white precipitate. The sodium and chloride ions remain dissociated in the top water.

Figure 2:

$NaOH + NaCl + H_2O + MAu \rightarrow$ dissociates $\rightarrow$

$Na^+ + OH^- + Na^+ + Cl^- + H^+ + OH^- + MAu^+ \rightarrow$ precipitates =

$MAuOH\downarrow + Na^+ + Cl^- + H_2O$

Experiments have demonstrated that the M-state elements will dissolve in aqueous solutions where the pH is below about 2.0 or are at pH 12 and above.

**Dry Process**:

In the earliest steps of the Sodium Burn process and the Lye Burn processes, the starting materials are burned at high heat with either pure sodium metal *or* with dry sodium hydroxide. These starting materials are normally either a *pure* form of metal or a very metallic ore, such as gold ore.

This action of heating these metallic materials with some form of salt with the intent to disaggregate the metal is nothing new. The corrosive nature of salt has been used for thousands of years to disaggregate metals. Modern man simply makes use of more modern and readily available corrosive agents, such as the pure sodium (Na) or sodium hydroxide (NaOH).

Once this burning is accomplished we will have a dry "matte" or "cake" containing the sodium (or sodium hydroxide), the metal that has been disaggregated to *some* degree and our M-state gold. As an example, if you were to burn one ounce of gold metal with three ounces of pure sodium metal, approximately 25% of the gold metal would be disaggregated enough to react during the next step where it is wetted again. (In a later step the burned material is boiled in sodium hydroxide solution. The remaining gold *metal* settles to the bottom of the boiling vessel and can be washed, dried and reused.) The M-state gold (M-gold) content would be that portion of the original gold metal that has had all of its metal-to-metal bonds broken and is represented in our equations as MAu and is now simply in its dry *elemental* form.

Once we have our dry cake it is further processed either by hammer and chisel or in a mortar with pestle until it is in a fine particle form.

The fine particles are then added to a sodium hydroxide solution and boiled, gently, for a few hours. This action is believed to leach the disaggregated portion of the now M-gold from the fine particles into solution.

We now separate the sodium hydroxide solution containing the MAu$^+$ from above the settled solids. However, you can see that this solution, while being similar to our seawater is different in several key ways.

First, the pH is around 13 and there is no chloride present. The MAu$^+$ is *free* within the sodium hydroxide solution. It is thought to relate in the same way as it relates to seawater. (See Figure 1). Second, there are few H+ ions present.

Hydronium ions that form in hydrochloric *acid* solution contain hydrogen atoms from which the electrons have been removed. The hydrogen atoms that donate an electron are also called protons. (Remember that hydrogen only has 1 proton and 1 electron.) This acidic HCl acts as a proton donor when added to water forming the hydronium ion H3O$^+$ and chloride Cl$^-$.

Figure 3:    $HCl + H_2O \rightarrow H_3O^+ + Cl^-$

If a solution containing hydronium ions is added to a solution containing the exact same amount of hydroxide ions the result would be simple water and its pH would be neutral at 7.0 pH.

Figure 4:     $H_3O^+ + OH^- \rightarrow 2H_2O$

Please note that the more modern way to explain this is to simplify the above equation using the simpler H+ ion as was used earlier in the Wet Process section:

Figure 4a:     $H_3O^+ + OH^- \rightarrow 2H_2O = H^+ + OH^- \rightarrow H_2O$

The properties of bases in water are thought to be due to the hydroxide ion $OH^-$. Most bases are ionic compounds containing positive ions from the metals group, such as sodium $(Na)^+$, potassium $(K)^+$ as well as calcium, magnesium and others.

The pH of a solution is a form of measurement of hydrogen ion $(H^+)$ concentration. The higher the pH, the lower the hydrogen ion concentration. A solution in this condition (above pH 7) is called a *base*.

The measurement of pH is exponential. Beginning at a neutral pH of 7.0 then, a pH of 8.0 is 10 times more basic than pH 7, meaning that its hydrogen ion concentration is also lower by a factor of 10. Thus pH of 9.0 is 100 times more basic than pH 7.0.

A solution that has a pH below pH 7.0 contains a larger concentration of hydrogen ions and is considered acidic. If the pH of an acid is 5.0 then it is 100 times more acidic than a neutral solution of pH 7.0.

As an acid is a proton donor, a base is a proton acceptor. The concept includes hydroxide ions and neutral molecules also. Some researchers believe that during these processes there are nuclear reactions (protonations) occurring. I interject this comment in order to point you toward those low energy nuclear reactions that I mentioned at the beginning of this chapter.

When the basic sodium hydroxide is neutralized by hydrochloric acid the result is water and salt.

Figure 5:     $NaOH + HCl \rightarrow H_2O + NaCl$ (salt)

The salt in our case however, is the M-gold hydroxide, MAuOH.

Next we perform a precipitation step by adding a 6N HCl solution, drop-by-drop, while stirring the NaOH solution containing our M-gold briskly.

Once we have added enough hydrogen ions, the pH of our solution begins to fall and our M-gold hydroxide forms. Since this new complex is no longer water soluble (due to the lowering of pH) it precipitates out of solution and falls to the bottom of the beaker. This begins to become more evident as the pH of our solution falls below pH 11.

Once this MAuOH complex forms it will remain intact and once all pH adjustments are made will settle to the bottom of the beaker where it can be collected and further processed by washing, etc.

This basic reaction is illustrated by the equations in figure 6 below.

Figure 6:

$$NaOH + MAu^+ + H_2O \rightarrow add\ HCl \rightarrow$$

$$MAu^+ + OH^- + Na^+ + Cl^- + H_2O \rightarrow precipitates =$$

$$MAuOH\downarrow + Na^+ + Cl^- + H_2O.$$

You can now understand that this situation is similar to, but different from the Wet Process and that it is simple but complicated.

Don Nance

# Glossary

**Acid** - pH values on a pH meter up to and not including pH 7.

**Alchemy** - An art practiced for thousands of years focused on: 1 Transforming base metals into more valuable metals coupled with the search for a universal solvent and elixir of life. 2 The regeneration and ultimate perfection of man, gained through self-knowledge. 3 Defined by Paracelsus as the ability to control, purify and transform nature by the living power of the spirit.

**Alchemical Oxygen** - One way of describing the degree of beneficial effects Ormus has on biological systems (Ormus is not oxygen-enriched).

**Alchemist** - An alchemy practitioner who practices alchemy.

**Alkaline** - Having alkalinity. See alkalinity.

**Alkalinity** - Hydroxyl ion concentration in a solution having values above pH 7 and up to pH 14.

**Aloe** - Name of succulent plant that is known to have high Ormus content especially when grown in volcanic soils.

**Animals and Ormus** - Hints and suggestions for animal use are found in Appendix XXI.

**Annealing** - Heating the extracted Ormus to 1 help raise the energy level 2 to remove impurities.

**Artephius** - A middle ages alchemist.

**Atom** - The smallest particle that comprises a chemical element having the properties of the element and consists of electrons around a nucleus comprised of protons and neutrons.

**Aura** - aka "Light Body." - An emanation or light that radiates out from the body and felt to be seen in Kirlian photography.

**Barry Carter** - A resident of Baker City, Oregon. Among other activities Barry maintains the most complete and comprehensive website on Ormus and subtle energies and is currently the moderator of many Ormus lists; he often conducts workshops, and holds seminars speaking on behalf of Ormus history and current research.

**Boiling Energy** - The elixir of life (life force energy) as defined in Southern African (Bushmen) culture.

**Bose-Einstein Condensate** - A group of atoms which are all in the same "quantum state."

**Boson** -Elements with an even number of sub-particles that can pair up into Bose-Einstein Condensates that behave as a single atom ceasing to behave as a particle and more like light by resonance-coupling oscillation.

**C-11** - Ormus prepared from seawater.

**Canons of Espagnet** - Common name for the *Areanum of Hermetic Philosophy*, written by Espagnet, which states that "the science of producing natures grand" (secret) involves the realm of metals and the principles of metals by analysis.

**Catalyst** - Substance that causes an acceleration of a chemical reaction by its presence and without being affected itself .

**Caustic** - 1 A highly alkaline substance with strong precautions regarding its use. 2 Corrosive or aggressive effect on living tissue.

**Charging** - A process of consciously imprinting an energy or thought into Ormus.

**Chi** - The elixir of life (life force energy) as defined in Chinese culture.

**Cobalt** - A hard, brittle metal, atomic number 27, that is occasionally used to make Ormus.

**Cold Extraction** - A lengthy process for extracting Ormus directly from a rock or stone source.

**Cold Fire Process** - A.K.A. Dry Process - Process that uses no external heat.

**Collector** - One who gathers.

**Colloid** - A mixture in which one substance is divided into minute particles, can be pure elemental metal, and dispersed throughout a liquid such as distilled water.  Is stable for a long time and will not settle because of particle size and electrical charge.

**Colloidal Gold Solution** - Elemental gold reduced to micro-clusters using electric current.

**Colloidal Silver Solution** - Elemental silver reduced to micro-clusters using electric current.

**Colloidal System** - aka colloid.  Combination of a colloid and the substance in which it is dispersed.  If left undisturbed, the particles in a colloidal system do not precipitate but remain dispersed.   The particles are larger than ordinary molecules but too small to be visible to the naked eye.

**Concord Grapes** - A good source for iridium and rhodium.

**Cooper-Pair Boson** - Elements with an odd number of sub-particles that can pair up into Bose-Einstein Condensates that behave as a single atom ceasing to behave as a particle and more like light by resonance-coupling oscillation.

**Copper Ormus** - aka M-1 copper.  Ormus made from elemental copper.

**Coulomb Field** - The electrostatic field around a charged particle.

**Coulomb Wave** - aka Scalar Wave - A wave of the coulomb field.  A postulation is that an atom of a monoatomic element is spinning out of balance and producing this wave that comes off the atom.

**David Hudson** - An Arizona farmer credited with the rediscovery and reintroduction of the study of monatomic elements related to alchemy.  David applied for patents on processes to produce ORME. Defined as "Orbitally Rearranged Monatomic Elements."

**Decant** - To pour from one container to another often without disturbing sediment if there is one.

**Dew** - Moisture that condenses out of the air and contains Ormus.

**Diatomic** - Element consisting of two atoms or two atoms per molecule.

**Disaggregate** - The process of reducing elements in an Ormus source material to a mono-atomic state during an Ormus collection process.

**Dissolved** - Cause to go into a solution.

**Distillation (Distilled)** --Heating a liquid to its boiling point then collecting the vapor through condensing into a concentrated form.  This can be used to separate the components in a liquid.

**Dowsing** - Obtaining information beyond the physical senses using various mechanisms, such as pendulum and witching.

**Drop Out** - One of several terms sometimes used to describe the precipitate that drops to the bottom of the container during an Ormus collection process.

**Doves** - One of several terms sometimes used to describe the precipitate that drops to the bottom of the container during the "Wet Process" Ormus collection process.

**Drawn seawater** - Seawater taken directly from the sea.

**Dry Process** - A process for extracting ORMUS substances from initially dry source material.

**Electron** - Negatively charged particles that continually orbit the nucleus of an atom and are held in orbit by attraction to the positive charge of the nucleus.

**Energetic** --Having energy or energies; possessing a capacity for vigorous action or for exerting force.

**Energetics** -- The method of the flow and transformation of energy within a particular system.

**Entrainment** - Formation of regular, predictable patterns in time and/or space when a designated space is used for one purpose only--such as Ormus collection--through interactions within or between systems (such as the zero point and our dimension).

**Espagnet** - (d'Espagnet.)  Hermetic philosopher (ca 1640).

**Essene** - An anonymous man who is credited by many in the Ormus network with developing the "Wet Process", "Dry Process" and "Sodium Burn Process" used to extract Ormus and also coined the phrase M-state for these elements.  Called Essene (not "the" Essene).

**Enlightened Consciousness** - - A consciousness that intuits or feels insights or wisdoms that recognizes that humans and all life are one thus causing life to be more harmonious and workable.

**Enlightenment** - The state of having an enlightened consciousness.

**Esoteric** - Hidden wisdom or inner wisdom that is now being made exoteric or revealed on Earth.

**Essiac Tea** - A Native American herbal tea.

**Fibonacci Series** - A series of numbers often found in nature "discovered" by Leonard Fibonacci (ca-1175-1250) and through computation create the "golden ratio" of (approximately) 1.618:1.

**Fractional Vaporization** - Vaporizing a material for analysis using the light spectrum it emits when boiling off in the sequence of the ingredients boiling temperature. The carbon electrode is bathed in inert gas to allow the longest burn time possible (300 seconds).

**Gel** - A colloid suspension in a semi rigid form.

**Gold Ore** - A rock or mineral or aggregate of minerals which basically contains gold and other elements.

**Golden Ratio** - aka divine proportion, golden mean or golden section. The number equal to (approximately) 1.618:1 that seems to arise out of the basic structure of our cosmos reminding us of the principle of "oneness" and acts as a continuous reminder of our relationship to the whole.

**Hermes Trismegistus** - A representation name from the melding of the Egyptian god Thoth and the Greek God Hermes who was believed to be the author, under this name of writings from probably the first to the third centuries AD.

**Hermetic** - A set of beliefs primarily upon Egyptian writings of Hermes Trismegistus.

**HDPE Plastic** - High-density polyethylene, a certified food grade plastic.

**HCl aka Hydrochloric Acid** - A very corrosive acid used in some processes to reduce elemental metals to mono-atomic state.

**Healing Crisis** - Part of a healing process where the body undergoes physical detoxification from toxins. This can be uncomfortable and cause symptoms such as fatigue and headache and even manifestations of previous illnesses.

**Heap Leach Process** - An advanced formula using toxic chemicals to extract Ormus from dry source material.

**Higher Energy State** - A system that has a higher energy than the ground state. The higher temperature is indicative of the level of excitation.

**Hot Rock Process** - An advanced process in which iodine is used to extract Ormus gold from certain types of rocks/ores.

**Hydrogen Peroxide (35%)** - A liquid solution used in some processes chemically known as $H_2O_2$.

**Hydrogen Peroxide (Gold) Process** - The process involves reducing metallic gold to fine shavings that are then chemically reduced to M-state.

**Humic Shale** - A layered sedimentary stone that has trapped minerals between the layers.

**Humans and Ormus** - Hints and suggestions for human use are found in Appendix XXI.

**Icosahedron** - aka Icosahedral. 20 sided polyhedron with each side made up of triangles that is the shape of water clusters that combine to make very large super clusters of water.

**Implicate Order** - A vast and deeper level of reality out of which our reality unfolds.

**Imprinting** - A process of unconsciously imparting an energy or thought into the Ormus.

**Interstitial** - Relating to small enclosed space.

**Ion** - An electrically charged atom or groups of atoms.

**Ionic** ~ aka ionic solutions ~Ions in solution and behaves as an electrically conductive medium.

**Isotope** - Atoms of the same element having the same number of protons and electrons but a different number of neutrons.

**Ki** - The elixir of life (life force energy) as defined in Japanese culture.

**Kirlian Photography** - Form of photogram made with a high voltage and felt by some to display the aura or light body.

**KOH** - The chemical formula for Potassium Hydroxide. This is an alternative to using lye in the wet process.

**Light Body** - aka Aura. Light that radiates out from the body and thought to be seen in Kirlian Photography.

**Live Oil Process** - A process for extracting ORMUS substances using oils such as grape seed oil.

**Living menstruum** - An "Ormus-containing lye medium" formed during dry Ormus collection processes and is at the core of the process.

**Lye** - 1 A very caustic compound with a chemical formula of NAOH, aka Sodium Hydroxide.  2 Useful In Ormus collection processes.

**Lye Boil** - A process used to reduce dry land based minerals into Ormus.

**Lye Burn** - A process using dry granular or powdered lye on a dry source material over a hot flame (or in a kiln/furnace).

**Lye Burn and Boil** - This process involves extracting Ormus by burning a source material in lye granules then boiling it in a liquid.

**M-1 Copper** - A copper Ormus made by first dissolving elemental copper.

**M-1 Gold - aka M-1**. A gold Ormus made by first dissolving elemental gold.

**M-3** - An M-state gold, iridium and rhodium mixture.

**M-State** - (Defined as "Meta-physical form" or "Manna-form.") 1 Another word, Ormus or Manna. One of several terms sometimes used to describe the precipitate that drops to the bottom of the container during an Ormus collection process. 2 Orme, Ormus and M-state all are generic terms which apply to any normally metallic elements in a spectroscopically "invisible non-metallic form. These terms apply regardless of which method was used to obtain them or the relative effectiveness of the element.

**Magnet Vortex Water Trap** - A magneto hydrodynamic device used to energize water and extract ORMUS substances from ground water.

**Magnetic field** - aka Electromagnetic field. 1 A created field produced by electric charges that move. 2 Also a natural field produced by nature called "The Earths Magnetic Field."

**Magnetite** - A natural occurring ferrous bearing mineral which is generally permanently magnetic

**Manna** - 1 One of several terms sometimes used to describe the precipitate that drops to the bottom of the container during an Ormus collection process. 2 The elixir of life (life force energy) as defined in Hawaiian culture.

**Matrix of Consciousness** - Describes the Ormus materials role as a connector or bridge between spirit and matter.

**Menstruum** - 1 A solvent 2 Any fluid or substance which dissolves a solid body. (See Living Menstruum.)

**Mercury** - A silvery metallic element, atomic number 80. which is a liquid at room temperature and is highly toxic.

**Meissner Effect** - The expulsion of a magnetic field from a superconductor and is produced when a superconductor has an external magnetic field applied to it.

**Micro-cluster** - A cluster of specific atoms that gather together and are the size of 10 - 1,000 atoms.

**Military Time** - Time referenced according to a 24-hour clock instead of AM and PM where 0000 is midnight and 2300 is 11PM.

**Molecule** - A cluster of atoms generally found to be 1-10 atoms.

**Monoatomic (Monatomic)** - Element consisting of a single atom or one atom per molecule.

**Moon Chart** - Shows the phases of the moon for each day of the month.

**Muriatic Acid** - aka hydrochloric acid.  1 An acid that is very "caustic."  2 Useful in dry processes.

**NaOH** - The chemical name of a very caustic common Lye.  (Sodium Hydroxide)

**Neutron** -- Uncharged or electrically neutral subatomic particle found in the nucleus of atoms which cluster with protons in the center of an atom and comprise its nucleus.

**Nickel** - A hard shiny white metallic element, atomic number 28.

**Nitrous Oxide** - aka Laughing Gas.  This is a nontoxic, non-flammable gaseous substance that is found in the air in small quantities.

**Nonlinear** - A property of a system whose output is not proportional to its input or not in a straight line.

**Orgone** - 1"Life Energy" discovered by Wilhelm Reich said to be collected in a box-like device and used to recharge one's sense of well-being. 2 A real physical energy that charges and animates the natural world.

**Orgone Accumulator** - A device that collects Orgone (sometimes referred to as a"black box").

**ORME** - 1 As defined in this writing refers to substances outlined in David Hudson's patent application that are said to be "Orbitally Rearranged Monatomic Elements." 2 Orme, Ormus and M-state all are generic terms which apply to any normally metallic elements in a spectroscopically "invisible non-metallic form.  These terms apply regardless of which method was used to obtain them or the relative effectiveness of the element.

**Orme-Sodium** - A theory that Ormus has tied to a sodium molecule and formed a collectable complex during an Ormus collection process.

**ORMUS** - 1 The term ORMUS has been used for many centuries.  Currently we use the word to identify transition elements in non-metallic form.  Most prominent of these are gold, silver, copper and the platinum group.  These seem to be a new or rediscovered class of mineral nutrients that are beneficial to life.  2 Orme, Ormus and M-state all are generic terms which apply to any normally metallic elements in a spectroscopically "invisible non-metallic form.  These terms apply regardless of which method was used to obtain them or the relative effectiveness of the element.  3 One of several terms sometimes used to describe the precipitate that drops to the bottom of the container during an Ormus collection process.

**Over-The-Hem** - A refining process using a glass retort aka still.  DO NOT refine using this process more than twice or the manna can become unstable (loses potency).

**Oxidize** - To combine (an element) with oxygen.

**Paracelsus** - (Phillip von Hohenheim 1493-1541 known as Paracelsus).  Alchemist, Physician and Astrologer who contributed towards philosophy, medicine, toxicology and psychotherapy.

**Paramagnetic Sand** - Sand often black in color that has a high iron content that allows localized concentration of the earth's natural magnetic field.  But it is not permanently magnetized.

**Paramagnatism** - 1 a weak magnetic condition of substances causing a  positive but small susceptibility to magnetism. 2 A form of magnetism which occurs only in the presence of an externally applied magnetic field. Paramagnetic materials are attracted to magnetic fields, hence have a relative magnetic permeability greater than one (or, equivalently, a positive magnetic susceptibility). The force of attraction generated by the applied field is linear in the field strength and rather weak. It typically requires a sensitive analytical balance to detect the effect. Unlike ferromagnets, paramagnets do not retain any magnetization in the absence of an externally applied magnetic field, because thermal motion causes the spins to become randomly oriented without it. Thus the total magnetization will drop to zero when the applied field is removed." (Wikipedia)

**Parkinsonism** - A disease of the nervous system, evident by shaking and uneven speech.

**Periodic Table** - This table shows the chemical symbols for all of the standard elements.

**Perturbation** - A weak disturbance to the system. (see Quantum Resonance Frequency).

**Phil Callahan** - Developed a fairly inexpensive meter for testing the magnetic qualities of soil and also wrote numerous books about Paramagnetism relating to soil.

**Philosopher's Stone** - While definitions may vary, most currently agree the stone is pure white powdered gold (white powder of gold).

**pH Meter** - A calibrated meter for measuring the alkalinity/acidity of any liquid.

**Plants and Ormus** - Hints and suggestions for plant use are found in Appendix XXI

**Platinum Metal Group** - - A group of six transitional metals on the periodic table. These are rhodium, iridium, ruthenium, palladium, osmium, and platinum. They are usually found in varying amounts in mineral deposits together with gold and silver.

**Polyhedron** - aka polyhedra (plural). Simple solid shapes. As the number of faces increase its shape becomes more spherical.

**Potassium Hydroxide** - A substitute for Lye as a chemical in the wet process. Chemical formula is (KOH).

**Prana** - 1 The elixir of life (life force energy) as defined in Hindu culture  2. An ancient name from the Middle East describing Ormus substances.

**Precipitate** - One of several terms used to describe the wet solid that forms when a reaction occurs or the resulting substance that forms and settles (drops out) to the bottom of the container during an Ormus collection process.

**Proton** - Positively charged sub atomic particle found in the nucleus of atoms

**Purple Grapes** - A source high in rhodium content.

**Pyramid** - A tuned resonate structured chamber or geometric solid, that resonates at a primary frequency equal to the wave length of its height. Also in all even harmonics.

**Qi** - Another word, Chi.

**Quantitative** - The use of numerical data to obtain information relating to quantity about an occurrence (as in calculating "percent yield").

**Quantum resonance** - An enhanced coupling between quantum states with the same energy.

**Quantum Resonance Frequency** - The quantum mechanics of non-linear "resonance containing" Resonance Zones. These zones have subspaces which upon perturbation undergoes a spreading of the measurable space and causes a growth in size and eventual overlapping of the spaces.

**Quantum State** - A state that is shared by many distinct locations and therefore allows an instant merging.

**Quintessence** - Defined as a first point or beginning of life it is also the purest and most concentrated essence of the life force.

**Rare Earth Elements** - Also known as the lanthanides. 1 Any of the series of metallic chemical elements with consecutive atomic numbers of 57-71 which closely resemble one another chemically. 2 Group of soft lustrous strongly paramagnetic and strongly reactive metals that are sometimes called rare earth metals. (Some are not that rare.)

**Reagent** - Any substance used in a chemical reaction that enters into the reaction for the purpose of producing other substances.

**Red Lion** - The end product of a collection process that is usually somewhat red crystalline in appearance.

**Resonance-Coupling Oscillation** - Materials that act as one by resonating at the same frequency.

**Sage** - An herb that is used in purification or ridding an area of negative energies.

**Salt Crystal Lamps** - Large salt crystals that are hollowed out to contain a small light bulb that illuminates the crystal from within.

**Sea Salt** - Crystal salts obtained by dehydrating seawater.

**Seawater Pump** - A system for safely obtaining water from the sea/ocean.

**Secret Fire** - The alchemical term that is used to describe the reaction during an Ormus process after a chemical such as NAOH or KOH is added to a mixture.

**Shem-an-na** - A bread believed to contain Ormus given the gods in ancient Egypt.

**Silver Ore** - A mineral deposit, which contains silver in quantity that is economically feasible to mine.

**Shift in Consciousness** - Shift inside the human psyche that allows the ability to view his world with a dramatic new perspective. Often considered in tandem with enlightenment.

**Silver Chloride** - A toxic substance (white precipitate, that is formed by mixing silver and hydrochloric acid. NOT RECOMMENDED!

**Sodium** - This element is an alkali metal, atomic number 11. It is volatile when in contact with water and most fluids.

**Sodium Burn** - A hazardous advanced process using sodium metal for disaggregating ORMUS substances from dry source material.

**Science** - Method to discover, understand or to understand better, how the physical world works by using observable physical evidence during the study as the basis of that understanding.

**Spirit** - The vital principle or animating force within living things.

**Spiritual Growth** - Type of life entering into a human causing the ability to know, understand and do things they normally would not. See enlightenment.

**Superconductor** - 1 A many atom system of atoms operating in two dimensions along a standing wave and is so in balance it does not allow any external magnetic fields inside the super conductor's domain. 2 Materials able to conduct electricity with virtually no resistance at relatively warm temperatures.

**Synthetic Magnetite** - A man made magnetite produced by firing in a kiln aka furnace.

**Telomeres** - Caps on the end of the chromosomes of the cells within the body.

**Tetrahedron** - aka tetrahedral. Four sided polyhedron composed of four triangular faces.

**The Drop** - One of several terms sometimes used to describe the precipitate that drops to the bottom of the container during an Ormus collection process.

**The "great work"** - Defined by Paracelsus as the ability to control, purify and transform nature by the living power of the spirit.

**Transition Elements** - These metals when reduced to mono-atomic form are thought to assist communication between cells in the body and between the body and spirit.

**Treatise** - A systematic written exposition including a description of the methodology for discovery, the principles involved, and the conclusions.

**Tuning to Ormus** - The body can adjust to the frequencies of the Ormus at which time the person may no longer experience any feeling from it.

**Vedic Alchemy** - Alchemical processes from Eastern India. (This book lists one process.)

**Volatile** ~ 1 Explosive: liable to lead to sudden change  2 Evaporates at room temperature.

**Vortex Water Trap** - A hydrodynamic device used to energize water and extract Ormus substances from ground water.

**Wet in Liquid** - 1 term to describe Ormus collected from the "Wet" and all the dry processes. 2 Wet liquid droplets in the liquid (versus solid particles such as earth particles held in a suspension of muddy water).

**Wet Process** - A process for extracting ORMUS material from salty fluid sources such as seawater or water that has had sea salt dissolved into it.

**White Dove** - A term sometimes used to describe the precipitate that drops to the bottom of the container during an Ormus collection process when the appearance is pure white.  Most commonly the source for this is seawater or water that has had sea salt dissolved into it.

**Wei Po-yang** - An Ancient Chinese alchemist.

**Zero Point** - 1 Considered the entryway of the "God" force energy into our world (and the universe). 2 A concept developed from Quantum physics & mechanics. It is a place in the Void of Time and Space where matter and antimatter merge

## ❧ THE AUTHOR

**CHRISTINE M. EMMONS** graduated from Pharmacy school in 1976 and owned a Pharmacy in Pontiac, Michigan until 1991 when she moved to South Florida. She observed alternative healing modalities in action as a close friend underwent a serious health crisis and this experience sparked an interest in the subject that led to knowledge of the Ormus material and its beneficial effects. Having a pharmacy background, she desired to know how to collect Ormus from

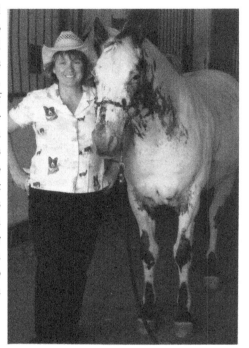

fresh water, seawater, organic matter, minerals and metals. Beginning in 2004 Chris devoted herself to finding and learning from those who could teach and explain proper technique. These included Ormus Researchers and a well-known commercial Alchemist. A friend, having heard about the culmination of these efforts, verbalized how the Ormus community-both current and future-could benefit by having a manual of Ormus collection processes and that Chris embodied professional training and personal traits to complete such a work. Because Chris never forgot how it feels to yearn for the knowledge of Ormus collection processes she began work on such a manual. It is now available to the Ormus community and the world. In addition to this work, Chris is an active member of the Ormus community, sponsors lab days that teach Ormus collection processes and is a member of the International Alchemy Guild. *cmemmons@bellsouth.net*

## Author's Note:

I must report how the "All" had a hand in bringing this book into the physical world. Consistently, just at the very time needed, individuals "happened" along the trail with knowledge that was required to help the book "arrive." Each generously merged their efforts with mine to place this book in the hands of the world and I thank each one. These included proofreaders, those who knew of publishers and printers as well as publishers themselves. There were writers, authors, copy editors, book formatters, an English teacher, chemist, graphic artist and webmaster. Now that the Ormus book is completed, I pause and fully recognize with appreciation and gratefulness the subtle hand of the "All" behind the convergence of so many lives. *www.ormusbook.com*

# ❄ LISTED CONTRIBUTORS

**BARRY CARTER** was born in 1949 and has been interested in science since he was a child. In 1995, he discovered the work of David Hudson on white gold and monatomic elements and began experimenting and researching Hudson's ideas full time. He has since proven and developed Hudson's original theories into a much more comprehensive and demonstrable science. He is also encouraging and coordinating research into the nature of the ORMUS materials, and has given scores of lectures on the subject around the world. Barry considers himself the "official greeter for ORMUS." Barry's goal is to get high quality ORMUS information out to as many people as possible as quickly as possible. His current

projects include: scheduling more presentations on ORMUS; setting up a non-profit funding structure for research; continue to help people get better acquainted with ORMUS individually; finish his new book on ORMUS; and he wants to find a research coordinator who has the time and resources to coordinate ORMUS research.

Website: *www.subtleenergies.com*

**DON NANCE** was born in Virginia on August 11, 1955. He was a professional musician for 35 years and is an accomplished lead guitarist and vocalist who also plays keyboard instruments and percussion. He holds a degree in electronics engineering with a minor in acoustical engineering. After being diagnosed with advanced colon cancer that apparently disappeared after three months of taking M-state/Ormus materials, he learned to master the processes needed to make, extract and purify them from 1999 to 2001. He is a tireless researcher who is attempting to bridge the gaps between the M-state/Ormus elements and our currently accepted paradigms of Chemistry, Solid State Physics and Quantum Mechanics. He gives lectures and teaches workshops on the state-of-our-art processes used to make, concentrate and purify the M-state/Ormus elements by the Wet Way and the Dry Way and the steps needed to make the white powder of gold from pure gold metal. He has accomplished the transmutation of the M-state/Ormus elements into silver, gold and several platinum group metals. He has contributed many scientific papers to internet forums and science workgroups. He continues to be a student of Alchemy and Nature and freely shares his knowledge. The fruits of his love are available at his web site below.

*http://www.oceanalchemy.com*

For information about availability for lectures or hands-on workshops his email address is: *swiftrock@juno.com*

Other contributing Ormus researchers requested anonymity.

Prologue by Dennis William Hauck

**DENNIS WILLIAM HAUCK** is an author, consultant, and lecturer working to facilitate personal and institutional transformation through the application of the ancient principles of alchemy. He writes and lectures on the universal principles of physical, psychological, and spiritual perfection to a wide variety of audiences that range from scientists and business leaders to religious and New Age groups. Hauck's interest in alchemy began while he was still in graduate school at the University of Vienna, and he has since translated a number of important alchemy manuscripts dating back to the fourteenth century.
Among his bestselling books are **The Emerald Tablet: Alchemy for Personal Transformation** (Penguin 1999), **Sorcerer's Stone: A Beginner's Guide to Alchemy** (Citadel 2004), and **The Complete Idiot's Guide to Alchemy** (Penguin Alpha 2008). Hauck is an officer in the Alchemy Guild *(www.AlchemyGuild.org)* and chief coordinator for the annual International Alchemy Conference *(www.AlchemyConference.com)*.

More information at *www.DWHauck.com.*

## ❋ A PRICE

*A long time ago I thought to write: "There is a Price." Friends asked: What is this? I answered: Everything has a price - and this has little to do with money.*

*Well, it has been 1 1/2 years now since beginning the Ormus book. Time periods between working, obligations and rest have pretty much been devoted to the work. Soon it will be completed.*

*But today I am reminded of that phrase I wrote long ago. You see, this journey has been fruitful and with the collated knowledge provided in Ormus: Modern Day Alchemy, I perceive the possibility of enrichment to the world.*

*But, on March 6 at 7:30pm my five-year old Duyvenbode lory parrot suffered a heart attack and today I am reminded of my price. Parrots live so long and I expected all that time together. The energy funneled to the book left less for her; and that was OK because it would end - instead cricket ended - first.*

*Cricket Emmons, my smart, energetic, loving, playful, sentient bird-child.*

*I acknowledge being heavy hearted: If I had only enjoyed more time with her this past 1 1/2 years - if I had only not been writing. Feeling love, joy and appreciation is elusive today and I hold out a hope that she finds a way to return to me.*

*Feeling so diminished, a good friend coached me. Now I acknowledge all the animals - all the parrots - whose lives may be enriched by Ormus because of this work.*

*I am still reminded though how a long time ago I wrote: "There is a Price."*

C.E.

# The Emerald Tablet

Traditional alchemists hold that Alchemy originated with Thoth in ancient Egypt. The *"Emerald Tablet"* said to be written by Thoth (Hermes Trismegistus) is considered the most important alchemical declaration ever found. Translations of the text were posted in the workshops of ancient alchemists and can be observed in images of that era. Modern alchemists also display these words in their work areas.

Sir Isaac Newton's Version Taken from his Personal Alchemy Notes:

- It is true without lying, certain and most true. That which is Below is like that which is Above & that which is Above is like that which is Below to do the miracles of one Only Thing.
- And as all things have been & arose from One by the mediation of One: so all things have their birth from this One Thing by adaptation.
- The Sun is its father; the Moon its mother;
- The Wind hath carried it in its belly; the Earth its nurse.
- The father of all perfection in the whole world is here.
- Its force or power is entire if it be converted into Earth.
- Separate thou the Earth from the Fire, the subtle from the gross, sweetly with great industry.
- It ascends from the Earth to the Heavens and again it descends to the Earth and receives the force of things superior and inferior.
- By this means you shall have the glory of the whole world and thereby all obscurity shall fly from you.
- Its force is above all force, for it vanquishes every subtle thing & penetrates every solid thing.
- So was the world created.
- From this are and do come admirable adaptations, whereof the process is here in this.

Hence I am called Hermes Trismegistus, having the three parts of the philosophy of the whole world.

That which I have said of the operation of the Sun is accomplished and ended.

NOTES:

NOTES:

Made in the USA
Coppell, TX
05 January 2021

47576327R00175